VOLUME 521

MAY 1992

THE ANNALS

of The American Academy *of* Political
and Social Science

RICHARD D. LAMBERT, *Editor*
ALAN W. HESTON, *Associate Editor*

DRUG ABUSE:

LINKING POLICY AND RESEARCH

Special Editor of this Volume

ERIC D. WISH

Center for Substance Abuse Research
University of Maryland
College Park

⑤ SAGE PUBLICATIONS *NEWBURY PARK   LONDON   NEW DELHI*

THE ANNALS

© 1992 *by* The American Academy *of* Political *and* Social Science

Editorial Office: 3937 Chestnut Street, Philadelphia, PA 19104.

For information about membership (individuals only) and subscriptions (institutions), address:*

SAGE PUBLICATIONS, INC.
2455 Teller Road
Newbury Park, CA 91320

From India and South Asia, *write to:* SAGE PUBLICATIONS INDIA Pvt. Ltd. P.O. Box 4215 New Delhi 110 048 INDIA		*From the UK, Europe, the Middle* *East and Africa, write to:* SAGE PUBLICATIONS LTD 6 Bonhill Street London EC2A 4PU UNITED KINGDOM

SAGE Production Staff: LINDA GRAY, LIANN LECH, and JANELLE LeMASTER
Please note that members of The Academy receive THE ANNALS with their membership.
Library of Congress Catalog Card Number 91-67477
International Standard Serial Number ISSN 0002-7162
International Standard Book Number ISBN 0-8039-4620-1 (Vol. 521, 1992 paper)
International Standard Book Number ISBN 0-8039-4619-8 (Vol. 521, 1992 cloth)
Manufactured in the United States of America. First printing, May 1992.

The articles appearing in THE ANNALS are indexed in *Book Review Index, Public Affairs Information Service Bulletin, Social Sciences Index, Current Contents, General Periodicals Index, Academic Index, Pro-Views,* and *Combined Retrospective Index Sets.* They are also abstracted and indexed in *ABC Pol Sci, Historical Abstracts, Human Resources Abstracts, Social Sciences Citation Index, United States Political Science Documents, Social Work Research & Abstracts, Sage Urban Studies Abstracts, International Political Science Abstracts, America: History and Life, Sociological Abstracts, Managing Abstracts, Social Planning/Policy & Development Abstracts, Automatic Subject Citation Alert, Book Review Digest, Work Related Abstracts,* and/or *Family Resources Database,* and are available on microfilm from University Microfilms, Ann Arbor, Michigan.

Information about membership rates, institutional subscriptions, and back issue prices may be found on the facing page.

Advertising. Current rates and specifications may be obtained by writing to THE ANNALS Advertising and Promotion Manager at the Newbury Park office (address above).

Claims. Claims for undelivered copies must be made no later than three months following month of publication. The publisher will supply missing copies when losses have been sustained in transit and when the reserve stock will permit.

Change of Address. Six weeks' advance notice must be given when notifying of change of address to ensure proper identification. Please specify name of journal. Send address changes to: THE ANNALS, c/o Sage Publications, Inc., 2455 Teller Road, Newbury Park, CA 91320.

The American Academy of Political and Social Science

3937 Chestnut Street   Philadelphia, Pennsylvania 19104

Origin and Purpose. The Academy was organized December 14, 1889, to promote the progress of political and social science, especially through publications and meetings. The Academy does not take sides in controverted questions, but seeks to gather and present reliable information to assist the public in forming an intelligent and accurate judgment.

Meetings. The Academy occasionally holds a meeting in the spring extending over two days.

Publications. THE ANNALS is the bimonthly publication of The Academy. Each issue contains articles on some prominent social or political problem, written at the invitation of the editors. Also, monographs are published from time to time, numbers of which are distributed to pertinent professional organizations. These volumes constitute important reference works on the topics with which they deal, and they are extensively cited by authorities throughout the United States and abroad. The papers presented at the meetings of The Academy are included in THE ANNALS.

Membership. Each member of The Academy receives THE ANNALS and may attend the meetings of The Academy. Membership is open only to individuals. Annual dues: $39.00 for the regular paperbound edition (clothbound, $54.00). California residents must add 7.25% sales tax on all orders ($41.82 paperbound; $57.91 clothbound). Add $9.00 per year for membership outside the U.S.A. Members may also purchase single issues of THE ANNALS for $12.00 each (clothbound, $17.00). California residents: $12.87 paperbound, $18.23 clothbound. Add $1.50 for shipping and handling on all prepaid orders.

Subscriptions. THE ANNALS (ISSN 0002-7162) is published six times annually—in January, March, May, July, September, and November. Institutions may subscribe to THE ANNALS at the annual rate: $120.00 (clothbound, $144.00). California institutions: $128.70 paperbound, $155.44 clothbound. Add $9.00 per year for subscriptions outside the U.S.A. Institutional rates for single issues: $23.00 each (clothbound, $28.00). California institutions: $24.66 paperbound, $30.03 clothbound.

Second class postage paid at Thousand Oaks, California, and additional offices.

Single issues of THE ANNALS may be obtained by individuals who are not members of The Academy for $15.95 each (clothbound, $25.00). California residents: $17.10 paperbound, $26.81 clothbound. Add $1.50 for shipping and handling on all prepaid orders. Single issues of THE ANNALS have proven to be excellent supplementary texts for classroom use. Direct inquiries regarding adoptions to THE ANNALS c/o Sage Publications (address below).

All correspondence concerning membership in The Academy, dues renewals, inquiries about membership status, and/or purchase of single issues of THE ANNALS should be sent to THE ANNALS c/o Sage Publications, Inc., 2455 Teller Road, Newbury Park, CA 91320. Telephone: (805) 499-0721; FAX/Order line: (805) 499-0871. *Please note that orders under $30 must be prepaid.* Sage affiliates in London and India will assist institutional subscribers abroad with regard to orders, claims, and inquiries for both subscriptions and single issues.

THE ANNALS

of The American Academy *of* Political *and* Social Science

RICHARD D. LAMBERT, *Editor*
ALAN W. HESTON, *Associate Editor*

─────────── FORTHCOMING ───────────

THE FUTURE: TRENDS INTO
THE TWENTY-FIRST CENTURY
Special Editors: Joseph F. Coates and Jennifer Jarratt
Volume 522   July 1992

AFFIRMATIVE ACTION REVISITED
Special Editors: Harold Orlans and June O'Neill
Volume 523   September 1992

POLITICAL ISLAM
Special Editors: I. William Zartman
and Charles E. Butterworth
Volume 524   November 1992

See page 3 for information on Academy membership and
purchase of single volumes of The Annals.

CONTENTS

BOOK DEPARTMENT CONTENTS

SOCIOLOGY

ECONOMICS

PREFACE

Drug abuse is a topic of intense public concern and therefore subject to considerable debate by policymakers and politicians. During the 1980s and 1990s, public opinion polls have frequently reported that much of the public ranked drug abuse as the most important problem facing the nation. With or without justification, drug abuse is often cited as a major cause of crime, violence, and family disruption across the United States. The cocaine epidemic of the 1980s and the burgeoning epidemic of acquired immune deficiency syndrome (AIDS) have pressured state and federal agencies to expand the resources devoted to addressing these problems.

While much of the federal funding has been used to increase law enforcement efforts to reduce the flow of drugs into and within the United States, substantial increases in funding for research have also occurred. Researchers have learned much about the types of persons who are at high risk for drug abuse and have studied many possible interventions. In view of this expanding base of knowledge, it is most disconcerting to see how little of this information makes its way into the political debates on drug abuse.

A common topic of discussion at meetings of drug abuse researchers is the disparity between what has been learned about drug abuse through research, and the low quality of the debate and solutions suggested at the highest levels of government. For example, federal legislators' discussions of revoking a person's driver's license as a punishment for illegal drug use demonstrated a lack of understanding of the types of extremely deviant youths most likely to be abusing illicit drugs.

Researchers are taught to be cautious about drawing policy implications from their research. Scholarly articles traditionally end with a call for additional research to confirm or extend the research findings. Unfortunately, policymakers need answers immediately and cannot wait for the perfect research study to be completed. My experience as a visiting fellow at the National Institute of Justice convinced me of the need for research scientists to speak out and to present their advice to policymakers. If scientists are silent, the debate continues without them and decisions are made, often by persons who are far less knowledgeable.

This volume was designed to offer leading drug abuse researchers an opportunity to present their most policy-relevant research findings. All authors contributing to this volume were encouraged to review the evidence in their area of expertise and to go out on a limb to interpret their findings to suggest directions for policymakers. The backgrounds of the authors reflect the diverse, multidisciplinary nature of drug abuse research. Contributing authors include physicians, psychologists, sociologists, economists, and crim-

8

inologists. The volume concentrates on the use of illicit drugs; although most illicit drug abusers also abuse alcohol, a discussion of alcohol abuse research and policy deserves a separate volume.

While some overlap exists, the articles have been classified into four sections. Section 1 is devoted to the topic of cocaine exposure in the newborn and to drug use among high-risk youths. Linda Mayes raises questions about the evidence for the long-term adverse effects of newborns' exposure to cocaine. Richard Dembo, Linda Williams, and James Schmeidler have been studying a cohort of juveniles arrested and detained by the criminal justice system in Tampa, Florida. In their article, Dembo et al. draw a sharp contrast between the considerable drug abuse, psychological, and behavioral problems typical of such high-risk youths and the paucity of services available for them.

Section 2 covers interventions that have been found to be effective with hard-core drug abusers. Two pioneering researchers on intravenous drug use and AIDS in the United States, Don Des Jarlais and Samuel Friedman, present compelling evidence regarding the effectiveness of programs that provide clean needles for drug injectors. Douglas Anglin and Thomas Maugh, in their article, provide a concise description of current drug abuse treatment programs and argue the effectiveness of programs that force referrals from the criminal justice system to enter and remain in treatment. It must be noted that many politicians still believe that drug abuse treatment programs are ineffective, even in the face of evidence to the contrary.

Advances in the technology for detecting drug use by the analysis of urine or hair specimens have spawned considerable controversy. The potential of these tests for detecting drug use by persons detained and monitored by the criminal justice system is enormous. And yet policymakers appear more interested in testing employee populations, where drug abuse—cocaine and heroin use—is relatively rare, than in testing offender populations, where dysfunctional drug abuse is extremely common. Section 3 provides important research findings on this topic.

Robert DuPont has written an insightful description of his attempts to use research findings to guide the development in the United States of a national program, Operation Tripwire, for testing criminals for illicit drug use. DuPont writes from a personal perspective about the political ramifications of suggesting a program well ahead of its time; he attributes losing his job as the first director of the National Institute on Drug Abuse partially to his Operation Tripwire proposal. As a coauthor with DuPont, I have written about the creation and uses of the Drug Use Forecasting program. In a long-overdue synthesis, Christy Visher critically reviews the growing research evidence on the effectiveness of pretrial drug-testing programs. Tom Mieczkowski discusses the research findings on the effectiveness of tests that can analyze hair specimens for evidence of illicit drug use, and the controversy that has occurred in reaction to the proposed introduction of these tests.

In section 4, Peter Reuter questions the usefulness of strategies designed to prevent the introduction of drugs into the United States. Mark Kleiman and Jonathan Caulkins are already looking toward the next drug problem as the current cocaine epidemic crests. Fearing a possible increase in heroin use, Kleiman and Caulkins describe a strategy for enabling the country to detect early any significant changes in the use of this drug in the United States. In a fitting conclusion to a volume dedicated to the link between research and policy, Douglas Lipton draws on his long career as the former director of the New York State Division of Substance Abuse Services and as an accomplished researcher to describe strategies that may enhance the use of research findings by policymakers.

Finally, this volume is dedicated to my mentor, Lee N. Robins, whose rigorous standard of research in the field of substance abuse has made possible the work of a number of the volume's contributors.

ERIC D. WISH

ANNALS, *AAPSS*, 521, May 1992

Prenatal Cocaine Exposure and Young Children's Development

By LINDA C. MAYES

ABSTRACT: The current state of knowledge about the neurodevelopmental sequelae of prenatal cocaine exposure is reviewed. Maternal cocaine use is associated with a number of other factors such as poor nutrition, inadequate prenatal care, and exposure to other substances, including alcohol and tobacco, that also affect neurodevelopmental outcome. The effects of postnatal maternal cocaine use on the mother's capacity to care for the infant as well as the association of cocaine use with more general environmental factors—for example, poverty, violence, neglect, and abuse—are discussed as important factors to consider when attempting to define whether or not prenatal cocaine exposure has specific and unique effects on the developing fetal brain. Six methodological problems commonly found in the literature on prenatal cocaine exposure are cited as issues to consider when attempting to evaluate the validity of currently available findings.

Linda C. Mayes is the Arnold Gesell Associate Professor of Child Development at the Yale Child Study Center. She received her M.D. from Vanderbilt University, where she also completed a fellowship in neonatology. From 1982 to 1984, she was a Robert Wood Johnson General Pediatrics Academic Fellow. She joined the faculty of the Child Study Center in 1985, and in 1986 she was named a William T. Grant Faculty Scholar. Dr. Mayes is currently involved in a longitudinal study of infants who were exposed to cocaine prenatally.

11

ALTHOUGH the prevalence of cocaine or crack use is declining in the general population—in 1990 an estimated 6.6 million individuals reported use in the preceding year compared to 12 million for 1988[1]—certain groups continue to use at high or increasing rates. Especially in the inner cities, more and more pregnant women are reporting use of cocaine during their pregnancies, with the result that increasing numbers of infants are born having been exposed to cocaine or crack in utero. A recent study of consecutively recruited women in routine prenatal care reported that 17 percent had used cocaine during pregnancy,[2] and national estimates across all socioeconomic groups estimate that 10 to 20 percent of infants are exposed to cocaine prenatally.[3] In some areas, childbearing populations are at much greater risk for abusing drugs than in other areas.[4] For example, in many inner-city populations, nearly 50 percent of women giving birth report or test positive for cocaine use at the time of delivery.[5]

The high rate of cocaine use among pregnant women has generated urgent concern about how their infants will be affected by exposure to cocaine during the critical periods of early gestation. Additionally, cocaine abuse intensifies already well-recognized environmental hazards for mothers and their infants—poverty, violence, abandonment, homelessness, multiple short-term foster placements, and inadequate or abusive parenting.[6] These can be significant factors in and of themselves inasmuch as styles of parenting occupy an important place in determining the child's early cognitive, social, and emotional development.[7] In this article, I summarize the findings of research to date on the effects of prenatal cocaine exposure on early behav-

1. U.S., Department of Health and Human Services, National Institute on Drug Abuse, National Household Survey on Drug Abuse, 1985, 1988, 1990.

2. Deborah A. Frank et al., "Cocaine Use during Pregnancy: Prevalence and Correlates," *Pediatrics*, 82:888-95 (1988).

3. Ira J. Chasnoff, Harvey J. Landress, and Mark E. Barrett, "The Prevalence of Illicit Drug or Alcohol Abuse during Pregnancy and Discrepancies in Mandatory Reporting in Pinellas County, Florida," *New England Journal of Medicine*, 322:102-6 (1990).

4. Hortensia Amaro, Barry Zuckerman, and Howard Cabral, "Drug Use among Adolescent Mothers: Profile of Risk," *Pediatrics*, 84:144-51 (1989); Barry Zuckerman et al., "Effects of Maternal Marijuana and Cocaine Use on Fetal Growth," *New England Journal of Medicine*, 320:762-68 (1989).

5. Hortensia Amaro et al., "Violence during Pregnancy and Substance Use," *American Journal of Public Health*, 80:575-79 (1990); John D. Osterloh and Belle L. Lee, "Urine Drug Screening in Mothers and Newborns," *American Journal of Diseases of Children*, 143:791-93 (1989).

6. Loretta Finnegan et al., "Evaluation of Parenting, Depression, and Violence Profiles in Methadone-Maintained Women," *Child Abuse and Neglect*, 5:267 (1981); Barry Zuckerman, *Selected Methodological Issues in Investigations of Prenatal Effects of Cocaine: Lessons from the Past*, National Institute on Drug Abuse Research Monograph Series (Rockville, MD: Department of Health and Human Services, National Institute on Drug Abuse, forthcoming).

7. Marc Bornstein, "Between Caretakers and Their Young: Two Modes of Interaction and Their Consequences for Cognitive Growth," in *Interaction in Human Development*, ed. Marc H. Bornstein and Jerome S. Bruner (Hillsdale, NJ: Lawrence Erlbaum, 1989), pp. 237-94.

ior and development. I will also outline how any consideration of the long-term effects of prenatal cocaine exposure must take into account the interactions between the biological exposure factor and the social or environmental conditions in which these children live. Finally, I will discuss the critical methodological issues that must be considered before using the available research to guide public policy toward and intervention strategies for cocaine-exposed children.

PHARMACOLOGY OF COCAINE

Cocaine—along with its synthetic equivalent, crack—is a central nervous system (CNS) stimulant. It is similar in structure and in neurochemical action to amphetamines. Cocaine affects both the dopaminergic and norepinephrine neurotransmitter systems in the CNS by blocking the reuptake of these neurotransmitters.[8] Each of these neurotransmitter systems is involved in the modulation of several basic neuropsychological functions including activity level, attention, and regulation of anxiety or other emotional states. Blocking a reuptake of such neurochemicals results in enhanced activity of these agents in the CNS and in specific behaviors and physiological reactions. For example, by blocking the reuptake of dopamine in the CNS, cocaine use magnifies the CNS pleasure response leading to a height-

ened sense of power, euphoria, and excitement.[9] Further, while in adult animal models, chronic cocaine exposure does not produce alterations in the content or morphology of dopamine systems, there is some suggestion that prenatal exposure results in a functional alteration of the dopaminergic neurotransmitter system. Animals exposed to cocaine prenatally show as adults abnormal behavioral responses to other stimulants such as amphetamines.[10]

Norepinephrine mediates the level of CNS arousal and controls the behavioral response to stress or to acutely frightening situations. In the peripheral nervous system, norepinephrine increases blood pressure, heart rate, blood glucose, and peripheral muscle activity, all of which are physiologically necessary for a response to danger. The exaggerated alertness, hypervigilance, tachycardia, and hypertension seen with cocaine use are related to the effect of cocaine on the norepinephrine system.[11] Because of the norepinephrine-related vasoconstrictive effects, in the pregnant animal, cocaine ingestion results in decreased uteroplacental blood flow, severe uteroplacental insufficiency (acute and chronic), maternal hypertension, and

8. Frank H. Gawin and Everett H. Ellinwood, Jr., "Cocaine and Other Stimulants," *New England Journal of Medicine*, 318:1173-82 (1988).

9. Henry L. Spitz and Jeffrey S. Rosecan, *Cocaine Abuse: New Directions in Treatment and Research* (New York: Bruner/Mazel, 1987).

10. Donald E. Hutchings and Diana Dow-Edwards, "Animal Models of Opiate, Cocaine, and Cannabis Use," *Clinics in Perinatology*, 18:1-22 (1991).

11. J. Murdoch Richie and Nicholas M. Greene, "Local Anesthetics," in *The Pharmacologic Basis of Therapeutics*, 7th ed., ed. A. G. Gilman et al. (New York: Macmillan, 1985), pp. 309-310.

fetal vasoconstriction.[12] Cocaine readily crosses the placenta as well as the blood brain barrier. Brain concentrations of cocaine have been as high as four times that of peak plasma levels.[13] Thus the developing fetal brain may be exposed to high levels of cocaine.

NEWBORN OUTCOME

In pregnancy, the vasoconstrictive effects of cocaine lead to a decrease in placental blood flow to the fetus that results in fetal hypoxia—that is, oxygen deficiency—and decreased fetal nutrition.[14] These vasoconstrictive effects on the placenta have been linked to a number of complications and malformations that are evident in the newborn period. Cocaine use has been associated with spontaneous abortion, premature labor, and abruption (placental separation).[15] While maternal cocaine use has been associated with an increased incidence of premature delivery in some studies,[16] this finding has not been confirmed by others.[17]

More consistent with placental vasoconstriction are the reported associations with low birth weight and a decrease in head circumference.[18] Cocaine affects fetal growth on multiple levels. First, the vasoconstrictive effects of cocaine on placental function decrease nutrient flow to the fetus.

12. Thomas R. Moore et al., "Hemodynamic Effects of Intravenous Cocaine on the Pregnant Ewe and Fetus," *American Journal of Obstetrics and Gynecology*, 155:883-88 (1986); James R. Woods, Mark A. Plessinger, and Kenneth E. Clark, "Effect of Cocaine on Uterine Blood Flow and Fetal Oxygenation," *Journal of the American Medical Association*, 257:957-61 (1987).

13. Henry C. Farrar and Gregory L. Kearns, "Cocaine: Clinical Pharmacology and Toxicology," *Journal of Pediatrics*, 115:665-75 (1989).

14. Woods, Plessinger, and Clark, "Effect of Cocaine on Uterine Blood Flow."

15. Cathy S. Lindenberg et al., "A Review of the Literature on Cocaine Abuse in Pregnancy," *Nursing Research*, 40:69-75 (1991); N. Bingol et al., "Teratogenicity of Cocaine in Humans," *Journal of Pediatrics*, 110:93-96 (1987); R. Cherukuri et al., "A Cohort Study of Alkaloidal Cocaine ('Crack') in Pregnancy," *Obstetrics and Gynecology*, 72:147-51 (1988).

16. Cherukuri et al., "Cohort Study of Alkaloidal Cocaine"; Scott N. MacGregor et al., "Cocaine Use during Pregnancy: Adverse Perinatal Outcome," *American Journal of Perinatal Outcome*, 157:686-90 (1987); Bertis B. Little et al., "Cocaine Abuse during Pregnancy: Maternal and Fetal Implications," *Obstetrics and Gynecology*, 73:157-60 (1989); Ira J. Chasnoff, Kathryn A. Burns, and William J. Burns, "Cocaine Use in Pregnancy: Perinatal Morbidity and Mortality," *Neurotoxicology and Teratology*, 9:291-93 (1987).

17. Zuckerman et al., "Effects of Maternal Marijuana and Cocaine Use"; Anthony J. Hadeed and Sharon R. Siegel, "Maternal Cocaine Use during Pregnancy: Effect on the Newborn Infant," *Pediatrics*, 84:205-10 (1989); L. Ryan, S. Erlich, and Loretta Finnegan, "Cocaine Abuse in Pregnancy: Effects on the Fetus and Newborn," *Neurotoxicology and Teratology*, 9:295-99 (1987).

18. Zuckerman et al., "Effects of Maternal Marijuana and Cocaine Use"; Cherukuri et al., "Cohort Study of Alkaloidal Cocaine"; MacGregor et al., "Cocaine Use during Pregnancy"; Chasnoff, Burns, and Burns, "Cocaine Use in Pregnancy"; Hadeed and Siegel, "Maternal Cocaine Use during Pregnancy"; Ryan, Erlich, and Finnegan, "Cocaine Abuse in Pregnancy"; Amy S. Oro and Suzanne D. Dixon, "Perinatal Cocaine and Methamphetamine Exposure: Maternal and Neonatal Correlates," *Journal of Pediatrics*, 111:571-78 (1987); Richard Fulroth, Barry Phillips, and David J. Durand, "Perinatal Outcome of Infants Exposed to Cocaine and/or Heroin In Utero," *American Journal of Diseases of Children*, 143:905-10 (1989).

Second, the increase in fetal metabolism caused by the increase in norepinephrine activity causes a depletion of fetal nutrient stores and eventually fetal malnutrition.[19] Third, cocaine abuse is associated with other maternal health factors that potentially compromise fetal status including maternal undernutrition and use of other drugs such as tobacco and alcohol.[20] Only one study that demonstrates a relationship between cocaine exposure and delay in fetal growth controlled for maternal nutritional status and alcohol and tobacco use.[21]

Prenatal cocaine exposure is also associated with a higher rate of congenital malformations including limb deformities, cardiac malformations, ocular impairments, and anomalies of the urinary tract.[22] The diversity of these malformations suggests that their association with cocaine is not because of a specific teratogenic—fetal-malformation—effect but rather because of effects of cocaine on blood flow to developing organ systems. In support of the possibility of more serious direct effects on fetal vasculature, Chasnoff described an instance of perinatal cerebral infarction associated with heavy maternal cocaine use 15 hours before delivery,[23] and Hoyme and colleagues described a group of anomalies in infants exposed to cocaine that were most consistent with disruption of fetal vasculature.[24] It should be noted that recent studies that control for confounding variables such as tobacco use again have not shown that cocaine exposure is associated independently with these various congenital anomalies.[25]

Reports of infant status after delivery describe a number of neurological and neurobehavioral abnormalities. Actual brain malformations have been reported in a study of

19. Kathleen Fiks, Helen Johnson, and Tove Rosen, "Methadone-Maintained Mothers: Three-Year Follow-up of Parental Functioning," *International Journal of Addiction*, 20:651-60 (1985).

20. Frank et al., "Cocaine Use during Pregnancy"; Zuckerman et al., "Effects of Maternal Marijuana and Cocaine Use."

21. Zuckerman et al., "Effects of Maternal Marijuana and Cocaine Use."

22. Ira J. Chasnoff, Gay M. Chisum, and William E. Kaplan, "Maternal Cocaine Use and Genitourinary Tract Malformations," *Teratology*, 37:201-4 (1988); Sherwin J. Isenberg, Abraham Spierer, Stanley H. Inkelis, "Ocular Signs of Cocaine Intoxication in Neonates," *American Journal of Ophthalmology*, 103:211-14 (1987); Gilberto F. Chavez, Joseph Mulinare, and José F. Cordero, "Maternal Cocaine Use during Early Pregnancy as a Risk Factor for Congenital Urogenital Anomalies," *Journal of the American Medical Association*, 262:795-98 (1989); Rodrigo Dominguez et al., "Brain and Ocular Abnormalities in Infants with In Utero Exposure to Cocaine and Other Street Drugs," *American Journal of Diseases of Children*, 145:688-95 (1991); S. E. Lipshultz, J. J. Frassica, and E. J. Orav, "Cardiovascular Abnormalities in Infants Prenatally Exposed to Cocaine," *Journal of Pediatrics*, 118:44-51 (1991); H. E. Hoyme et al., "Prenatal Cocaine Exposure and Fetal Vascular Disruption," *Pediatrics*, 85:743-47 (1990).

23. Ira J. Chasnoff et al., "Perinatal Cerebral Infarction and Maternal Cocaine Use," *Journal of Pediatrics*, 108:456-59 (1986).

24. Hoyme et al., "Prenatal Cocaine Exposure."

25. Zuckerman et al., "Effects of Maternal Marijuana and Cocaine Use"; Barry Zuckerman and Deborah A. Frank, "Marijuana and Cocaine: Clinical Implications," in *Maternal Substance Abuse and Neural Development*, ed. I. Zagon and T. Slotkin (New York: Academic Press, forthcoming).

stimulant-exposed—cocaine plus amphetamines—asymptomatic infants in which 35 percent showed marked morphological alterations in brain structure primarily in the frontal lobe and basal ganglia.[26] One study reported electroencephalographic abnormalities in infants exposed to cocaine that were not predictable on the basis of the severity of any perinatal symptoms and resolved within six months after delivery.[27] Similarly, abnormalities in CNS auditory function have been reported that are consistent with neurological impairment or dysfunction in the auditory system.[28] As with the electroencephalographic patterns, these auditory dysfunctions seem to revert to normal by three to six months. Seizures in the neonatal period have been reported in a number of individual case studies, and a proportion of these infants, though not all, continued to have seizures after six months of age.[29] While cocaine abuse does lower the seizure

threshold in adults,[30] it is not clear what the true incidence of cocaine-related seizures is in infants with no other risk factors.[31]

Neonatal neurobehavioral symptoms related to cocaine exposure have been reported in several studies, but the findings are sufficiently inconsistent to warrant caution about drawing any firm conclusion about the effects of cocaine on neurobehavioral functioning. While infants exposed to cocaine do not show withdrawal symptoms in the neonatal period,[32] they are often poorly responsive and difficult to arouse. Once alert, they may quickly become irritable and difficult to engage. Several studies have evaluated the neurobehavioral functioning of cocaine-exposed infants using the Brazelton Neonatal Behavioral Assessment Scale (NBAS), which assesses such functions as ease of arousal, capacity to attend to animate and inanimate objects, and ability to tolerate stimulation of differing intensity. In a series of studies, Chasnoff reported

26. Suzanne D. Dixon and Raul Bejar, "Echoencephalographic Findings in Neonates Associated with Maternal Cocaine and Methamphetamine Use: Incidence and Clinical Correlates," *Journal of Pediatrics*, 115:770-78 (1989). These findings have yet to be replicated by other investigators.

27. Tatiana M. Doberczak et al., "Neonatal Neurologic and Electroencephalographic Effects of Intrauterine Cocaine Exposure," *Journal of Pediatrics*, 113:354-58 (1988).

28. A. Salamy et al., "Brain-Stem Transmission Time in Infants Exposed to Cocaine In Utero," *Journal of Pediatrics*, 117:627-29 (1990); L. Shih, B. Cone-Wesson, and B. Reddix, "Effects of Maternal Cocaine Abuse on the Neonatal Auditory System," *International Journal of Pediatric Otorhinolaryngology*, 15:245-51 (1988).

29. L. D. Kramer et al., "Neonatal Cocaine-Related Seizures," *Journal of Child Neurology*, 5:60-64 (1990).

30. Frank H. Gawin and Herbert D. Kleber, "Evolving Conceptualizations of Cocaine Dependence," *Yale Journal of Biology and Medicine*, 61:123-36 (1988).

31. Zuckerman and Frank, "Marijuana and Cocaine."

32. Ira J. Chasnoff et al., "Cocaine Use in Pregnancy," *New England Journal of Medicine*, 313:666-69 (1985); Ira J. Chasnoff and Dan R. Griffith, "Cocaine: Clinical Studies of Pregnancy and the Newborn," *Annals of the New York Academy of Science*, 562:260-66 (1989); Patrick E. LeBlanc et al., "Effects of Intrauterine Exposure to Alkaloidal Cocaine ('Crack')," *American Journal of Diseases of Children*, 141:937-38 (1987); John D. Madden, Terrence F. Payne, and Sue Miller, "Maternal Cocaine Abuse and the Effect on the Newborn," *Pediatrics*, 77:209-11 (1986).

that on the NBAS, cocaine-exposed infants have increased state lability, for instance, more shifts from alert to crying or alert to sleep; increased startles; and decreased interactive behaviors, for example, attention to animate objects such as examiner's face.[33] In contrast, a recent study found no differences on NBAS scores between cocaine-exposed and unexposed newborns in the first 72 hours.[34]

Other factors such as maternal alcohol use, concomitant opiate exposure, or obstetric complications such as length of labor may contribute to some of the reported relations between cocaine exposure and neonatal irritability.[35] Further, other factors, especially intrauterine growth retardation, may contribute to the variability in neurobehavioral profiles found among cocaine-exposed infants. It may be that these factors influence neurobehavioral functioning through different mechanisms, that is, that cocaine has both a specific effect on brain functioning and an indirect effect through the influence on fetal nutritional status. In support of a specific effect of cocaine on brain functioning are the findings of atypical fetal breathing patterns and altered respiratory control in exposed infants.[36] Neonatal cry characteristics lend support to the hypothesis about a direct and indirect effect of cocaine on neurobehavioral functioning.[37] The potentially direct effects of cocaine exposure on brain development and/or function are hypothesized to result in cry features that characterize an excitable pattern. In contrast, fetal malnutrition and intrauterine growth retardation result in a series of acoustic characteristics characterized as depressed neurobehavioral functioning.

In summary, in the newborn period a number of neurological and neurobehavioral dysfunctions and impairments have been reported as related to cocaine exposure. Many of these findings have not been replicated in more carefully designed studies that include comparison groups and also take into account other perinatal factors including use of other substances such as alcohol. Further, a number of the reported dysfunctions appear transient and are no longer apparent by six months of age. The variability in findings may in part reflect mixed etiologies; that is, different findings may be due

33. Chasnoff, "Cocaine Use in Pregnancy"; Ira J. Chasnoff et al., "Prenatal Drug Exposure: Effects on Neonatal and Infant Growth and Development," *Neurobehavior, Toxicology and Teratology*, 8:357-62 (1986); Ira J. Chasnoff et al., "Temporal Patterns of Cocaine Use in Pregnancy," *Journal of the American Medical Association*, 261:1741-44 (1989).

34. Daniel R. Neuspiel and Sara C. Hamel, "Cocaine and Infant Behavior," *Journal of Developmental and Behavioral Pediatrics*, 12:55-64 (1991).

35. Lisa N. Eisen et al., "Perinatal Cocaine Effects on Neonatal Stress Behavior and Performance on the Brazelton Scale," *Pediatrics*, 88:477-80 (1991).

36. Jeannine Gingras et al., "Atypical Fetal Breathing Patterns Associated with In Utero Cocaine Exposure," *Pediatric Research*, 25:3, abstract no. 1844 (1989); Warren W. Wasiewski and Thomas N. Hansen, "Intrauterine Cocaine Exposure Alters Respiratory Control in Newborn Rabbit Pups," ibid., 27:74A.

37. Barry M. Lester et al., "Neurobehavioral Syndromes in Cocaine Exposed Newborn Infants," *Child Development*, 62:694-705 (1991).

to the direct effect of cocaine on fetal brain development or may be accounted for through the indirect effects on uterine blood supply with the resulting fetal hypoxia.

LONG-TERM EFFECTS OF PRENATAL COCAINE EXPOSURE

Very little is known about any long-term neurological sequelae of prenatal exposure to cocaine and crack, and what is currently available deals with infants exposed to both cocaine and opiates. There are no published studies of the development of children exposed prenatally to cocaine alone that follow children beyond the newborn period. However, the findings from the newborn period previously cited—such as small head circumference, persistent seizures, or structural damage to selective areas of the brain found on cranial ultrasound—do raise significant concerns regarding long-term neurological and behavioral effects related to cocaine. Recently, some investigators studying cocaine-exposed infants have begun to discuss apparently persistent problems in attention regulation and impulse control through the second year of life. For example, in a study of mother-infant attachment, 18-month-old children exposed to cocaine, along with a mixture of other drugs, demonstrated more disorganized behavior and less representational play.[38] A number of anecdotal reports from schools describe children who are markedly impulsive and show severe attentional impairments.[39]

Data from several animal models would suggest that the mechanisms for the neuroregulation of states of arousal and attention may be affected by prenatal cocaine exposure. Animal studies indicate that prenatal cocaine exposure produces offspring with an impaired ability to perform associative learning soon after birth. Several have found that adult animals, exposed prenatally, show depressed hippocampal function, which is responsible for the consolidation of memory.[40] Second, as cited earlier, prenatal exposure to cocaine seems to alter central dopaminergic function.[41] The neurotransmitters, norepinephrine and dopamine, play an important role in central control of basic processes including the regulation of attention, response to sensory stimuli, and the modulation of mood states.[42] By altering neurotransmitter activity, chronic prenatal exposure to cocaine

38. Carol Rodning, Leila Beckwith, and Judy Howard, "Characteristics of Attachment Organization and Play Organization in Prenatally Drug Exposed Toddlers," *Development and Psychopathology*, 1:277-89 (1990).

39. Sandra Blakeslee, "Parents Fight for a Future for Infants Born to Drugs," *New York Times*, 19 May 1990; Susan Chira, "Crack Babies Turn 5 and Schools Brace," ibid., 25 May 1990; Nicole Wise, "Drug Users' Children Need Help at School," ibid., 19 Aug. 1990.

40. Diana Dow-Edwards, Laurel A. Freed, and T. A. Fico, "Structural and Functional Effects of Prenatal Cocaine Exposure in Adult Rat Brain," *Developmental Brain Research*, in press.

41. Hutchings and Dow-Edwards, "Animal Models of Opiate, Cocaine, and Cannibis Use."

42. Barry L. Jacobs, "Overview of the Activity of the Brain Monoaminergic Neurons across the Sleep-Wake Cycle," in *Sleep-Neurotransmitters and Neuromodulators*, ed. A. Wauquier et al. (New York: Raven Press, 1985), pp. 1-14.

may adversely affect these functions in the developing nervous system of exposed infants. That prenatal cocaine exposure does alter neurotransmitter function and activity is suggested by the finding that elevated circulating norepinephrine levels and heart rates are found in prenatally exposed infants at two months of age.[43]

Thus there are data suggesting that prenatal cocaine exposure does have specific direct effects on neurological functioning and that these effects may be manifest in the regulation of attention, functions of memory, and modulation of anxiety and other mood states. To date, however, no study has examined these outcomes in a group of infants exposed to cocaine prenatally and followed longitudinally. The question of whether or not prenatal exposure to cocaine results in specific neurodevelopmental sequelae remains a significant one for predicting the needs for intervention and educational services in the future. Establishing cause-effect relationships between prenatal cocaine exposure and neurodevelopmental deficits can be problematic, however, given the number of confounding variables that might affect vulnerability to such neurodevelopmental outcomes.[44] At the

very least, developmental outcomes such as attentional regulation, anxiety regulation, and memory function, while neurocognitive or neurophysiological functions, are dramatically influenced by environmental circumstances. Any longitudinal study examining the long-term effects of cocaine on development will need to take into account the psychosocial conditions in which these children live.

THE INTERACTIONS BETWEEN BIOLOGICAL AND ENVIRONMENTAL FACTORS

As Zuckerman and others have emphasized, the potential developmental sequelae of prenatal exposure to cocaine are best conceptualized by considering the interaction between biological and environmental factors.[45] By directly affecting brain development as well as through the effects on fetal blood flow and maternal nutrition, cocaine contributes to a biologically based vulnerability for neurodevelopmental impairments. These dysfunctions heighten the child's vulnerability to the effects of inadequate or inconsistent caretaking. On the other hand, many early neurodevelopmental dysfunctions may be partially or completely compensated for both because of brain plasticity in early infancy and childhood and through the effects of adequate caretaking.

43. Sally L. D. Ward et al., "Circulating Catecholamines and Adrenoreceptors in Infants of Cocaine Abusing Mothers," *Pediatric Research*, 27:74A (1990); M. S. Woo et al., "Elevated Heart Rates in Infants of Cocaine Abusing Mothers during Normoxia and Hypoxia," *American Review of Respiratory Diseases*, 141:A807 (1990).

44. Stephen J. Suomi and J. Dee Higley, "Rationale and Methodologies for Developing Nonhuman Primate Models of Prenatal Drug Exposure" (Manuscript, National Institute of Child Health and Development, Laboratory of Comparative Ethology, 1990).

45. Zuckerman and Frank, "Marijuana and Cocaine."

For example, if mothers' substance abuse continues after delivery, their capacities to respond to their infants may be impaired.[46] The association between substance abuse and greater incidence of parental psychopathology, such as depression,[47] provides additional risks of impaired maternal interactions with the infant.[48] Any of the developmental outcomes —whether more general measures of mental age or cognitive performance or more specific outcomes such as attentional regulation—are influenced by maternal interactive style.[49] Because of the effects of substance abuse on maternal behavior as well as on more general environmental factors, sorting out the biological effects of prenatal cocaine exposure on development from the effects mediated by the influence of cocaine on the caregiving environment requires detailed studies of maternal style as well as of selected infant neurodevelopmental outcomes.

Among human infants, the relation between perinatal factors and neurodevelopment is most apparent in the first year of life. Subsequently, much of the individual variation in outcome is related to social and environmental factors.[50] Particularly among infants exposed to opiates prenatally, the quality of the postnatal environment and not the amount of prenatal exposure seems to be the more important contributor to outcome.[51] Early motor-coordination difficulties among methadone-exposed infants tend to disappear by the second year of life unless the dysfunction is combined with environments of high social risk.[52] There is no reason to expect that the effects of environment on the development of cocaine-exposed infants will be mediated differently.

The parenting capacities of mothers using cocaine and/or other substances may be markedly impaired, which in turn influences the interactions between these mothers and their infants. Functionally, it is the cumulative effect of these interactions that most influences the infant's developmental functioning[53] and affects whether or not the envi-

46. Pamela S. Bauman and Frank E. Dougherty, "Drug-Addicted Mothers' Parenting and Their Children's Development," *International Journal of Addiction*, 18:291-302 (1983).

47. Bruce J. Rounsaville et al., "Heterogeneity of Psychiatric Diagnosis in Treated Opiate Addicts," *Archives of General Psychiatry*, 39:161-66 (1982).

48. Michael Fendrick, Virginia Warner, and Myrna Weissman, "Family Risk Factors, Parental Depression, and Psychopathology in Offspring," *Developmental Psychology*, 26:40-50 (1990).

49. Catherine S. Tamis-LeMonda and Marc H. Bornstein, "Habituation and Maternal Encouragement of Attention in Infancy as Predictors of Toddler Language, Play, and Representational Competence," *Child Development*, 60:738-51 (1989).

50. Helen Bee et al., "Prediction of IQ and Language Skill from Perinatal Status, Child Performance, Family Characteristics, and Mother-Infant Interaction," *Child Development*, 53:1134-56 (1982).

51. Marta Lifshitz et al., "Factors Affecting Head Growth and Intellectual Function in Children of Drug Addiction," *Pediatrics*, 75:269-74 (1985).

52. Sydney L. Hans, "Developmental Consequences of Prenatal Exposure to Methadone: Prenatal Abuse of Licit and Illicit Drugs," *Annals of the New York Academy of Sciences*, 562:195-207 (1989).

53. Victor J. Bernstein, Rita J. Jeremy, and Joseph Marcus, "Mother-Infant Interaction in Multiproblem Families: Finding Them at

ronmental input will facilitate recovery from early neurodevelopmental dysfunctions. For example, clinical depression occurs frequently among drug-using women[54] and impairs their ability to respond consistently to their infant's needs. Children of depressed mothers tend to have more behavior and learning problems and tend to have more difficulties with regulation of affect than do children raised by nondepressed mothers.[55] These outcomes are similar to the ones of interest in questions about the effects of prenatal cocaine exposure. Further, infants exposed to cocaine may be difficult to arouse or bring to an alert attentional state. For such infants, mothers ideally provide external support to facilitate the infant's gradually developing more adequate arousal, or state, regulatory patterns; that is, they provide stimulation when an infant is underaroused and carefully reduce external stimulation when the infant is overexcited. These types of state regulatory dysfunctions, difficult for any parent, are particularly difficult for mothers using drugs.

Other environmental factors that tend to occur more often in the families of drug-exposed infants include poverty, repeated episodes of violence, neglect and abuse of the child, and multiple foster placements.[56]

Risk," *Journal of American Academy of Child Psychiatry*, 25:631-40 (1986).

54. Barry Zuckerman et al., "Depressive Symptoms during Pregnancy: Relationship to Poor Health Behavior," *American Journal of Obstetrics and Gynecology*, 160:1107-11 (1989).

55. Barry S. Zuckerman and William Beardslee, "Maternal Depression: An Issue for Pediatricians," *Pediatrics*, 79:110-17 (1987).

56. Amaro et al., "Violence during Pregnancy."

Any one of these factors is also associated with a variety of developmental dysfunctions. Differentiating the importance of the multiple poor health behaviors prenatally and postnatal environmental factors associated with parental drug use from the importance of neurophysiological manifestations specific to the actions of prenatal cocaine exposure is essential in order to inform policy and appropriate interventions.

METHODOLOGICAL ISSUES

A significant problem in interpreting the currently available findings about the relationship between prenatal cocaine exposure and developmental outcome is that the scientific literature is plagued by a number of methodological problems. In brief, these include issues such as sample definition, controlling for confounding variables, and selecting outcomes specifically targeted to assess the hypothesized effects of cocaine on fetal and neonatal brain functioning and on individual behavior and performance.

Most important is the issue of identification of exposure. In any study of possible teratogenic effects, identifying the specific agents, the timing, the frequency, and the intensity of the exposure is critical. First, the relative purity and potency of cocaine varies over time, across regions, and often from exposure to exposure. Thus there are few ways to judge dosage of exposure. Additionally, cocaine is often diluted with a number of adulterants of which the user may be unaware, including talcum, ether, or lidocaine—each of which may also have unknown fetal effects.[57] Timing of exposure is equally important and difficult to determine. Is an infant who is exposed to cocaine early in the first trimester at equal risk with an infant whose mother continues to use the drug throughout pregnancy? Is there a sensitive period during pregnancy in which exposure becomes most harmful?[58] The frequency and timing of cocaine use by pregnant women vary. In one of the few prospective studies conducted, one-third of cocaine users used less than once per month, and 50 percent used at least weekly.[59] Only one study has evaluated outcomes in newborns based on different patterns of maternal use.[60]

Determining the nature of exposure to cocaine is further complicated by the tendency of cocaine users to use other drugs—for example, alcohol, heroin, marijuana, tobacco—and to practice other poor health behaviors, such as inadequate nutrition and prenatal care.[61] The specific effects of cocaine on fetal development may be additive to, or synergistic with, these other factors. For example, in one study, infants of mothers who had a positive urine assay for cocaine during pregnancy were approximately 400 grams smaller in birthweight than infants of mothers who did not use cocaine. Only 25 percent of the weight decrement could be attributed directly to cocaine, however. The remainder was attributable to the effect of cigarettes and marijuana, other drugs, and poor nutrition.[62]

A second methodological issue is the identification of users. Because cocaine, along with other agents such as marijuana or heroin, is illegal, determination of exposure based solely on maternal report will fail to identify many infants who are exposed. In one study, 24 percent of women who used cocaine would not have been identified had not urine assays been conducted.[63] In another study, only 43 percent of cocaine-exposed infants identified by urine screening were identified by a clinical history.[64] Urine assays at the birth of the child also provide limited information because positive urines identify only women who have used the drug within one to four days of the assay. Urine assays performed on mothers postpartum identify only 25 percent of cocaine users, and these are most likely to be the heavier users.[65] If cocaine users, especially more moderate ones, are misclassified as nonusers and the outcomes of interest are less severe compared to those of

57. Zuckerman and Frank, "Marijuana and Cocaine."

58. Marc H. Bornstein, "Sensitive Periods in Development: Structural Characteristics and Causal Interpretations," *Psychological Bulletin*, 105:179-97 (1989).

59. Amaro, Zuckerman, and Cabral, "Drug Use among Adolescent Mothers."

60. Ira J. Chasnoff et al., "Temporal Patterns of Cocaine Use in Pregnancy," *Journal of the American Medical Association*, 261:1741-44 (1989).

61. Zuckerman et al., "Effects of Maternal Marijuana and Cocaine Use."

62. Ibid.

63. Ibid.

64. Mark G. Neerhof et al., "Cocaine Abuse during Pregnancy: Peripartum Prevalence and Perinatal Outcome," *American Journal of Obstetrics and Gynecology*, 161:633-38 (1989).

65. Frank et al., "Cocaine Use during Pregnancy"; Zuckerman et al., "Effects of Maternal Marijuana and Cocaine Use"; Zuckerman, "Selected Methodological Issues."

the heavier users, the user group will have a falsely elevated rate of severe outcomes. Conversely, if users are misclassified as nonusers, differences between the two groups in the outcomes of interest that might truly be attributable to cocaine may be minimized and hence overlooked. Thus identification and classification of prenatal cocaine use constitute a critical issue. If assay techniques that reflect longer periods of exposure, such as detection in meconium, can be validated, classification of women and their infants would improve.[66]

How samples are selected represents a third methodological issue. Study populations are often not well defined or are not generalizable to the larger population of women using cocaine during their pregnancy. Generalizing from poorly defined or highly selective samples is risky. Common study samples consist of women whose drug use is evident enough for them to be referred to drug treatment programs prenatally or for the clinical staff to detect it at the time of delivery.[67] The mothers of these infants constitute a small percentage of the pregnant women who use cocaine and probably represent the most frequent users of cocaine.[68] They may also reflect the prevailing socioeconomic prejudices regarding those who use drugs. Chasnoff recently reported that clinicians were 10 times more likely to report a woman for substance abuse if she were low-income and black even though actual rates of prenatal use of illicit drugs were no different in this group from those of white women delivering on the private obstetric service.[69]

The issue of nonrepresentative samples becomes more complicated with any attempt to follow these infants over time inasmuch as the children and families who are retained in long-term studies may be quite different from those who are lost or withdraw from the study.[70] It may be that families who are better functioning and more motivated continue in the study and that these are the families who are least affected by substance abuse. In this case, results may be biased toward children of lower psychosocial risk of developmental impairments. Conversely, it may also be that families with more apparently impaired children remain in the study, in which case the samples are skewed toward more dysfunctional infants. At the very least, identifying the characteristics of those children lost to follow-up and comparing them to those retained is necessary in order to evaluate the validity and generalizability of the outcome data.

Sample selection raises a fourth methodological issue, which is the

66. Zuckerman and Frank, "Marijuana and Cocaine"; Edward C. Maynard, Louis P. Amoruso, and William Oh, "Meconium for Drug Testing," *American Journal of Diseases of Children*, 145:650-52 (1991).

67. Bingol et al., "Teratogenicity of Cocaine in Humans"; Oro and Dixon, "Perinatal Cocaine and Methamphetamine Exposure"; Chasnoff et al., "Cocaine Use in Pregnancy"; Madden, Payne, and Miller, "Maternal Cocaine Abuse."

68. Zuckerman, "Selected Methodological Issues."

69. Chasnoff, Landress, and Barrett, "Prevalence of Illicit Drug or Alcohol Abuse."

70. Zuckerman and Frank, "Marijuana and Cocaine."

use of comparison groups and the administration of measures by individuals blinded to the infant's exposure status. Ideally, the comparison group should be comparable to the cocaine-exposed sample on factors that are most likely to influence developmental outcome. Inasmuch as most exposed children come from minority, impoverished families, selecting comparison groups from these same populations is imperative. Further, a number of the neurobehavioral or neurodevelopmental measures are likely to be distorted by the examiner's knowledge of the child's exposure status. For example, many of the NBAS items require subjective examiner judgments about how interactive or neurologically organized an infant is. Knowledge of drug exposure status may well bias the examiner to score that infant higher or lower depending on the examiner's notions about the effects of prenatal cocaine exposure.

A fifth methodological issue concerns elucidating the specific functions in children that are likely to be compromised by cocaine. General measures of developmental outcome may not provide critical information on how cocaine harms children or which specific functions may be affected, information needed if appropriate intervention or remediation is to be designed. Well-standardized measures such as the Bayley Scales of Infant Development may not tap into the specific areas of dysfunction such as attentional regulation. On the other hand, measures of the more specific functional areas, such as attention, likely to be affected by co-

caine, though more sensitive to subtle impairments, are more difficult to administer. Further, any study of long-term outcome needs to include measures of postnatal drug exposure, of the home environment, and of caretaker functioning with the child.

The sixth and final methodological issue concerns the number of confounding variables to be considered in any hypotheses about the effect of prenatal cocaine exposure. As discussed earlier in this article, cocaine use is strongly associated with a number of maternal characteristics and health behaviors that correlate significantly with poor pregnancy outcome and elevated risk for developmental impairments. Also as discussed, in the postnatal period, the drug culture exerts confounding negative effects on the child's family and community environments and is strongly correlated with poverty, violence, abandonment, homelessness, and inadequate or abusive parenting. As long as addiction prevents mothers from adequately caring for their children even in the most basic ways, children born to addicts will frequently face inadequate parenting or, alternatively, multiple, short-term foster placements and/or repeated moves over short periods of time, a situation that brings with it the added developmental risk of multiple separations and losses in the early years. Differentiating the relative importance of environmental effects from neurophysiological manifestations specific to the actions of prenatal cocaine exposure on the central nervous system will be essential and difficult.

CONCLUSION

Despite a significant amount of research to date, many important questions about prenatal cocaine exposure remain unanswered, including issues of prevalence, mechanism of neurobiological effect, and neurodevelopmental outcome. The central challenge for studies of outcome in these children is to understand how much of their adaptive difficulties are due to the effects of prenatal cocaine exposure on developing brain and how much results from the environmental effects of inadequate caretaking. Because of its urgent and potentially catastrophic nature, prenatal cocaine exposure has attracted a great deal of attention from the press, investigators, educators, and policymakers. Despite the problems in the currently available evidence, infants exposed to cocaine in utero are often represented as severely or even irrevocably brain damaged—to the point that they may never function normally in society.

On this account, a very large group of children is being written off. Moreover, a social sentiment has arisen that the loss of these children is entirely attributable to the prenatal effects of cocaine, a permanent biological factor. Apparently, such a sentiment is not informed by the currently available research findings about the developmental and physical status of cocaine-exposed infants since present knowledge is simply too scant and/or contradictory to assume irremediable brain damage due to cocaine exposure. Though, as we have outlined, prenatal cocaine exposure does pose certain risks for the developing fetal brain, the postnatal factors that these children do inevitably face—poor nutrition, poverty, exposure to violence—are well-documented risk factors for developmental impairments.

There are many reasons for educators, clinicians, and policymakers to adhere to a belief that cocaine-exposed infants are invariably impaired simply and only because of their prenatal exposure to the drug. Among these, perhaps the most powerful is the wish to absolve society from having to face other explanations of the children's plight that are far more complex than presence or absence of a prenatal exposure and run deep within the societal fabric. Seriously considering explanations for these children's problems that take into account poverty, community violence, inadequate education, and diminishing employment opportunities requires us to critically review wider social values. These are problems that are simply far more difficult to solve or even to remedy. In principle, preventing prenatal cocaine exposure is simple: stop mothers' use of the drug by educating them about the risks, and, if need be, legislate prohibitions in the form of mandatory reporting of child abuse if mothers use cocaine during their pregnancy. But these measures do not work either to prevent prenatal exposure or to ensure that mothers are adequately cared for during their pregnancy.

Our history of success in prohibiting the use of illegal or even legal toxic substances does not lead us to believe that preventing cocaine use will occur quickly or simply. Mothers' use of cocaine reflects more than their addiction. It is part of the same complex array of social factors that also become risk factors for their children—inadequate education, threats of violence, unemployment. Moreover, legislation that punishes mothers by automatically removing their infants more likely drives them away from health care for they fear they will be reported. Paradoxically, they and their infants are placed at far greater risk for serious perinatal complications and resultant long-term sequelae because they do not receive adequate prenatal care.

The urgency to label prenatally cocaine-exposed children as irrevocably damaged also carries with it significant medical and psychosocial risks for the children. Labels such as "severely brain damaged" have a way of becoming self-fulfilling. Minimally, expectations for such children are lowered.[71] The attribution of irremediable damage makes it more difficult to find services for these children that are geared toward effective remediation rather than basic caretaking. Even more damaging is the difficulty in finding adequate homes for such children, since potential foster or adoptive parents are often concerned about assuming the care of cocaine-exposed children because of their perceived impairments.[72]

Labels also carry with them a risk of biasing and undermining clinical

decisions and scientific investigations. A 1989 report in *Lancet* indicates that abstracts regarding the impact of prenatal cocaine use were more likely to be accepted for presentation at the annual meeting of the Society for Pediatric Research if they reported positive results—that is, evidence of impairment—than if they failed to show such results, even though the rejected papers with negative findings tended to be methodologically more rigorous.[73] Clinical decisions are also affected by underlying attitudes. Another study shows that, given an equivalent extent of use of illegal drugs by pregnant women, physicians and clinics are more likely to report to law enforcement agencies black women or women on welfare than white or middle-class women.[74] Prejudice exists, and it can well bias referral to services, identification of children at risk for developmental impairment, or even which study results are given the most attention and weight.

Finally, labeling and isolating infants and young children because of their prenatal experience may lead us to overlook what we have long known about the remediating effects of early intervention.[75] Studies of preterm or ill newborns fail to support biological determinism.[76] Environ-

71. Robert Rosenthal and Lenore Jacobson, *Pygmalion in the Classroom: Teacher Expectation and Pupils' Intellectual Development* (New York: Holt, Rinehart & Winston, 1968).

72. Blakeslee, "Parents Fight for a Future"; J. C. Barden, "Foster Care System Reeling, despite Law Meant to Help," *New York Times*, 21 Sept. 1990.

73. G. Koren et al., "Bias against the Null Hypothesis: The Reproductive Hazards of Cocaine," *Lancet*, 16 Dec. 1989, pp. 1440-42.

74. Chasnoff, Landress, and Barrett, "Prevalence of Illicit Drug or Alcohol Abuse."

75. S. J. Meisels and J. P. Shonkoff, *Handbook of Early Childhood Intervention* (New York: Cambridge University Press, 1990).

76. Lyla Beckwith and Arthur H. Parmelee, Jr., "EEG Patterns of Preterm Infants, Home Environment and Later IQ," *Child*

ments contribute significantly to the outcome of infants with biological vulnerabilities at birth.[77] Even among infants exposed to narcotics prenatally, the home environment and not the amount of narcotics seems to be the more important predictor of developmental outcome.[78]

A fuller understanding of the problems of intrauterine cocaine exposure will require careful attention to the fundamental methodological issues previously outlined. Information derived from good science is needed to make sound clinical and public policy decisions.[79]

While we await research findings regarding discrete neurodevelopmental problems that may require specific therapeutic interventions, sufficient data are available from other sources to show that providing comprehensive services for these infants and their mothers around the drug-related health and environmental risk factors will improve outcome.[80] For the infants, such services include adequate nutrition, health care, and early developmental intervention programs, and for the mothers, drug treatment, health care, and family-support assistance. Providing key services such as pediatric health care, drug treatment, child-development services, and family planning in one location with one appointment system and the same staff may facilitate compliance with these services and improve the health and well-being of both mother and child.

Development, 57:777-89 (1986); Infant Health and Development Program, "Enhancing the Outcomes of Low-Birthweight, Premature Infants: A Multisite, Randomized Trial," *Journal of the American Medical Association*, 263:3035-42 (1990).

77. Arnold J. Sameroff, "Developmental Systems: Contexts and Evolution," in *Handbook of Child Psychology*, vol. 1, *History, Theory and Methods*, ed. W. Kessen and P. H. Mussen (New York: John Wiley, 1983), pp. 237-94.

78. Lifshitz et al., "Factors Affecting Head Growth."

79. U.S., Congress, House, Committee on Ways and Means, Subcommittee on Human

Resources, testimony of B. Zuckerman, 3 Apr. 1990.

80. L. C. Mayes et al., "The Problem of Prenatal Cocaine Exposure: A Rush to Judgement," *Journal of the American Medical Association*, 267:406-8 (1992).

ANNALS, *AAPSS*, 521, May 1992

Drug Abuse among Juvenile Detainees

By RICHARD DEMBO, LINDA WILLIAMS,
and JAMES SCHMEIDLER

ABSTRACT: Although recent surveys of youths in the general population indicate that drug use has declined, drug use among juvenile detainees remains at a high level. These youths, who are often experiencing multiple problems, are a seriously underserved population group in our society. A review of the literature, and results from an ongoing longitudinal study of juvenile detainees in Tampa, Florida, documenting their drug use and related problems, lead to the identification of five key areas for policy and program development: early intervention; quality screening and assessment; providing quality, community-based services; improving linkages between community agencies; and continuity of services. Youths entering the juvenile justice system often require repeated interventions over a protracted period, reinforced by improvements in their social, vocational, and educational skills, if their lives are to be directed in socially responsible ways. A national effort is needed to address the poignant issues presented by these youths and their families.

Richard Dembo, Ph.D., is a professor of criminology at the University of South Florida, Tampa. Since 1969, he has conducted research on drug use and delinquency and, with his associates, has published numerous articles and book chapters on this topic.

Linda Williams (B.A., criminology) is a research associate at the University of South Florida, Tampa, where she is working on a longitudinal study involving detained youths.

James Schmeidler, Ph.D., is an assistant professor in the Department of Psychiatry and Biomathematical Sciences at Mount Sinai School of Medicine, New York City.

RECENT surveys indicate that drug use is decreasing among youths in the general population.[1] The mass media, and some public officials, have made interpretational leaps from these figures, suggesting that they signify that the "war on drugs" is being won. Perhaps it is being won among sectors of the middle class.

These surveys substantially underrepresent, however, the kinds of youths who are most likely to use illicit drugs and engage in other forms of deviant behavior, including crime. Surveys of high school seniors do not include dropouts, who are estimated to account for 15 percent of each class and who, research has shown, have higher rates of drug use than students who regularly attend school.[2] National household surveys exclude institutionalized youths. A recent report from the National Institute of Justice's Drug Use Forecasting Program notes that urine-test data from male juvenile arrestees or detainees in eight cities ranged from 8 percent positive, in San Jose, to 37 percent positive, in Los Angeles, with Cleveland and Washington, D.C., having positive rates of 20 percent and 18 percent, respectively.[3]

High-risk youths—young people who come to the attention of public service agencies for behavior problems in the community and who are likely to move into delinquent lifestyles—represent a seriously underserved population group in our society. For a variety of reasons, a number of which we review in this article, their needs and those of their immediate families are, in general, insufficiently addressed. The consequences of this neglect for these youths and for society as a whole are as poignant as they are financially staggering. What is needed is a national effort to redirect the lives of as many of these young people as possible in socially responsible ways.

THE FLOW PROCESS INTO
THE JUVENILE JUSTICE SYSTEM

Although there are exceptions, there is a general pattern in the process by which youths move into the juvenile justice system.[4] In the earliest school grades, these high-risk youths are distinguishable from oth-

1. U.S., Department of Health and Human Services, National Institute on Drug Abuse, *NIDA Capsules: Overview of the 1988 National Household Survey on Drug Abuse* (Rockville, MD: National Institute on Drug Abuse, 1989); idem, *NIDA Notes* (Rockville, MD: National Institute on Drug Abuse, 1991); Jerald G. Bachman, L. D. Johnston, and Patrick M. O'Malley, "Explaining the Recent Decline in Cocaine Use among Young Adults: Further Evidence That Perceived Risks and Disapproval Lead to Reduced Drug Use," *Journal of Health and Social Behavior*, 31:173-84 (1990); Jerald G. Bachman et al., "Explaining the Recent Decline in Marijuana Use: Differentiating the Effects of Perceived Risks, Disapproval, and General Lifestyle Factors," ibid., 29:92-112 (1988).

2. Denise B. Kandel, "Reaching the Hard-to-Reach: Illicit Drug Use among High School Absentees," *Addictive Diseases*, 1:465-80 (1975).

3. U.S., Department of Justice, National Institute of Justice, *Drug Use Forecasting Second Quarter: April to June 1990* (Washington, DC: National Institute of Justice, 1991).

4. We are indebted to the ideas of Dr. Robert DuPont in the development of this section. See Robert L. DuPont, *Stopping Alcohol and Other Drug Use before It Starts: The Future of Prevention* (Rockville, MD: Office of Substance Abuse Prevention, 1989).

ers by their aggressive antisocial behavior, particularly a combination of shyness and aggression,[5] and by an indication of school adjustment problems, with an emphasis on truancy. By the late elementary grades, these youths show evidence of school failure[6] now joined by aggressive behaviors and the initiation of illicit drug use and acts of delinquency. By adolescence, there are strong indications of low commitment to school, academic failure,[7] delinquency, drug-using friends, alienation from conventional society, and rebelliousness.[8] Many of these youths become drug involved themselves, drop out of school, and, as a consequence of official agency response to their increasingly troubled behavior in the community, move into the juvenile justice system. Hence, by the time these youths become known to the juvenile courts, they have already had a lengthy history of increasingly troubled behavior and failure in conventional activities.

PROBLEMS EXPERIENCED BY JUVENILE DETAINEES

Youths entering the juvenile justice system are often experiencing multiple difficulties. These high-risk young people, many of whom are from ethnic minority groups[9] and derive from economically stressed families and communities, often report troubled pasts, including physical abuse, sexual victimization, alcohol and other drug abuse, and involvement in other delinquent behavior.[10] Related to these difficulties, these youths tend to have significant deficits in the areas of educational and vocational skills. These personal difficulties, coupled with their families' experience of alcohol and other drug abuse, mental health problems, and involvement with the criminal justice system,[11] place a combination of impediments to these youths' development into socially responsible and productive adults.

Correspondingly, these youths can be seen as having been failed by society and its safety net. Many of them

5. Shepard G. Kellam and H. Brown, *Social Adaptational and Psychological Antecedents of Adolescent Psychopathology Ten Years Later* (Baltimore, MD: Johns Hopkins University, 1982).

6. K. Polk et al., "Becoming Adult" (Final report to U.S., Department of Health and Human Services, National Institute of Mental Health, 1981).

7. Denise B. Kandel, "Epidemiological and Psychosocial Perspectives on Adolescent Drug Use," *Journal of American Academic Clinical Psychiatry*, 21:328-47 (1982).

8. G. M. Smith and C. P. Fogg, "Psychological Predictors of Early Use, Late Use and Nonuse of Marijuana among Teenage Students," *Longitudinal Research on Drug Use: Empirical Findings and Methodological Issues*, ed. D. B. Kandel (Washington, DC: Hemisphere, 1978).

9. Barry Krisberg et al., *The Incarceration of Minority Youth* (Minneapolis: University of Minnesota, H. H. Humphrey Institute of Public Affairs, 1986).

10. Richard Dembo et al., "Examination of the Relationships among Drug Use, Emotional/Psychological Problems and Crime among Youths Entering a Juvenile Detention Center," *International Journal of the Addictions*, 25:1301-40 (1990).

11. Richard Dembo et al., "Examining a Structural Model of the Role of Family Factors, Physical Abuse and Sexual Victimization Experiences in a Sample of High Risk Youths' Alcohol/Other Drug Use and Delinquency/Crime over Time" (Report, Department of Criminology, University of South Florida, 1991).

were born into economically strained circumstances, often raised by families who neglected or abused them or in other ways did not provide for their nurturance and wholesome development. At an early age, they came to the attention of an overburdened and underresourced public service system, which was unable to provide them and their families with the quality, deep-reaching services they needed. The youths' specific problems became more serious and tended to cumulate over time.

The drug use of these youths is often associated with high-rate criminal behavior.[12] Their rates of use of alcohol and other drugs—particularly marijuana, hashish, and cocaine—are much higher than those reported by youths interviewed in national household surveys on drug abuse.[13] Further, large proportions of juvenile detainees report experiencing adverse effects related to their use of alcohol or other drugs.[14]

*Urine testing for drug
use by juvenile detainees*

Urine testing, particularly the EMIT (enzyme multiplied immunoassay technique) procedure, has proven to be a

valuable technique for identifying recent drug use by youths as they enter the juvenile justice system. The threshold for a test result that is positive for drugs can be set quite high to reduce the rate of false positives—that is, test identification of recent drug use where no use has occurred—and initial positives are usually confirmed by another, more sensitive test.[15]

Urine testing of a sample of 399 youths entering the Hillsborough Regional Juvenile Detention Center in Tampa, Florida, between December 1986 and April 1989 yielded high rates of positive test results. Marijuana and cocaine were found in the urine specimens of 37 percent and 10 percent of the youths, respectively. There was an increase by age in the percentage of youths who tested positive for cocaine, ranging from 4 percent at age 13 to 15 percent at age 17 or 18.[16] These findings are similar to those found in comparable samples of youths.[17]

Urine testing is a necessary supplement to self-reports for identifying drug use among juvenile arrestees. In one study, the more unacceptable the use of a given drug, the more likely these youths were to deny its use.[18] Youths reported accurately the use of marijuana but underreported their recent use of cocaine.

With the support of the Office of Juvenile Justice and Delinquency

12. Eric D. Wish and Bernard A. Gropper, "Crime and Justice," in *Drugs and Crime*, ed. M. Tonry and J. P. Wilson (Chicago: University of Chicago Press, 1990).

13. Dembo et al., "Relationships among Drug Use, Emotional/Psychological Problems and Crime."

14. Richard Dembo et al., "Examining a Structural Model of the Relationships among Alcohol Use, Marijuana/Hashish Use, Their Effects and Emotional/Psychological Problems over Time in a Cohort of High Risk Youths," *Deviant Behavior*, in press.

15. Wish and Gropper, "Crime and Justice."

16. Richard Dembo et al., *Urine Testing of Detained Juveniles to Identify High-Risk Youth* (Washington, DC: Department of Justice, 1990).

17. Wish and Gropper, "Crime and Justice."

18. Dembo et al., "Relationships among Drug Use, Emotional/Psychological Problems and Crime."

Prevention, the American Correctional Association and the Institute for Health and Behavior are developing policies and procedures for the drug testing of juveniles entering detention centers. These promise to provide an important adjunct to current detainee-screening procedures.

As Wish and Gropper note,[19] the onset of illicit drug use usually begins with the use of marijuana or phencyclidine (PCP), which typically occurs in early adolescence. Involvement in the use of other drugs, such as cocaine or heroin, tends to occur in the late teens. Identifying juvenile arrestees who are using illicit drugs in early adolescence and involving them in effective educational, vocational, and drug treatment programs hold the promise of reducing their progression to more serious drug abuse problems.

JUVENILE-DETAINEE DRUG USE AND ITS CONNECTION WITH OTHER PROBLEMS

Illicit drug use is a marker for other problem behavior. For example, detainees whose urine tests positive for marijuana are more likely to be involved in delinquency than those whose test results are negative for this drug. Studies of different samples of juvenile detainees in Tampa indicate that detainees who test positive for the recent use of marijuana have significantly higher rates of referral to juvenile court for non-drug-related felonies—especially such property offenses as burglary, auto theft, and grand larceny—than do

19. Wish and Gropper, "Crime and Justice."

marijuana-negative detainees.[20] These results indicate that marijuana use among these detainees may be a marker for criminal behavior, much as the use of cocaine or heroin is for adults.[21] Importantly, it is easier and more cost effective to intervene in the lives of marijuana-using detainees than in the lives of users of other illicit drugs such as cocaine.

Detainees who test positive for cocaine tend to be highly involved in crime. In the first phase of the longitudinal study of juvenile detainees in Tampa, those who tested positive for cocaine had a significantly greater number of previous referrals to juvenile court on drug felony charges and reported almost four times as many drug-sale crimes as detainees who tested negative.[22] An additional analysis examined factors differentiating detainees who were cocaine positive or negative during their follow-up interviews approximately one year later. Again, previous delinquent behavior figured prominently in this

20. Dembo et al., "Relationships among Drug Use, Emotional/Psychological Problems and Crime"; Richard Dembo et al., "Heavy Marijuana Use and Crime among Youths Entering a Juvenile Detention Center," *Journal of Psychoactive Drugs*, 19:47-56 (1987); Richard Dembo et al., "Further Examination of the Association between Heavy Marijuana Use and Crime among Youths Entering a Juvenile Detention Center," ibid., pp. 361-73.

21. Wish and Gropper, "Crime and Justice"; Eric D. Wish, "U.S. Drug Policy in the 1990s: Insights from New Data from Arrestees," *International Journal of the Addictions*, 25:377-409 (1990-91).

22. Dembo et al., "Relationships among Drug Use, Emotional/Psychological Problems and Crime"; Dembo et al., *Urine Testing of Detained Juveniles*.

analysis. Detainees who were cocaine positive had a significantly larger number of referrals to juvenile court for felony drug offenses, misdemeanor disorderly-conduct offenses, and misdemeanor drug offenses prior to their first interviews, and they reported more drug sales and crimes against persons in the year preceding their initial interviews[23] than did cocaine-negative detainees.

The Tampa longitudinal study also tracked the official arrests and referrals to juvenile court for the detainees for three and a half years following their initial interviews. Youths who tested positive for cocaine at the time of their initial interviews had a significantly higher rate of referral or arrest for property offenses during this 42-month period—56 percent—than did cocaine-negative youths, whose rate was 42 percent. Since official arrest data substantially underrepresent involvement in criminal behavior, the cocaine-positive youths in the study were probably heavily involved in crime during this follow-up period.[24]

Among the males in the Tampa longitudinal study, involvement in drug sales in the year prior to the first interview was a significant predictor of a urine test positive for cocaine at the time of the follow-up interview. This finding indicated that involvement in drug distribution is an activity at high risk of resulting in a deepening, personal involvement in cocaine use over time, particularly among the white males in the study.[25]

Drug use and other problems

Illicit drug use has also been found to be related to a number of traumatic experiences and other difficulties. Preliminary indications that physical and sexual abuse are related to illicit drug use[26] have been confirmed by longitudinal research. Analyses of data collected on youths in the Tampa juvenile-detainee longitudinal study, examining a developmental-damage view of the role of child maltreatment in the youths' drug use, found that their physical abuse and sexual victimization experiences were interrelated, antecedent events that related significantly to their marijuana or hashish use and delinquency over time.[27] These findings support the

23. Richard Dembo et al., "A Longitudinal Study of the Relationships among Marijuana/Hashish Use, Cocaine Use and Delinquency in a Cohort of High Risk Youths," *Journal of Drug Issues*, 21:271-312 (1991).

24. Richard Dembo et al., "Recidivism in a Cohort of Juvenile Detainees: A 3-1/2 Year Follow-Up," *International Journal of the Addictions*, in press.

25. Richard Dembo et al., "The Relationships between Cocaine Use, Drug Sales and Other Delinquency among a Cohort of High Risk Youths over Time," in *Drugs and Violence: Causes, Correlates, and Consequences*, ed. M. De La Rosa, E. Y. Lambert, and B. Gropper (Rockville, MD: Department of Health and Human Services, National Institute on Drug Abuse, 1990).

26. B. R. Russe and D. C. McBride, "Childhood Sexual Abuse and Cocaine Use" (Report, Health Services Research Center, University of Miami, 1985); Richard Dembo et al., "Physical Abuse, Sexual Victimization and Illicit Drug Use: A Structural Analysis among High Risk Adolescents," *Journal of Adolescence*, 10:13-33 (1987); Richard Dembo et al., "Physical Abuse, Sexual Victimization and Illicit Drug Use: Replication of a Structural Analysis among a New Sample of High Risk Youths," *Violence and Victims*, 4:121-38 (1989).

27. Richard Dembo et al., "Examining a Structural Model of the Relationship between

findings of related longitudinal efforts that highlight that the physical abuse or sexual victimization experiences of young people are severely traumatizing events that significantly influence their development of troubled life-styles.[28] Related analyses of data on youths in the Tampa juvenile-detainee study found significant linkages between the youths' physical or sexual abuse experience and their family's alcohol or other drug abuse and mental health problems and involvement in crime; and between the youths' physical or sexual abuse, family mental health problems and involvement in crime, and the youths' marijuana or hashish use and participation in delinquency.[29]

In many ways, the cocaine-using youths in the Tampa study were those who had the most problems at the time of the initial interview. Compared to cocaine-negative detainees, youths who tested positive for cocaine at the follow-up interview reported experiencing more different kinds of physical abuse prior to their first interviews; and their self-report and urine test data for cocaine at the initial interview indicated significantly greater involvement with this drug.[30]

The results from these studies urge that youths entering the juvenile justice system be seen holistically, not one problem at a time. The piecemeal approach is a major limitation in public agency response to these youths. Their continued involvement in drug use and delinquent behavior is related to seriously troubled life-styles, which can often be traced to their earliest years. Programs that focus on one problem at a time, in neglect of the multiple difficulties many of these youths are experiencing simultaneously, are likely to fail. They and their families need deep-reaching, effective intervention services over a protracted period if their lives are to be redirected along more salutary paths.

The delinquent or criminal behavior of the youths in the Tampa study, and their counterparts elsewhere, will not decline until their multiple needs in the areas of education, vocational training and employment, and drug misuse are addressed. In part due to the limited treatment intervention and resources available for the youths in the study, many of them have moved into the Florida Department of Corrections (DOC). In the 42 months following their initial interviews, 52 percent of the youths had Florida DOC numbers, and many of these youths spent time confined in a DOC institution.[31]

POLICY IMPLICATIONS

A number of policy implications can be drawn from our work and from the work of others in the field. At

Physical Abuse, Sexual Victimization, Marijuana/Hashish Use and Delinquency among a Cohort of High Risk Youths over Time," *Violence and Victims*, in press.

28. C. S. Widom, "Child Abuse, Neglect, and Violent Criminal Behavior," *Criminology*, 27:251-69 (1989); idem, "The Cycle of Violence," *Science*, 244:160-66 (1989).

29. Dembo et al., *Examining a Structural Model*.

30. Dembo et al., "Relationships among Marijuana/Hashish Use, Cocaine Use and Delinquency."

31. Dembo et al., "Recidivism in a Cohort of Juvenile Detainees."

least five key areas for program or policy development or improvement can be identified: (1) early intervention with troubled youths and their families before the youths become deeply involved with the juvenile justice system; (2) quality screening and assessment of youths entering the juvenile justice system, especially those admitted to detention centers; (3) providing quality, community-based services; (4) improving linkages between community agencies; and (5) providing for continuity of services to supply needed intervention and support programs to troubled youths and their families.

Early intervention

The most effective reduction of drug use and delinquency and crime in our society lies in prevention or early intervention. Previous research has documented that the nature and quality of family life has an influence on youths' drug use and other delinquent behavior and that fragmented and dysfunctional families tend to have high rates of substance misuse and other problem behavior. Investing in effective services for these youths and their families early in their lives could save much human potential and reduce the personal and social costs of their delinquent or criminal behavior.[32]

Workers in the juvenile justice system generally do not become seriously concerned over the behavior of a youth until he or she has appeared in court several times. At this point, the youngster has probably failed in

a number of informal and loosely structured programs and has developed serious problems in school and delinquent behavior, including the misuse of various drugs. An assistant state attorney in Florida recently commented that several arrests usually occur before the juvenile justice system takes youths seriously; at that point, they have developed a criminal-behavior life-style, and it is often too late to turn them around.[33] Our findings suggest that resources should be placed in assessing and providing needed services to youths and their families at the first point of contact with the juvenile justice system, rather than targeted to youths with repeated contact with the juvenile courts.

Quality screening and assessment

Proper assessment of youths entering the juvenile justice system is a promising method for identifying youngsters with difficulties in a variety of problem areas. Further, assessment of youths should not only identify the difficulties they may be experiencing but seek to link troubled youths and their families with appropriate services.

Using screening units at detention centers is a very promising approach to identifying youths with mental health or substance abuse problems. For many youths, being placed in a detention center represents their first prolonged contact with the juvenile justice system. Detention consti-

32. DuPont, *Stopping Alcohol and Other Drug Use before It Starts.*

33. Joe Guidry, "Cloak of Evil Not Worn by Adults Alone," *Tampa Tribune* (Florida), 18 June 1991.

tutes an important juncture at which youths who are at high risk for future drug use and delinquent behavior can be identified. Detention therefore also creates the opportunity for constructive interventions to be made in their lives.

For a number of reasons, especially budget constraints, quality screening and assessment of youths in detention centers remain the exception rather than the rule. At the same time, experience indicates that these services benefit both detainees and staff.[34] In recent years, serious efforts have been made to develop assessment instruments for juveniles.[35] An important, ambitious effort, the Adolescent Assessment/ Referral System, (AARS), is being supported by the National Institute on Drug Abuse.[36]

The AARS consists of three main elements. One is the Problem Oriented Screening Instrument for Teenagers (POSIT). Available in Spanish and English versions, the POSIT consists of 139 items and probes for difficulties in 10 potentially problematic functional areas: substance use/ abuse, physical health status, mental

health status, family relationships, peer relations, educational status, vocational status, social skills, leisure and recreation, and aggressive behavior and delinquency. A personal history questionnaire is also part of the POSIT. The second AARS component is the Comprehensive Assessment Battery (CAB), which includes psychometrically validated assessment protocols probing in more depth each problem area tapped by the POSIT. The CAB instruments are used when the POSIT has indicated that a problem may exist in a given functional area. The third element of the AARS is a referral system guide, which assists the case manager or referral agent in placing troubled youths in services to address their medical, psychiatric, educational, and psychosocial needs. The AARS holds considerable promise for identifying troubled youths and placing them in needed service programs.

Providing quality, community-based services

The results of our research on Tampa detainees indicate that there is a serious need for innovative educational and vocational programs for these youths, as well as for services to address their substance misuse or mental health needs. The delinquent or criminal behavior of these youths will not decline unless the impediments they have developed, and which serve to alienate them from conventional society, are remedied. In this effort, they need to be provided with opportunities to develop their educational and vocational skills to a level that will permit them

34. Richard Dembo et al., "Setting up a Screening/Triage Unit at a Juvenile Detention Center" (Report, Department of Criminology, University of South Florida, 1990).

35. National Association of State Alcohol and Drug Abuse Directors, *Drug Offender Assessment Monograph* (Washington, DC: National Association of State Alcohol and Drug Abuse Directors, 1991); U.S., Department of Health and Human Services, National Institute on Drug Abuse, *The Adolescent Assessment/Referral System* (Rockville, MD: National Institute on Drug Abuse, 1991).

36. National Institute on Drug Abuse, *Adolescent Assessment/Referral System*.

to access and compete successfully in their communities as socially responsible young adults. These efforts should avoid stigmatizing these youths, and they should involve a collaborative relationship with the youths' families.

In recent years, public responses to these high-risk youths have been punitive in their approach, emphasizing commitment in large residential facilities. These facilities were often intimidating and otherwise stressful environments, where the youths' educational and other rehabilitative needs were ignored. Another disturbing trend has been an increase in the direct filing of these youths from the juvenile to the adult justice systems. This is partly a result of the increased work load in many local juvenile justice systems and a belief among juvenile judges that the services provided to youths in the juvenile system are inadequate.

At the same time, evidence has been accumulating that expensive programs that isolate troubled youths from the general society are ineffective and have no significant impact on reducing recidivism.[37] For example, a recent study by the U.S. Department of Justice indicated that 69 percent of a group of young parolees were rearrested for a serious crime within six years of their release from prison. Fifty-three percent were convicted on a new offense, and 49 percent were returned to prison.[38]

Based on these experiences, increased interest has been shown in identifying high-risk youths at a sufficiently early point in their lives and involving them in effective, nonresidential, community-based intervention programs to reduce the likelihood that they will move into adult criminal careers. This alternative to the incarceration model is growing in its attractiveness with the appreciation that failure to remedy these youths' impediments to socially responsible behavior in the community results in the consumption of a large and growing amount of state resources as they grow older.[39]

Unfortunately, treatment services for troubled youths, particularly those in the public sector, are sorely lacking in most parts of the country. For example, many youths in the Tampa longitudinal study needed serious treatment intervention, especially to address their substance use difficulties. Very few of them, however, received such help for any length of time during the follow-up period. During their follow-up interviews, many youths reported poi-

37. Peter Greenwood and F. Zimring, *One More Chance: The Pursuit of Promising Intervention Strategies for Chronic Juvenile Offenders* (Santa Monica, CA: RAND, 1985).

38. U.S., Department of Justice, *Recidivism of Young Parolees*, NCJ-104916 (Washington, DC: Department of Justice, Bureau of Justice Statistics, 1987).

39. U.S., Department of Justice, *Report to the Nation on Crime and Justice*, 2d ed. (Washington, DC: Department of Justice, 1988); Wharton Econometric Forecasting Associates, Inc., "The Income of Organized Crime," by S. Fishman, K. Rodenrys, and G. Schink, in *President's Commission on Organized Crime, The Impact: Organized Crime Today* (Washington, DC: Government Printing Office, 1986), pp. 413-39; Henrick J. Harwood et al., *Economic Costs to Society of Alcohol and Drug Abuse and Mental Illness: 1980* (Research Triangle Park, NC: Research Triangle Institute, 1984).

gnant experiences regarding their seeking help for a drug problem. Some youths claimed they were attending treatment on an outpatient basis and that they were abruptly terminated when their money ran out. Some youths claimed they and their families lacked the resources to pay for their treatment.

Research has repeatedly found that criminal behavior increases following addiction and that arrests for drug offenses and property crimes decline with decreasing frequency of drug use.[40] These results stress the value of treatment in reducing crime among drug-dependent persons.

Whenever possible, systematic urine testing should be completed on all youths entering the juvenile justice system. This information, together with other data collected during their screening and assessment, should be used to determine whether the youths would benefit from placement in early intervention programs, designed to reduce the likelihood that they will move on to develop more serious personal problems and become more involved in substance use and crime. Although much more needs to be learned about these problems, juvenile detention centers represent a key contact point for trou-

bled youths, around which creative and effective programming can and should occur.[41] Such activities should involve a strong research component, so that the needs for various services can be documented and new patterns of abuse identified.

Efforts should be made to place drug-involved youths in treatment programs. Our state of knowledge about the effectiveness of adolescent drug programs leads to four major conclusions: (1) some treatment is better than no treatment; (2) few comparisons of treatment method have consistently demonstrated that one method is superior to another; (3) posttreatment relapse rates are high; and (4) more controlled studies of adolescent treatment are needed.[42] In addition, there is a general need to establish and employ common definitions of relapse and to use early intervention and a classification system for adolescent substance-related problems. Available information indicates that youngsters with more severe drug histories and extensive criminal records may benefit from longer or more intensive treatment experiences and that treatment programs need to encourage youths' ac-

40. William H. McGlothlin, M. D. Anglin, and B. D. Wilson, "Narcotic Addiction and Crime," *Criminology*, 16:293-315 (1987); John C. Ball, J. W. Shaffer, and David N. Nurco, "Day to Day Criminality of Heroin Addicts in Baltimore: A Study in Continuity of Offense Rates," *Drug and Alcohol Dependence*, 12:119-42 (1983); M. D. Anglin and G. Speckart, "Narcotics Use and Crime: A Multisample, Multimethod Analysis," *Criminology*, 26:197-233 (1988).

41. Michael Klitzner et al., "Report to the Robert Wood Johnson Foundation on Strategies for Early Intervention with Children and Youth to Avoid Abuse of Addictive Substances" (Pacific Institute for Research and Evaluation, Bethesda, MD, 1991); Dembo et al., "Setting up a Screening/Triage Unit."

42. Richard Catalano et al., "Evaluation of the Effectiveness of Adolescent Drug Abuse Treatment, Assessment of Risks for Relapse, and Promising Approaches for Relapse Prevention," *International Journal of the Addictions*, 25:1085-1140 (1990-91).

ademic and vocational educational experiences. Length of treatment has been found to lead to improvement in posttreatment outcome, especially for youths in residential programs. Having families involved in treatment has been found to result in higher rates of program completion and reduction in problem behavior among treated adolescents.

Unfortunately, many youths are unable to sustain the gains they achieve during treatment. Posttreatment support programs are needed to provide the continued assistance many youths require as they face the pressures of community life. Such assistance programs should help youths deal with cravings to return to drug use and involve them in satisfactory leisure activities and productive activities such as work and school.[43]

Therapeutic communities for substance abuse have proven to be effective in remedying the troubled lives of youths who are seriously drug involved.[44] These programs are based on a social learning process, which seeks to make life-style changes in a social context, and they are particularly effective for youths and young adults of the urban underclass who have been the driving force behind

43. Ibid.
44. George DeLeon and J. T. Ziegenfuss, eds., *Therapeutic Communities for Addictions* (Springfield, IL: Charles C Thomas, 1986); Rod Mullen and Naya Arbiter, "Against the Odds: Therapeutic Community Approaches to Underclass Drug Abuse," in *Drug Policy in the Americas* (La Jolla, CA: Institute of the Americas, Center for Iberian and Latin American Studies, forthcoming).

the dramatic growth in the number of persons on probation, on parole, in jail, and in prison.

*Improving
linkages between
community agencies*

There is also a need to improve the linkages and coordination between various community-based agencies dealing with high-risk youths. There is a particular need for coordination between schools and vocational and employment resources and services addressing the substance misuse and mental health needs of these youths and their families. Such an effort would reduce duplication of effort and respond to these youths in a holistic, comprehensive manner. Greater integration of community agencies would smooth the transition of these youths from program to program and reduce the likelihood that youths will slip through the gaps in the community support system.

For example, 21 percent of reinterviewed youths in the Tampa detainee longitudinal study claimed they had repeated a grade in school during the follow-up period, and 48 percent of the youths reporting that they were held back felt it was related to their being in detention or incarcerated. Almost half of the youths noted that they had dropped out of school since their initial interviews, and nearly 30 percent indicated that they had been expelled or suspended from school during the follow-up year. Further, only 10 percent of the youths graduated high school or obtained a general education degree (GED). Clearly, much work needs to be done to improve the educational skills of the youths in the study and their counterparts elsewhere and to build and strengthen linkages between school and other community agencies.[45]

Continuity of services

Juvenile justice agencies tend to have an episodic interest in troubled youths. The interest centers around the behavioral reason for a youth's contact with the system and the judicially imposed consequences of that behavior. Once the sanction, program, or supervision period ends, agency interest in the youth's case ceases—unless he or she comes to the attention of a juvenile justice agency again. However, this manner of providing services to troubled young people fails to incorporate the knowledge that, for many youths, their problem-laden lives can be traced to their early years and that their problems may become more serious as they proceed through adolescence. The delinquent behavior of these youths reflects a chronic involvement in personally and socially damaging activities.

Serious consideration needs to be given to providing long-term assistance to seriously troubled youths. For example, in treating a person for dysfunctional drug use, it is important to appreciate that altering a drug-dependent existence is often a prolonged process involving periodic

45. Richard Dembo et al., "Educating Kids at Risk: The Continuing Challenge" (Report, Department of Criminology, University of South Florida, 1991).

relapses to drug use. Repeated interventions over a protracted period, which are reinforced by improvements in the social, vocational, and educational skill levels of the individuals in treatment, are the type of intervention most likely to be successful. Service-delivery systems, and associated support services, need to address the chronic nature of many of these youths' difficulties.

A NATIONAL COMMITMENT TO TROUBLED JUVENILES

The program and policy areas we have addressed represent attempts to strengthen existing weaknesses in the juvenile justice system. In too many states in this country, faced with budget cuts, categorical funding that targets specific problem behaviors while neglecting others, and lack of coordination between juvenile service agencies, the term "system" is a misnomer, and what there is of juvenile justice is often chaotic. What is needed is a national effort to provide as many youths as possible with the opportunity to develop themselves in socially responsible ways.

Society pays dearly for continuing to neglect addressing the needs of the many troubled youths who enter the juvenile justice system. The juvenile system serves as a conveyer belt into the adult corrections system, with all its associated costs. Beyond this more visible economics is the reality of lives lost to useful purpose, and the pain this failure causes these youths, their families, and the community. As the philosopher Santayana noted, those who do not learn from history are condemned to repeat it. As regards juvenile justice, the issues and the effects of failing to address them are clearer than ever. What is needed is a dedicated effort to make a constructive difference. Do we have the will to rise to this challenge?

AIDS and Legal Access to Sterile Drug Injection Equipment

By DON C. DES JARLAIS and SAMUEL R. FRIEDMAN

ABSTRACT: Legal access to sterile injection equipment has been a primary strategy for preventing the acquired immune deficiency syndrome (AIDS) among persons who inject illicit drugs in almost all developed countries. This strategy has remained highly controversial in the United States, with only a small number of localities adopting it. This article reviews different techniques of providing legal access—over-the-counter sales and syringe exchanges—research design issues relevant to evaluating legal-access programs, and the findings from the large number of studies conducted to date. The findings are consistent in showing no increase in illicit drug use related to legal access and decreases in AIDS risk behavior related to legal-access programs. The design of legal-access programs for maximal impact and the ultimate effect of the decreases in AIDS risk behavior on transmission of the human immunodeficiency virus (HIV) remain to be determined.

Don C. Des Jarlais, Ph.D., is director of research with the Chemical Dependency Institute of Beth Israel Medical Center and professor of community medicine at Mount Sinai's Department of Community Medicine. He has published extensively in the fields of AIDS and intravenous drug use. A member of the U.S. National Commission on AIDS, he is a consultant to the Centers for Disease Control and the World Health Organization.

Samuel R. Friedman, Ph.D., is a senior principal investigator at Narcotic and Drug Research, Inc. He has been involved in AIDS research since 1983 and has consulted for the National Institute on Drug Abuse, the World Health Organization, and other agencies.

THE sharing of equipment while injecting illicit drugs is becoming an increasingly important part of the epidemic of the human immunodeficiency virus (HIV) and the acquired immune deficiency syndrome (AIDS) throughout the world. In the United States, almost one-third of the recently diagnosed cases of AIDS were related to the sharing of drug injection equipment, including cases among injecting drug users (IDUs) themselves, as well as among their heterosexual partners and their children.[1] In Europe, the sharing of drug injection equipment has become the single most common mode of transmission among recent cases.[2] HIV infection among IDUs has also emerged as a major public-health problem in Asia—Thailand, Myanmar, and northern India—and in South America, specifically in Argentina and Brazil.[3]

In almost all countries where HIV infection among IDUs has emerged as a potential problem, the primary public-health approach to preventing further transmission of the virus among IDUs has been providing legal access to sterile injection equipment. The rationale for this strategy is relatively simple: since it is the sharing

1. *HIV/AIDS Surveillance, Year-End Edition: U.S. AIDS Cases Reported through December 1990* (Atlanta, GA: Centers for Disease Control, 1991).

2. WHO-EC Collaborating Center on AIDS, *AIDS Surveillance in Europe: Quarterly Report No. 27* (Geneva: World Health Organization, 1990).

3. For a recent review of the epidemiology of AIDS and HIV among drug injectors, see Samuel R. Friedman and Don C. Des Jarlais, "HIV among Drug Injectors: The Epidemic and the Response," *AIDS Care*, 3(3):237-48 (1991).

of drug injection equipment that actually transmits HIV, reducing multi-person use of the equipment can reduce the transmission of the virus. This approach separates the specific issue of AIDS prevention from the related issue of generally reducing or eliminating injection of illicit drugs, a much more difficult problem.

In this article, we will first describe the different types of legal-access programs and the opposition to these programs. Since all of the research conducted to date on legal-access programs has been criticized on methodological grounds, we first outline what would be needed to conduct a randomized clinical trial of legal-access programs. Such trials are the standard method for demonstrating the potential effectiveness of a public-health intervention, but in this case such a trial would require an extremely expensive, time-consuming, and logistically difficult research study in order to evaluate the effectiveness of legal-access programs. The main section of the article is a review of the existing studies of legal-access programs. The final section of the article discusses the findings that emerge from the existing research and possible reasons why these findings have rarely been incorporated into public policy in the United States.

TYPES OF LEGAL ACCESS

Two major approaches to providing legal access to sterile injection equipment have emerged as AIDS prevention strategies: over-the-counter sales at standard prices, which tend to be very low, and syringe-exchange programs. Both are most effective in the absence of "narcotics paraphernalia" laws that criminalize the possession of equipment for the injection of illicit drugs.

Over-the-counter sales and syringe-exchange programs both provide legal access to sterile injection equipment, but there are corresponding advantages and disadvantages to each as AIDS prevention strategies. Over-the-counter sales utilize the existing network of pharmacies (and in some instances grocery stores) within a geographic area, so that there are minimal start-up costs to implementing this strategy. Pharmacies also tend to be widely dispersed throughout most communities and to be open for relatively long hours, so that coverage—an essential practical aspect of the legal availability of sterile injection equipment—will be relatively thorough. Pharmacies in urban areas tend to be more anonymous than syringe exchanges, so that IDUs can obtain the injection equipment with less chance that they will become identified as illicit drug users. In small towns, on the other hand, syringe exchange by outreach workers —that is, not at a fixed site—may be necessary to protect the confidentiality of the IDUs.

In contrast to the simple over-the-counter sale of injection equipment, syringe-exchange programs do not charge for injection equipment but rather trade new sterile injection equipment for used equipment. Syringe exchanges are usually staffed by persons whose primary responsibility is to provide the exchange service (and related other services) and thus have moderate staffing and location expenses. Syringe exchanges are typically located in high-drug-use neighborhoods and normally try to be open during the hours when IDUs are likely to be in need of injection equipment. The primary advantages of syringe exchanges over simple over-the-counter sales are that the IDUs will interact with the staff on the exchange and that the exchange will be able to properly dispose of the potentially HIV-contaminated used injection equipment. The interaction with staff facilitates (1) AIDS education, including counseling about heterosexual and perinatal transmission of HIV; (2) distribution of condoms and equipment in addition to syringes needed for sterile injection—cotton, an alcohol swab, and a cooker; and (3) distribution of bleach for disinfecting injection equipment if not enough is available. The interaction with staff may also permit some on-site health care services, such as tuberculosis testing, and referral to other needed medical and social services, particularly to drug abuse treatment.

While over-the-counter sales and syringe exchanges should be thought of as two different methods of providing legal access to drug injection equipment, some programs are hybrids of these two methods. The syringe exchanges in Amsterdam, for example, will sell, at low cost, sterile needles and syringes to IDUs who come to the exchange without used equipment to trade in. Some of the syringe exchanges in Australia and New Zealand sell sterile injection equipment to IDUs but will give a discount if the IDU trades in used injection equipment. Most countries that provide legal access to drug injection equipment utilize both over-the-counter sales and syringe exchanges. Over-the-counter sales are typically done on a nationwide basis, so that all IDUs in the country will have some legal access to injection equipment, and syringe exchanges typically concentrate on the high-drug-use areas of the major cities, where the large numbers of IDUs can justify the costs of the extra services, and the need for safe disposal of potentially contaminated injection equipment is likely to be greater.

OPPOSITION TO
LEGAL ACCESS

Although legal access to sterile injection equipment has been adopted as a national AIDS prevention strategy in almost all other countries with problems of HIV infection among IDUs, the policy of providing free needles to drug users has been quite controversial in the United States. The National Academy of Sciences has repeatedly recommended large-scale research on "safer injection" programs,[4] including legal access to sterile injection equipment, and the United States National Commission

on AIDS recently recommended removing the legal restrictions on access to drug injection equipment.[5] U.S. opponents of legal access to drug injection equipment have argued that the programs would not work to reduce HIV transmission, would "encourage" or "condone" illicit drug use, would "send the wrong message" and would "undermine our war on drugs."[6] Opponents have accused those who advocated even limited syringe-exchange programs of "genocide."[7]

It is important to note that the opposition to legal access to drug injection equipment should not be seen as a traditional liberal-conservative difference of opinion. Opposition to legal access comes both from extreme conservatives, such as Senator Jesse Helms of North Carolina, and from traditional liberals, such as Congressman Charles Rangel of New York. In Western Europe, the greatest restrictions on legal access to drug injection equipment are in Sweden, where the government is controlled by the Social Democratic

4. Institute of Medicine and National Academy of Sciences, *Confronting AIDS: Directions for Public Health, Health Care, and Research* (Washington, DC: National Academy Press, 1986); idem, *Confronting AIDS: Update 1988* (Washington, DC: National Academy Press, 1988); Heather G. Miller, Charles F. Turner, and Lincoln E. Moses, eds., *AIDS: The Second Decade* (Washington, DC: National Academy Press, 1990); Charles F. Turner, Heather G. Miller, and Lincoln E. Moses, eds., *AIDS: Sexual Behavior and Intravenous Drug Use* (Washington, DC: National Academy Press, 1989).

5. National Commission on AIDS, *Report: The Twin Epidemics of Substance Use and HIV* (Washington, DC: Government Printing Office, 1991), pp. 10-11.

6. Herbert D. Kleber, "Exchanges Increase Risk," *USA Today*, 22 Aug. 1991; Mitchell S. Rosenthal, "Giving Away Needles Won't Stop AIDS," *New York Times*, 17 Aug. 1991.

7. See these histories of the New York City Health Department syringe-exchange program: Stephen C. Joseph and Don C. Des Jarlais, "Needle and Syringe Exchange as a Method of AIDS Epidemic Control," *AIDS Updates*, 2(5):1-8 (Sept.-Oct. 1989); Warwick Anderson, "The New York Needle Trial: The Politics of Public Health in the Age of AIDS," *American Journal of Public Health*, in press.

Party, while in the United Kingdom, the Conservative Party under Margaret Thatcher implemented a nationwide program of syringe exchanges in addition to the over-the-counter sales that were permitted prior to the AIDS epidemic.

In the United States, opposition to legal access to drug injection equipment has gone beyond scientific and media debates and has been incorporated into law. The U.S. laws requiring prescriptions for the sale of injection equipment and the laws criminalizing the mere possession of paraphernalia for the injection of illicit drugs are all state laws and all were enacted before the AIDS epidemic. At the federal level, however, an amendment to the 1989 appropriations bill for the Department of Health and Human Services forbade any federal support for syringe-exchange programs unless the secretary of health and human services certified that such programs were both safe and effective.[8] The actual policy of the federal government to date has been not only not to fund any syringe-exchange programs in the United States but also not to fund

8. The amendment was adopted in response to an amendment sponsored by Senator Jesse Helms that would have banned federal support for both syringe-exchange programs and bleach-distribution programs unless the President certified them to be safe and effective. The substitute amendment thus provided for continued federal support of bleach-distribution programs while providing an opportunity for the Senate to vote "against drug abuse." For a more detailed discussion of this issue, see Don C. Des Jarlais and William Bailey, "Almost Banning Bleach" (Paper delivered at the conference of the American Psychological Association, Boston, Aug. 1990).

any research on syringe exchanges.[9] The federal government has thus placed itself in something of a catch-22 position regarding support of syringe-exchange programs. It cannot support syringe exchanges until there is sufficient evidence that these programs are safe and effective, but as long as it refuses to fund research in the area, it is unlikely that there will be enough data to make a rigorous scientific determination of safety and efficacy.

A CLINICAL TRIAL
RESEARCH DESIGN FOR
EVALUATING LEGAL ACCESS TO
DRUG INJECTION EQUIPMENT

Designing a rigorous evaluation of the effectiveness of legal access to drug injection equipment as a method of reducing transmission of HIV is not a very difficult task. Both the National Academy of Sciences and the Department of Health and Human Services have considered what would be involved in such a study. First, it is clear that a classic double-blind clinical trial—in which neither the researcher nor the subjects are aware of who is receiving the true experimental treatment and who is receiving a placebo control— would be neither practical nor ethical in this case. The psychological influences resulting from changes in legal

9. In the absence of any federal support for research on the topic, the American Foundation for AIDS Research (AmFAR) has become the leading source of funding for research on syringe exchanges in the United States. AmFAR supports research on the syringe-exchange programs in Portland, OR; Tacoma, WA; and San Francisco, CA.

access to injection equipment may themselves be an important part of successful AIDS prevention programs for IDUs. Likewise, the enthusiasm and commitment of many workers in syringe-exchange programs may have important effects toward increasing a generalized concern about health for the IDUs. Moreover, knowledge that government officials are willing to change laws and implement new programs to protect the health of IDUs may also lead the IDUs to overcome mistrust of public officials and hence become more willing to utilize other services such as drug abuse treatment programs.

The true starting point for a scientifically rigorous evaluation would be to use communities—not individual IDUs—as the unit of analysis. Self-selection effects and possible "herd immunity" effects would make it very difficult to evaluate legal access to injection equipment by comparing seroconversions among IDUs within a single community. Moreover, the fact that AIDS risk reduction among IDUs appears to be a social process—involving peer modeling and new social norms rather than simple individual decisions[10]—also argues for using communities as the unit of analysis.

A clinical trial evaluation of legal access to injection equipment would probably require 30 to 60 communities in the experimental-treatment

conditions—syringe exchange only, over-the-counter sales only, or both—and would probably also require 20 to 30 communities in a control condition, that is, with no legal access to injection equipment. Great care would need to be taken to ensure proper implementation of the experimental and control conditions. The experimental conditions would probably also require repeal or suspension of narcotics paraphernalia laws. The legal-access condition communities would have to ensure that pharmacists would be willing to sell equipment to IDUs and that syringe exchanges would be conveniently located for IDUs. The control communities would need some active enforcement of laws that prohibited distribution of injection equipment to illicit drug users and criminalized the possession of such equipment. The actual extent of the enforcement of these laws would have to be carefully assessed.[11]

In addition, a real clinical trial would, of course, include random assignment of experimental and control conditions to the participating communities.

Actual transmission of HIV among IDUs would be the primary outcome measure in such a study. HIV seroconversion rates can vary greatly within the same community over

10. Samuel R. Friedman and Don C. Des Jarlais, "AIDS and Self-Organization among Intravenous Drug Users," International Journal of the Addictions, 22(3):201-19 (1987); Samuel R. Friedman et al., "Social Intervention against AIDS among Injecting Drug Users," British Journal of Addictions, in press.

11. There are some difficulties in enforcing these laws, as law enforcement officials may not give them high priority compared to other criminal offenses, and trials of underground syringe-exchange staff in Massachusetts, New York, and California all failed to produce convictions. On the other hand, an active police presence outside a legal fixed-site syringe exchange may serve to discourage drug users from using the program.

short time periods,[12] so that it would be necessary to monitor these communities for relatively long time periods, at least five years and perhaps much longer. Both prospective cohort studies—those that follow the same individuals over time—and serial cross-sectional studies—those that assess different individuals at regular intervals—would probably be needed to follow HIV transmission in the communities under study. Cohort studies generally provide the most accurate counting of HIV seroconversions, but participation in a cohort study may in itself have a strong influence on HIV risk behaviors, so that such studies would not be sufficient by themselves. Because of the concern of opponents that legal access to injection equipment might encourage illicit drug injection, the study would also have to monitor the rates of injection among persons who were already injecting at the start of the study and the rates of initiation of new persons into illicit drug injecting.

Assuring confidentiality for the research subjects would be a critical issue in such a large study. Many of the studies that will be discussed later found it necessary to forgo collecting any identifying information from the subjects in order to obtain participation of active drug injectors in the research. Lack of identifying information, however, makes it very difficult to follow subjects over time, so that a cohort study may not be able to collect enough outcome data for drawing conclusions.

From this brief description, it should be clear that even if the U.S. federal government should change its present policy and decide to support research in this area, it is very unlikely that a clinical trial research study will ever be conducted. Such a study would be quite expensive, costing in the tens of millions of dollars. The study would also be logistically complicated, with difficulties in equating subject-recruitment methods and in measuring or estimating numbers of new injectors. The study would also be extremely difficult from a political perspective. The controversial nature of legal-access programs in the United States tends to polarize community leaders around the topic, so that it is unlikely that a large number of communities could be found that would be willing to accept random assignment to either the experimental or the control conditions.[13]

It is even less likely that a clinical trial of legal access would be conducted outside of the United States. As will be discussed later in this article, the experience with legal access has typically led other countries to expand and attempt to improve their legal-access programs, rather than expend resources attempting to provide a scientifically definitive measurement of effectiveness. The evidence to date from other countries has led some researchers to conclude that legal access to injection equipment should be considered the present standard of

12. Friedman and Des Jarlais, "HIV among Drug Injectors"; Don C. Des Jarlais and Samuel R. Friedman, "HIV Infection among Persons Who Inject Illicit Drugs: Problems and Prospects," *Journal of the Acquired Immune Deficiency Syndromes*, 1(3):267-73 (1988).

13. Don C. Des Jarlais and Bruce Stepherson, "History, Ethics and Politics in AIDS Prevention Research," *American Journal of Public Health*, in press.

care and that it would be unethical to conduct research in which IDUs were denied legal access simply to comply with a research design.[14]

Given the low probability of a full-scale clinical trial of legal access, most research on this topic is likely to continue to rely upon the case-study approach. For legal-access programs in the United States, these are likely to be simple pre-post comparison case studies, where the frequencies of different AIDS risk behaviors and other measures are compared. Studies in Europe, Australia, and Asia are likely to be time-extended case studies, where factors associated with the utilization of legal access over extended time periods are central questions.

The rest of this article will review the research that has been conducted on legal access to drug injection equipment, using a modified case-history format. Length restrictions prohibit full descriptions of all of the studies, and for some studies only highlights of the research will be reviewed. The studies will be presented in approximate chronological order. Since there has been extensive international communication among researchers and practitioners in the area of preventing HIV infection among IDUs, with many of the studies building on previous work, reviewing the studies in chronological order provides some sense of how the field has developed over time.

NEW YORK

The earliest studies of HIV—then called either lymphadenopathy-asso-

ciated virus (LAV) or human T-cell leukemia/lymphoma virus III (HTLV-III)—infection among IDUs were conducted in New York City and New Jersey.[15] These studies showed an unexpectedly high rate of exposure—approximately 50 percent—in both New York City and northern New Jersey. Studies of the reasons why IDUs had been sharing injection equipment indicated that sharing was firmly integrated in the drug injection subculture and that there were multiple reasons why equipment was shared. Major reasons included the limited availability of injection equipment and fear of arrest if caught by the police while carrying injection equipment.[16] The early New York studies also showed that the majority of IDUs in the city were already changing their behavior to reduce their risks of developing

14. Anderson, "New York Needle Trial."

15. Thomas J. Spira et al., "Prevalence of Antibody to Lymphadenopathy-Associated Virus among Drug-Detoxification Patients in New York" (letter), *New England Journal of Medicine*, 311(7):467-68 (Aug. 1984); Henry W. Cohen et al., "Behavioral Risk Factors for HTLV-III/LAV Seropositivity among Intravenous Drug Abusers" (Paper delivered at the First International Conference on AIDS, Atlanta, GA, Apr. 1985); Stanley H. Weiss et al., "Risk for HTLV-III Exposure and AIDS among Parenteral Drug Abusers in New Jersey" (Paper delivered at the First International Conference on AIDS, Atlanta, GA, Apr. 1985).

16. Don C. Des Jarlais, Samuel R. Friedman, and Donald Strug, "AIDS and Needle Sharing within the Intravenous Drug Use Subculture," in *The Social Dimensions of AIDS: Methods and Theory*, ed. D. Feldman and T. Johnson (New York: Praeger, 1986), pp. 111-25; Peter A. Selwyn et al., "Knowledge about AIDS and High-Risk Behavior among Intravenous Drug Abusers in New York City," *AIDS*, 1(4):247-54 (Dec. 1987).

AIDS.[17] In particular, IDUs in New York had increased their use of sterile injection equipment obtained on the illicit market.[18] (We should explain in passing that, just as drugs are sold in an illicit market, so, too, are needles and syringes. This injection equipment is usually diverted or stolen from legitimate medical sources. Moreover, the low cost of needles and syringes and the large market for standard medical uses of injection equipment make it virtually impossible for law enforcement efforts ever to shut off the supply of illicitly obtained injection equipment.) In summary, the New York City situation served both as a negative example of large-scale spread of HIV prior to prevention efforts and as a positive example of drug users' willingness to utilize sterile injection equipment as an AIDS prevention method.

AMSTERDAM

Legal access to sterile injection equipment and a formal syringe-exchange program actually existed in Amsterdam even before any concern about AIDS among IDUs. There had been no laws criminalizing the possession of injection equipment or requiring prescriptions for the sale of injection equipment. The absence of a prescription requirement, however, did not mean that individual phar-

macists were obligated to sell injection equipment to persons suspected of injecting illicit drugs. Indeed, in 1984, a pharmacy in central Amsterdam that had been a major source of injection equipment changed its policy and would no longer sell to those believed to be illicit IDUs. The MDHG, an organization of current IDUs, former IDUs, and concerned professionals, then proposed a syringe exchange in order to reduce the transmission of hepatitis B among IDUs in the city. This exchange was then initiated on a modest scale, with 25,000 syringes exchanged beginning in the fall of 1984 and 100,000 exchanged in 1985.

During 1985, when the HIV antibody test became available, testing was conducted on historically collected serum samples from IDUs in Amsterdam, and it became clear that HIV was already well established among IDUs in the city. A massive expansion of the syringe exchange was then undertaken, with 300,000 syringes exchanged in 1986, 500,000 in 1987, 600,000 in 1988, and up to the current level of approximately 700,000 per year for an estimated 3000 IDUs in the city.

Research was also undertaken to monitor the further spread of HIV in Amsterdam, including determination of risk factors associated with HIV exposure among IDUs. The studies have shown an increase in the reported use of the syringe exchange commensurate with the official expansion, yet without an increase in drug injection among persons already injecting[19] or an increase in the

17. Friedman and Des Jarlais, "AIDS and Self-Organization"; Selwyn et al., "Knowledge about AIDS."

18. Don C. Des Jarlais, Samuel R. Friedman, and William Hopkins, "Risk Reduction for the Acquired Immunodeficiency Syndrome among Intravenous Drug Users," *Annals of Internal Medicine*, 103(5):755-59 (Nov. 1985).

19. Johanna A. R. van den Hoek, Harry H.J.A. van Haastrecht, and Roel A. Coutinho,

overall number of persons injecting drugs in the city.[20] The mean age of IDUs in the city has increased moderately since the initial expansion of the syringe-exchange program, again indicating the absence of any influx of new IDUs. Although not reduced to zero, there have been substantial declines in both the hepatitis B incidence rates (from 48 per 10,000 in 1984 to 8.6 per 10,000 in 1989) and the HIV seroconversion rates (from 10.7 per 100 person-years in 1986 to 5.5 per 100 person-years in 1989) among IDUs in Amsterdam, along with a stabilization of the HIV seroprevalence rate.[21]

In Amsterdam there is a large-scale drug abuse treatment system, offering both drug-free and methadone maintenance treatment, intensive AIDS education efforts for IDUs, as well as both over-the-counter sales of injection equipment and the large-scale syringe exchange.[22] It is therefore difficult to attribute the reduction in HIV and hepatitis B seroconversions to any single specific component of the AIDS prevention program for IDUs in the city. The most recent study of HIV seroconverters in Amsterdam does not show a protective effect from using the syringe exchange as compared to obtaining sterile injection equipment from other sources—primarily from pharmacies.[23] The one positive benefit that can be most directly associated with the large-scale expansion of the syringe exchange is the reduction in the number of discarded needles and syringes found in public areas of the city.[24]

Other Dutch cities have also implemented syringe-exchange programs; providing syringe exchanges is essentially a national policy for preventing HIV transmission among IDUs in the country. Studies from Rotterdam indicate that the sharing of injection equipment has greatly declined, with an episode of sharing now considered as the exception to the new social rule among injectors, which now disapproves of sharing.[25]

"Risk Reduction among Intravenous Drug Users in Amsterdam under the Influence of AIDS," *American Journal of Public Health,* 79:1355-57 (1989).

20. Ernst C. Buning, "The Role of the Needle Exchange Project in Preventing HIV Infection among Drug Users in Amsterdam" (Paper delivered at the "What Works Conference: An International Perspective on Drug Abuse Treatment and Prevention Research," New York, Oct. 1989).

21. Harry J. A. van Haastrecht et al., "The Course of the HIV Epidemic among Intravenous Drug Users in Amsterdam, the Netherlands," *American Journal of Public Health,* 81(1):59-62 (Jan. 1991).

22. Ernst C. Buning et al., "Preventing AIDS in Drug Addicts in Amsterdam" (letter), *Lancet,* ii:1435 (June 1986).

23. Erik J. C. van Ameijden, Johanna A. R. van den Hoek, and Roel A. Coutinho, "Risk Factors for HIV Seroconversion in Injecting Drug Users in Amsterdam, the Netherlands" (Paper delivered at the Seventh International Conference on AIDS, Florence, Italy, June 1991).

24. Ernst C. Buning, G.H.A. van Brussel, and G. W. van Santen, "Amsterdam's Drug Policy and Its Implications for Controlling Needle Sharing," in *Needle Sharing among Intravenous Drug Abusers: National and International Drug Perspectives,* National Institute on Drug Abuse, Research Monograph Series no. 80, ed. R. J. Battjes and R. W. Pickens (Rockville, MD: National Institute on Drug Abuse, 1988), pp. 59-74.

25. Jean-Paul C. Grund, Charles D. Kaplan, and Nico F. P. Adriaans, "Needle Sharing in the Netherlands: An Ethnographic Analysis, *American Journal of Public Health,* in press.

EDINBURGH

Edinburgh experienced one of the most rapid spreads of HIV among IDUs of any city in the world. Historically collected sera indicate that HIV exposure among IDUs in the city reached approximately 50 percent within two years after the introduction of the virus into the city.[26] Yet injection equipment could be purchased without a prescription before the introduction of the virus into the community, and there were no laws criminalizing the possession of the equipment. At about the same time that the virus entered Edinburgh, however, the police persuaded the local pharmacists not to sell equipment to IDUs. Moreover, this very rapid spread of HIV in Edinburgh did occur in the absence of any AIDS awareness among the IDUs in the city. Such rapid spread prior to AIDS awareness had also occurred in New York—where, as noted earlier in this article, there were also severe restrictions on legal access to injection equipment—but also in several locations in Italy,[27] where there were rel-

atively few restrictions on legal access to injection equipment. Despite the numerous possible complex relationships between awareness of AIDS, legal restrictions, and practical restrictions on access to injection equipment in the spread of HIV among IDUs, the Edinburgh experience served as a powerful example against legal restrictions in policy debates over the next several years.

Over-the-counter sales and limited syringe exchange have since been implemented in Edinburgh, along with outreach to IDUs in the city. The HIV seroprevalence rate among IDUs in the city has also stabilized.[28]

UNITED KINGDOM

The United Kingdom did not have legal restrictions on injection equipment, although, as noted previously, there were some practical restrictions. Some local syringe-exchange programs—notably, the program in Liverpool—were started soon after AIDS among IDUs became a concern in 1985-86. In April 1987, a national syringe-exchange program was started that included a national evaluation. This evaluation focused on operational issues as well as on measuring outcome variables such as the sharing of injection equipment. There was wide variation in many of the operational characteristics of the exchanges, which was related to their ability to attract clients.[29] Exchanges

26. J. R. Robertson et al., "Epidemic of AIDS-Related Virus (HTLV-III/LAV) Infection among Intravenous Drug Abusers," *British Medical Journal*, 292:527-29 (Feb. 1986).

27. Fausto Titti et al., "Human Immunodeficiency Virus (HIV) Seropositivity in Intravenous (IV) Drug Abusers in Three Cities of Italy: Possible Natural History of HIV Infection in IV Drug Addicts in Italy," *Journal of Medical Virology*, 23:241-48 (1987); F. Bortolotti et al., "The Changing Epidemiology of Acute Type B Hepatitis: Results of an 11-Year Prospective Study in Padua (Northern Italy)," *Infection*, 17(6):364-68 (1989); Anita de Rossi et al., "Trends of HTLV-I and HIV Infections in Drug Addicts" (letter), *European Journal of Cancer and Clinical Oncology*, 24(2):279-80 (1988).

28. J. F. Peutherer et al., "HTLV-III Infection in Intravenous Drug Abusers in Edinburgh" (Paper delivered at the Second International Conference on AIDS, Paris, June 1986).

29. Gerry V. Stimson et al., *Injecting Equipment Exchange Schemes: Final Report*

that were able to attract clients were user friendly. They had locations and hours that were convenient for the IDUs. The staff were knowledgeable about the drug scene and took a non-judgmental attitude toward the clients. The staff were ready to refer clients to drug abuse treatment (and to other potentially needed medical and social services) but did not attempt to persuade clients that it was necessary for them to enter drug abuse treatment.[30] There was a minimum of bureaucratic hurdles for entering the program, and clients were recruited into the evaluation typically only after trust had been established. The user-friendly programs permitted large numbers of syringes to be exchanged at a single time, with some clients exchanging a hundred or more syringes at one time. These clients were clearly exchanging for groups of friends and were in effect serving as satellite exchange agents. This was particularly common in small-city or rural areas where travel to the exchange was often a problem.

The satellite exchange agent phenomenon can become a real problem if an exchange program does not anticipate it. One recent study from northern England found that, at an exchange which limited the number of syringes that could be exchanged at any one time to five, frequent users of the exchange actually passed used injection equipment to others at a higher rate than did persons who did not use the exchange frequently.[31] This occurred because the frequent users of the exchange had become known in the local drug-user community as persons who usually had injection equipment. Other drug injectors who needed equipment during hours when the exchange was not open would then seek out the frequent users and socially pressure them to provide equipment, even if it had been already used. It should be stressed that this is the only study to date that has shown a higher rate of a transmission-related behavior among frequent users of an exchange compared to infrequent users or nonusers of the exchange.

Nevertheless, the problems of frequent exchangers' serving as satellite exchange agents—and thus needing to exchange large numbers of syringes at one time—and of drug injectors' needing equipment at hours when the exchanges or the pharmacies are not open, appear to be universal for legal-access programs. The simplest solution is to supply enough syringes at one time for some users to act as satellite exchange agents. Another partial solution is for syringe-exchange programs to distribute bleach also, so that it will be possible for the drug injectors to disinfect the injection equipment if two or more persons are going to use it. Most exchanges in the United States already distribute bleach kits, and European exchanges

---

(London: Monitoring Research Group, Goldsmith's College, 1988).

30. One exchange program, operated by a drug abuse treatment program, did attempt to use the exchange primarily as a means of recruiting clients, and eventually it closed because it was not able to attract enough clients.

31. Hilary Klee et al., "The Sharing of Injection Equipment among Drug Users Attending Prescribing Clinics and Those Using Needle-Exchanges," British Journal of Addiction, 86:217-23 (1991).

are increasingly doing so. Another partial solution currently being considered is the use of vending machines that would provide syringes when special tokens were inserted. These tokens would be distributed by outreach workers or syringe-exchange staff in order to provide some opportunities for face-to-face contact and counseling about AIDS.

In any event, the results of the national syringe-exchange evaluation indicated that retention of clients was a considerable problem, with less than 10 percent returning for multiple visits to the syringe exchange. Part of the reason many clients did not continuously use the exchange is that sterile injection equipment was also available from pharmacies. The IDUs who used the syringe exchanges reduced significantly but did not eliminate their sharing of injection equipment. There was substantial variation across individuals, with a very small number who even increased their sharing after starting to use the exchange.

The research included a comparison group of IDUs who were not utilizing the exchange programs. These nonusers were generally younger, had shorter injection histories, and were less likely to already have started AIDS risk reduction. These comparisons are important to the ultimate findings in several ways. They provide strong evidence that syringe exchanges were not recruiting new persons into drug injection. The finding that persons coming to syringe exchanges tended to be established rather than new IDUs has since been replicated in all other studies of syringe exchanges. While these find-

ings clearly refute the argument that syringe exchanges would recruit new, inexperienced persons into drug injecting, they also raise the problem of by what other means health authorities will be able to reach new injectors, hopefully before they are exposed to HIV. Finally, the differences suggest that there were no readily available comparison groups for assessing syringe-exchange programs.

HIV seroconversion studies have recently been conducted in relation to the syringe exchanges in Liverpool and London. No HIV seroconversions have been noted among IDUs using the exchange in Liverpool[32] and few if any have been seen among IDUs using a London exchange.[33] To be precise, two seroconverters were observed during this study, but the timing of the seroconversion was such that the actual HIV infections of these two may well have occurred before the subjects started to participate in the exchange. There has also been a recent report of an apparent increase in HIV seroprevalence among IDUs in London.[34] Whether this apparent increase is an artifact of changed sampling procedures, of

32. Russell Newcombe, "The Liverpool Syringe Exchange Scheme for Drug Injectors: Initial Evidence of Effectiveness in HIV Infection" (Paper delivered at the First International Conference on the Global Impact of AIDS, London, Mar. 1988).

33. Graham J. Hart et al., "Evaluation of Needle Exchange in Central London: Behaviour Change and Anti-HIV Status over One Year," AIDS, 3(5):261-65 (May 1989).

34. Adam N. Crosier et al., "Prevalence of HIV Infection among Injecting Drug Users in London" (Paper delivered at the Seventh International Conference on AIDS, Florence, Italy, June 1991).

HIV-seropositive IDUs migrating to London, or of an actual increase in HIV transmission among IDUs in the city has not yet been determined.

SWEDEN

Sweden may be second only to New York City in the complexity of its policies and practices regarding legal access to injection equipment. Prior to AIDS, Sweden did have a law requiring prescriptions for dispensing injection equipment. This law has not been changed. Nevertheless, a group of physicians in southern Sweden, in the cities of Malmö and Lund, began a syringe exchange in 1986, including collecting data on participants in the syringe exchange. HIV-antibody counseling and testing is widely used throughout Sweden as an AIDS prevention technique, and participants in the exchange were encouraged to be regularly tested every three months. This testing then provided important data for assessing the effectiveness of the exchange.[35]

The Swedish National Welfare Board conducted an evaluation of the exchange and recommended that the exchange be expanded into a national system. The Swedish parliament, however, rejected this recommendation and permitted continuation of the exchange only in southern Sweden. The research on the exchange users has continued. Almost a thousand IDUs have used the syringe exchange, with

182 classified as "regular" users. To date there have been no known HIV seroconversions among the users of the syringe exchange. While this series of studies does not have a control group, it is noteworthy that HIV seroprevalence among IDUs in other parts of Sweden is substantially higher than among IDUs in southern Sweden.[36]

SYDNEY

Prior to the AIDS epidemic, over-the-counter sales of injection equipment were permitted in Australia and there were no narcotics paraphernalia laws there. In response to concerns about AIDS, syringe-exchange programs were also established. Initially, these were limited to discounts on the purchase of new injection equipment when drug users returned used equipment. Intravenous drug users' own organizations were also established in Australia, with government support. These organizations have implemented outreach exchange programs, with mobile units traveling through high-drug-use areas to exchange injection equipment at no cost to the drug users.

Two studies were conducted that addressed the potential efficacy and lack of harm of the syringe exchanges in Sydney. In the first study, blood in syringes returned to an exchange was tested for the antibody to HIV. The percentage of syringes containing anti-HIV antibodies remained stable over time, indicating that HIV was

35. Bengt Ljungberg et al., "HIV Prevention among Injecting Drug Users: Three Years of Experience from a Syringe Exchange Program in Sweden," *Journal of the Acquired Immune Deficiency Syndromes*, 4(9):890-95 (Sept. 1991).

36. Kerstin I. Kall and Robert G. Olin, "HIV Status and Changes in Risk Behavior among Intravenous Drug Users in Stockholm 1987-88," *AIDS*, 4(2):153-57 (Feb. 1990).

not greatly increasing among the users of the exchange.[37] In the second study, since the syringe exchange was coincidentally located only a block from a methadone maintenance program, urinalysis results from the methadone patients were examined for the time periods before and during the operation of the syringe-exchange program. The urinalysis results showed no evidence of an increase in illicit drug use, despite the proximity of the syringe exchange. These two studies were innovative in their use of biological measures rather than self-reported behavior, and the results were fully consistent with self-reported data from the European studies of syringe exchanges.

PARIS

Prior to the AIDS epidemic, France had a national law requiring prescriptions for the sale of injection equipment. The earliest HIV studies among IDUs showed high seroprevalence among IDUs in southern France and in Paris. As a result of the concern about AIDS among IDUs, the prescription law was repealed, and a national training program was established to train pharmacists in how to sell injection equipment, and to provide limited HIV counseling and education to IDUs. The French program thus recognized the importance of the cooperation and attitudes of pharmacists in actually supplying sterile injection equipment to IDUs.

The effectiveness of these measures was assessed in two studies. Espinoza and colleagues interviewed IDUs entering prison in Paris. They found that the use of sterile injection equipment increased substantially after the repeal of the prescription requirement and the training of pharmacists.[38] Ingold and Ingold interviewed IDUs recruited from treatment programs and from street settings in Paris, in two suburbs of Paris, and in three other French cities. They also found that the change in the prescription requirement had an "obvious" effect on reducing the sharing of injection equipment among French IDUs.[39] Neither study, however, reported a complete elimination of sharing of injection equipment, and both called for additional measures to prevent AIDS among IDUs.

INNSBRUCK

Austria did not have a prescription requirement law prior to the AIDS epidemic, but informal discretionary practices among pharmacists served to limit the actual availability of sterile injection equipment. In Innsbruck, for example, pharmacists normally

37. Jael S. Wolk et al., "HIV Seroprevalence in Syringes of Intravenous Drug Users Using Syringe Exchanges in Sydney, Australia, 1987" (Paper delivered at the Fourth International Conference on AIDS, Stockholm, Sweden, June 1988); idem, "Syringe HIV Seroprevalence and Behavioral and Demographic Characteristics of Intravenous Drug Users in Sydney, Australia, 1987," AIDS, 2(5):373-77 (1988).

38. Pierre Espinoza et al., "Has the Open Sale of Syringes Modified the Syringe Exchanging Habits of Drug Addicts?" (Paper delivered at the Fourth International Conference on AIDS, Stockholm, Sweden, June 1988).

39. F. R. Ingold and S. Ingold, "The Effects of the Liberalization of Syringe Sales on the Behaviour of Intravenous Drug Users in France," Bulletin on Narcotics, 41(1-2):67-81 (1989).

would sell injection equipment only in lots of 100 needles and syringes. As a result of concern about AIDS, public health officials in Innsbruck prevailed upon the local pharmacists and convinced them to sell injection equipment to illicit drug users in single units. HIV seroprevalence among IDUs in Innsbruck subsequently stabilized at approximately 30 percent.[40] While it is not possible to draw a simple cause-and-effect inference from the increased availability of injection equipment and the stabilization of HIV seroprevalence in Innsbruck, it should be noted that in other areas where HIV seroprevalence had reached 30 percent among IDUs, seroprevalence then continued to rapidly rise to between 40 and 50 percent: for example, New York,[41] Edinburgh,[42] Milan,[43] and Bari, Italy.[44] The other notable instance of a leveling off of rapid rises after reaching 30 percent is Amsterdam, which had also greatly increased the legal availability of injection equipment prior to the stabilization of HIV seroprevalence among IDUs.

NEW YORK REDUX

The situation in New York City with regard to legal availability of drug injection equipment has probably been the most complicated of any city in the world. As noted before, the early studies from New York showed both the possibility of rapid transmission of HIV among IDUs and the willingness of IDUs to reduce their AIDS risk by increasing their use of sterile equipment, which was obtained through an expanding illicit market for such equipment. New York has both a narcotics paraphernalia law and a prescription requirement. The prescription requirement law does, however, permit the state health commissioner to make exceptions in certain cases. Discussions of providing legal access to injection equipment in New York began in 1984, became public in late 1985,[45] and finally led to a pilot program research study that opened on 7 November 1988. The discussions of a possible syringe-exchange program were often quite heated,[46] and the program that finally opened was quite limited. It was permitted to operate out of only a single site, one not in a neighborhood with a high rate of injecting drug use but quite near the police headquarters, and it was prevented from having the proposed research comparison group. The program had complicated admission procedures

40. Dietmar Fuchs et al., "Anti-HIV-1 Antibodies, Anti-HTLV-1 Antibodies and Neopterin Levels in Parenteral Drug Addicts in the Austrian Tyrol," *Journal of the Acquired Immune Deficiency Syndromes*, 1(1):65-66 (1988).

41. Don C. Des Jarlais et al., "HIV-1 Infection among Intravenous Drug Users in Manhattan, New York City, from 1977 through 1987," *Journal of the American Medical Association*, 17 Feb. 1989, pp. 1008-12.

42. Buning et al., "Preventing AIDS in Drug Addicts."

43. Titti et al., "Human Immunodeficiency Virus Seropositivity."

44. G. Angarano et al., "Rapid Spread of HTLV-III Infection among Drug Addicts in Italy," *Lancet*, ii:1302 (1985).

45. Don C. Des Jarlais and William Hopkins, " 'Free' Needles for Intravenous Drug Users at Risk for AIDS: Current Developments in New York City," *New England Journal of Medicine*, 5 Dec. 1985, p. 1476.

46. Joseph and Des Jarlais, "Needle and Syringe Exchange"; Anderson, "New York Needle Trial."

and mandatory services such as tuberculosis testing. Admission to the program was limited to persons already waiting for open positions in drug abuse treatment programs. Of the persons admitted to the program, 39 percent were successfully placed into treatment programs, often before they had had significant use of the exchange. This pilot program was then closed after the election of a new mayor in November 1989.[47] This official New York program nonetheless illustrated both the importance of a user-friendly service in terms of attracting drug users, and the ability of syringe-exchange programs to place drug users into treatment programs.[48]

AIDS activists, including ACT UP and the AIDS Brigade, have been operating modest-scale syringe-exchange programs since the closing of the city Health Department program. Ten of these activists arranged to have themselves arrested in the hope that a court trial would compel the new city administration to reconsider its opposition to syringe exchange. The judge accepted a defense of public-health necessity and returned a not-guilty verdict. Subsequent reports from the syringe exchange in New Haven, Connecticut, and the recommendation of the National Commission on AIDS in support of syringe exchanges have led the current city government to announce that it is reconsidering its

position on syringe exchange, and fully authorized exchanges are expected to open in late 1991 or early 1992.[49]

Throughout this whole period of the debates and modest-scale exchange operations in New York City—from 1984 to the present—HIV seroprevalence has remained stable among IDUs in the city, with a low to moderate rate of new HIV infections.[50] This reduced rate of new infections is probably best attributed to large-scale AIDS risk reduction among IDUs,[51] facilitated by a large-scale expansion of the illicit market for sterile injection equipment.[52]

TACOMA

The first syringe exchange in North America was started by David Purchase in Tacoma, Washington, in 1988. Acting as a concerned citizen, he first discussed the project with local health and law enforcement officials to obtain prior assurance that they would not interfere. He then started doing syringe exchange in a high-drug-use area, donating his own time and using private donations for the purchase of the needed equip-

47. Anderson, "New York Needle Trial."

48. *The Pilot Needle Exchange Study in New York City: A Bridge to Treatment: A Report on the First Ten Months of Operation* (New York: New York City Department of Health, Dec. 1989).

49. Des Jarlais and Stepherson, "History, Ethics and Politics."

50. Des Jarlais et al., "HIV-1 Infection among Intravenous Drug Users"; idem, "Risk Reduction and Stabilization of HIV Seroprevalence among Drug Injectors in New York City and Bangkok, Thailand" (Paper delivered at the Seventh International Conference on AIDS, Florence, Italy, June 1991).

51. Friedman and Des Jarlais, "AIDS and Self-Organization"; Friedman et al., "Social Intervention against AIDS."

52. Des Jarlais, Friedman, and Hopkins, "Risk Reduction."

ment. Several months later, the Tacoma/Pierce County Health Department assumed official responsibility for the exchange. In addition to providing syringe exchange, the operation also provides general information about AIDS, distributes condoms and bleach, makes referrals to drug abuse treatment and other services—indeed, the Tacoma exchange has become the single largest referral source for drug abuse treatment in the county—and provides on-site screening for tuberculosis.

Evaluation of the Tacoma syringe-exchange program has been conducted since 1989. IDUs using the exchange typically have long histories of drug injection, with a mean of 15 years since first injection; fewer than 4 percent began injecting within the previous two years. Pre-post comparisons of AIDS risk behavior among syringe-exchange users show reductions of 76 percent in using potentially contaminated equipment—borrowing or renting previously used injection equipment—and of 63 percent in passing on equipment after injecting, a means of potential transmission. These pre-post comparisons also showed no changes in the rates of drug use among users of the exchange. Comparison with IDUs who do not use the syringe-exchange program showed higher frequencies of injection among the exchange users, but lower rates of AIDS risk behaviors.

At one point, the state attorney general in Washington attempted to close the syringe-exchange program, and a civil suit was required to resolve the dispute. As part of the suit, the Sanitation Department filed an affidavit certifying that the number of used needles and syringes discarded in the city had decreased since the opening of the syringe exchange. There are similar reports of decreases in the discarding of potentially contaminated injection equipment since the large-scale expansion of the exchange in Amsterdam[53] and since the opening of the exchange in Portland, Oregon.[54]

Monitoring of HIV and hepatitis B infection rates has been included as part of the evaluation of the Tacoma syringe exchange.[55] The HIV seroprevalence rate among IDUs in Tacoma not using the exchange (7 percent) is higher than among the users of the exchange (2 percent). HIV seroprevalence among IDUs in Tacoma overall has remained stable since the opening of the exchange, while hepatitis B among IDUs has actually declined since the opening of the exchange.[56]

SAN FRANCISCO

In terms of AIDS prevention among IDUs, San Francisco is probably best known for the development of bleach distribution for disinfecting

53. Van Ameijden, van den Hoek, and Coutinho, "Risk Factors for HIV Seroconversion."

54. K. Oliver, personal communication, Aug. 1991.

55. Holly Hagan et al., "Lower HIV Seroprevalence, Declining HBV Incidence and Safer Injection in Relation to the Tacoma Syringe Exchange" (Paper delivered at the Seventh International Conference on AIDS, Florence, Italy, June 1991).

56. Holly Hagan et al., "The Incidence of HBV Infection and Syringe Exchange Programs" (letter), *Journal of the American Medical Association*, in press.

used injection equipment.[57] The use of bleach for disinfecting injection equipment has been widely accepted by IDUs in San Francisco.[58] Bleach distribution has also been adopted by many of the cities in the National Institute on Drug Abuse's National AIDS Demonstration Research projects and has been increasingly incorporated within syringe-exchange programs. San Francisco is also the location of Prevention Point, a privately run syringe-exchange program, the largest in North America, which has been in operation since 1988.

Yet the exact legal status of the syringe exchange in San Francisco remains unclear. California does have a prescription requirement for dispensing syringes that the program clearly has not been following. In fact, the program was started with the expectation that the operators would be arrested and that the resulting trial would force the city and state governments to address the issue of a syringe-exchange program. Arrests were made, but charges were not pressed, and there was no trial. In any event, the exchange has continued, relying upon private donations of time and money for supplies. The mayor of San Francisco publicly praised Prevention Point in his address to the Sixth International AIDS Conference in San Francisco,[59] but no government financial or staff support has so far been provided, because of the apparent technical illegality of the operation. An arrest for distributing sterile injection equipment was made in nearby Redwood City, California, that resulted in an 11-to-1 hung jury for acquittal. In fact, the jury foreman in that case was sufficiently convinced of the benefits of syringe exchange that, after the trial, he became a volunteer worker for the exchange.

An evaluation of the San Francisco syringe exchange based on self-reported risk behavior has been conducted. The results showed that frequent use of the syringe exchange was strongly associated with a lower probability of having shared injection equipment in the month prior to the study interview. The study found an odds ratio of 2.8 for recent sharing of injection equipment when nonusers or infrequent users of the exchange were compared to frequent users of the exchange, that is, to persons who had used the exchange 25 times or more.[60] Data on the age at first injection among persons using the syringe exchange shows that exceedingly few of the exchangers are new injectors, so that there is no evidence for the exchange's attracting new persons

57. John A. Newmeyer et al., "Preventing AIDS Contagion among Intravenous Drug Users," *Medical Anthropology*, 10(2-3):167-75 (1987).

58. Richard E. Chaisson et al., "HIV, Bleach and Needle Sharing" (letter), *Lancet*, 1:1430 (1987); John K. Watters, D. M. Iura, and K. W. Iura, *AIDS Prevention and Education Service to Intravenous Drug Users through the Midcity Consortium to Combat AIDS: Administrative Report of the First Six Months* (San Francisco, CA: Midcity Consortium, 1986), p. 9.

59. Art Agnos, Mayor of San Francisco, opening-ceremony address to the Sixth International Conference on AIDS, San Francisco, CA, 1990.

60. John K. Watters et al., "Epidemiology and Prevention of HIV in Intravenous Drug Users in San Francisco, 1986-1989" (Paper delivered at the Sixth International Conference on AIDS, San Francisco, CA, June 1990).

into drug injection. Since the implementation of the bleach distribution and syringe-exchange programs in San Francisco, HIV seroprevalence has stabilized among IDUs.[61]

NEW HAVEN

In the spring of 1990, the state of Connecticut passed legislation permitting syringe exchanges. The legislation also required evaluation of the exchanges. An exchange program was implemented in the city of New Haven. As in other exchanges, the IDUs who utilized the exchange typically had long histories of injecting drugs; there was no evidence that new injectors were recruited as a result of the existence of the exchange.[62] The exchange program also became a major source of referral for encouraging IDUs to enter drug abuse treatment programs, although the shortage in overall treatment program capacity in the city has reduced the total numbers of persons who have actually entered treatment.

In addition to the questionnaire and referral data, the evaluation study utilized polymerase chain reaction (PCR) testing of HIV residues in the syringes that were returned to the exchange, PCR being an extremely sensitive method for detecting HIV in blood. Syringes distributed in the exchange program were marked; hence it was possible to determine whether a particular syringe was being returned by the same person to whom the syringe had originally been given. Thus PCR testing was done with a means of ascertaining which returned syringes were unlikely to have been shared (those that had been given to and returned by the same person) and which were likely to have been shared (those given to one person but returned by a different person). The proportion of probably unshared to probably shared syringes remained relatively constant throughout the operation of the exchange. The PCR HIV seroprevalence remained constant in the unlikely-to-have-been-shared syringes, while the PCR HIV seroprevalence in the likely-to-have-been-shared syringes declined substantially over time, indicating less frequent sharing of each of those syringes. Using a mathematical model of HIV transmission, the evaluators then estimated that HIV transmission among IDUs in the city had been reduced by one-third.

The PCR results showing decreasing HIV contamination in the likely-to-have-been-shared syringes can be taken as clear evidence that these syringes were being shared less over time. The projection to an actual reduction in new HIV infections, however, must be considered at best an estimate that needs to be tested further against estimates derived from other mathematical models of the spread of HIV among IDUs. The use of mathematical models in evaluation research is still a developing field that may yet have great poten-

61. John K. Watters et al., "Update on Changes in HIV-1 Seroprevalence and Risk Behavior among Intravenous Drug Users in San Francisco" (Paper delivered at the annual meeting of the American Public Health Association, Boston, MA, Nov. 1988).

62. Elaine O'Keefe, Edward Kaplan, and Kaveh Khoshnood, *Preliminary Report: City of New Haven Needle Exchange Program* (New Haven, CT: New Haven Health Department, 1991).

tial. If such models can be empirically validated, they would greatly reduce the time and expense needed in order to draw sound inferences about the effectiveness of different AIDS prevention programs.

BALTIMORE

Recruitment of a very large number of IDUs into an HIV seroprevalence study permitted researchers in Baltimore to examine the relationship between having diabetes and exposure to HIV.[63] For all the other medical conditions that have been studied in relationship to HIV exposure among IDUs, there were either no differences between HIV-positive and HIV-negative IDUs, or else injectors who were HIV-positive were also more likely to have had the other medical condition. These otherwise consistent findings may be the result of life-style or behavioral differences that are associated with HIV risk behavior,[64] or they may have occurred because HIV infection may precipitate the development of a wide variety of other infections among IDUs.[65] The Baltimore study also found that, in general, the HIV seropositives were more likely to have had a wide variety of other diseases, with the notable exception that HIV-seronegative IDUs were more likely to have had diabetes. Having had diabetes would, of course, lead to having longstanding access to prescriptions for large amounts of sterile drug injection equipment.

Baltimore is also noteworthy as an example of a place where the mayor of the city has been publicly supportive of syringe-exchange programs, but no program has been implemented because of political opposition. Since the mayor announced support for a syringe-exchange program, new HIV infections among IDUs have continued at moderate levels, indicating a need for more effective prevention programs.[66]

DISCUSSION

These case-history studies certainly illustrate the complexity of the issues surrounding AIDS among IDUs and legal access to drug injection equipment. The studies were conducted in the contexts of different pre-AIDS legal restrictions, different stages in HIV epidemics, and different national and local political cultures with respect to illicit drug use as a social problem. These studies also often used different research designs and different outcome measures. Despite all these differences, there appear to be at least four conclusions that can be drawn from this body of research.

63. Kenrad E. Nelson et al., "Diabetes Is Protective against HIV Infections in IV Drug Users" (Paper delivered at the Sixth International Conference on AIDS, San Francisco, CA, June 1990).

64. Samuel R. Friedman, Paula H. Kleinman, and Don C. Des Jarlais, "History, Biography, and HIV Infection among Drug Injectors: A Methodological Caution" (letter), *American Journal of Public Health*, in press.

65. Rand L. Stoneburner et al., "A Larger Spectrum of Severe HIV-Related Disease in Intravenous Drug Users in New York City," *Science*, 11 Nov. 1988, pp. 916-19.

66. Kenrad E. Nelson et al., "HIV-1 Seroconversions in a Cohort of Intravenous Drug Users" (Paper delivered at the Seventh International Conference on AIDS, Florence, Italy, June 1991).

First, there is an imperfect correlation between laws governing access to sterile injection equipment and actual use of sterile injection equipment by IDUs. Indeed, without any change in the laws, actual access to sterile injection equipment may increase through an illicit market in response to AIDS-related demand. This occurred in New York City, and it probably has been the most important early factor in reducing HIV transmission among IDUs in that city. Conversely, the absence of legal restrictions on drug injection equipment does not by itself mean that IDUs will actually have sterile injection equipment at the times when they are about to inject drugs.

Second, programs to increase the legal use of sterile injection equipment by IDUs appear to have almost universally achieved their desired effect of reducing AIDS risk behavior. Such programs may or may not have required changes in laws. They have required training and AIDS competence for the persons who sell or provide the injection equipment and AIDS education for the IDUs. The variety of outcome measures used in studies of these programs does not permit precise determination of an average effect size for these programs, but the consistency of the reported results in reducing AIDS risk behavior is quite striking. Admittedly, many of the studies were conducted by persons operating programs, and almost all were conducted with at least the cooperation of program staff, raising the issue of possible bias in the findings. Nevertheless, the findings did not vary sig-

nificantly by whether the study was conducted by program staff or by an outside evaluator, nor by whether outcome was measured by self-report alone or also with HIV or hepatitis B data.

The findings are also very consistent in showing that the AIDS risk reduction associated with these programs has not yet attained complete risk elimination. This is true partly because these programs are not utilized by all IDUs in the community and, even among persons who could be considered regular clients, there is a residual level of risk behavior and some variation involving relapses over time. The reasons for such limitations on the effectiveness of programs are an important subject for future research. Some of the limitations are likely to be related to operational issues of the specific programs, and others may be related to fundamental aspects of illicit drug injection, such as the strong craving to use drugs that occurs during withdrawal or psychological denial of AIDS risk in sharing injection equipment within very close personal relationships.

The experience of these programs also suggests a great need to more effectively link them with other forms of AIDS prevention, including treatment programs for drug abuse and programs to prevent sexual transmission of HIV. Legal access to injection equipment will clearly be of limited effectiveness where it is the only strategy used for preventing AIDS among IDUs. Indeed, one of the major strengths of the legal-access programs has been the opportunities these programs present for recruiting IDUs to other AIDS, health, and social services.

The outcome research has been so consistent on legal-access programs that the relevant question no longer is, Can these programs work? but rather, How can they be made to work better, and how can they best be integrated with other programs?

The research findings are also remarkably consistent in showing that the programs do not lead to increased illicit drug use either by persons who are already injecting drugs or by inducing new persons to start injecting drugs. This can most readily be seen in the longitudinal studies of clients of the programs, the numbers of clients who have been referred to drug abuse treatment, and the relatively long histories of drug injection prior to entering the programs. The absence of any increased illicit drug use raises two important questions for future research. First, how can or should legal-access programs and AIDS prevention programs reach persons who are starting to inject illicit drugs? The socially preferred prevention goal would, of course, be to prevent them from starting to inject or get them to stop injecting. Yet preventing transmission of HIV among those who nonetheless continue to inject would also be an important public-health goal, toward which the current studies of legal access provide little guidance.

The absence of harmful effects associated with legal-access programs also raises the question of how political opposition to these programs is maintained in the absence of supporting data. Obviously, scientific data are very rarely the only factor in public-health policy. Still, AIDS must plainly be considered a very important public-health problem in the United States, as well as in many countries throughout the world. Hence continued effective opposition to legal-access programs, in the absence of empirical support for the arguments based on the hypothesized harmful effects, is in itself a subject worthy of investigation. Examining the bases of such opposition to legal-access programs is beyond the scope of the present article, and to our knowledge, little relevant data have been collected. Nevertheless, we would suggest that the following interrelated factors may be relevant: (1) the highly stigmatized nature of illicit drug use; (2) the potential for synergistic stigmatization among illicit drug use, AIDS, and minority-group membership; and (3) the mutual lack of trust and empathy between illicit IDUs and most public officials. We would also note that the drug abuse problem in the United States and elsewhere is quite complicated and not amenable to fast or inexpensive solution. Difficulties in quickly reducing the drug abuse problem may create increased political utility for actions that symbolically express social disapproval of illicit drug use, such as criminalizing the possession of drug paraphernalia, even if these actions do not lead to any demonstrable benefit in reducing illicit drug use, and may incur the unintended but enormous cost of increased HIV transmission among illicit drug users, as well as from IDUs to their sexual partners and newborn children.

The public-health importance of AIDS among IDUs, their sexual partners, and their children, however, creates great pressure for finding effective prevention strategies. Based on the international evidence to date, programs that provide legal access to sterile injection equipment would appear to be one important—although not sufficient—component of an effective overall prevention strategy.

ANNALS, *AAPSS*, **521**, May 1992

Ensuring Success in Interventions with Drug-Using Offenders

By M. DOUGLAS ANGLIN and THOMAS H. MAUGH II

ABSTRACT: A significant proportion of crime in the United States is directly related to the use of illicit drugs. Substantial reductions in crime at all levels could be obtained by enlarging or targeting appropriate interventions for drug-using offenders. Accumulated research findings have demonstrated conclusively that treatment for drug use does work, and a growing body of evidence suggests that treatment is equally effective when imposed on drug-using criminal offenders by the criminal justice system. In this article, we suggest appropriate strategies for implementing treatment programs within criminal justice settings and for maximizing their chances of success.

M. Douglas Anglin, Ph.D., is an adjunct associate professor at the Neuropsychiatric Institute at the University of California, Los Angeles, and Thomas H. Maugh II, Ph.D., is a research consultant with the institute. Both are senior staff members at the UCLA Drug Abuse Research Center. Their major areas of research interest include drug abuse etiology, epidemiology, treatment outcome, and social policy.

NOTE: Partial support for this article was provided by grants DA05544 and DA07699 from the National Institute on Drug Abuse and grant 87-IJ-CX-042 from the National Institute of Justice. Dr. Anglin is also supported by Research Scientist Development Award (DA00146) from the National Institute on Drug Abuse.

A major impetus driving society's concern about illicit drugs is the association between drug use and crime. The morbidity, mortality, reduced economic productivity, and social dysfunctioning of users also cause concern, but crime and community safety are paramount. Empirical data suggest that drug use is both a direct and indirect cause of crime at all levels, including violent, property, and financial crime.

Where violent crime is concerned, most acts occur in transaction disputes or marketing conflicts. In the black market economy associated with illicit drugs, drug use incites trafficking and property crimes.[1] In this respect, numerous studies have documented the disproportionate amount of crime perpetrated by drug-dependent offenders.[2] In particular, individuals dependent on heroin and cocaine have been found to have extremely high crime rates.[3] As levels of personal use increase, the frequency and severity of criminal behavior also rise dramatically.[4] Not surprisingly, many surveys show that a relatively few severe-level drug users are responsible for an extraordinary proportion of crime.[5]

In addition to crime, drug-using offenders generally have life-styles characterized by hedonistic, self-destructive, and antisocial behaviors; they also have problems related to poor social skills, the absence of job training, dependence on others, and frequent contact with criminal jus-

1. Gregory P. Falkin, Harry K. Wexler, and Douglas S. Lipton, *Establishing Drug Treatment Programs in Prisons* (New York: Narcotic and Drug Research, 1990); National Criminal Justice Association, *Treatment Options for Drug-Dependent Offenders* (Washington, DC: National Criminal Justice Association, 1990).

2. Marcia R. Chaiken, "Crime Rates and Substance Abuse among Types of Offenders," in *Crime Rates among Drug-Abusing Offenders: Final Report to the National Institute of Justice*, ed. Bruce D. Johnson and Eric Wish (New York: Narcotic and Drug Research, 1986); Bruce D. Johnson et al., *Taking Care of Business: The Economics of Crime by Heroin Abusers* (Lexington, MA: Lexington Books, 1985); James A. Inciardi, "Heroin Use and Street Crime," *Crime & Delinquency* (July 1979), pp. 335-46.

3. Johnson et al., *Taking Care of Business*; John C. Ball et al., "The Criminology of Heroin Addicts When Addicted and When off Opiates," in *The Drugs-Crime Connection*, ed. James A. Inciardi (Beverly Hills, CA: Sage, 1981); John C. Ball, "The Hyper-Criminal Opiate Addict," in *Crime Rates among Drug-Abusing Offenders*, ed. Johnson and Wish; Jan M. Chaiken and Marcia R. Chaiken, "Crime Rates and the Active Offender," in *Crime and Public Policy*, ed. James Q. Wilson (New Brunswick, NJ: Transaction Books, 1983); James J. Collins, Robert L. Hubbard, and J. Valley Rachal, "Expensive Drug Use and Illegal Income: A Test of Explanatory Hypotheses," *Criminology*, 23(4):743-64 (1985); George R. Speckart and M. Douglas Anglin, "Narcotics and Crime: A Causal Modeling Approach," *Journal of Quantitative Criminology*, 2:3-28 (1986).

4. Chaiken, "Crime Rates and Substance Abuse among Types of Offenders"; Collins, Hubbard, and Rachal, "Expensive Drug Use and Illegal Income"; Speckart and Anglin, "Narcotics and Crime"; Jan M. Chaiken and Marcia R. Chaiken, *Varieties of Criminal Behavior* (Santa Monica, CA: RAND, 1982).

5. Johnson et al., *Taking Care of Business*; Inciardi, "Heroin Use and Street Crime"; John C. Ball, J. W. Shaffer, and David N. Nurco, "Day-to-Day Criminality of Heroin Addicts in Baltimore: A Study in the Continuity of Offense Rates," *Drug and Alcohol Dependence*, 12:119-43 (1983); Bernard A. Gropper, *Probing the Links between Drugs and Crime* (Washington, DC: Department of Justice, 1985).

tice authorities.[6] Those who are involved in the regular use of hard drugs or the use of multiple substances are typically at high risk of recidivism after their release from incarceration.[7]

IMPACT OF DRUG USE ON THE CRIMINAL JUSTICE SYSTEM

Drug use by offenders is most striking, and most objectively assessed, in arrestees. Studies conducted in over 20 cities nationwide by the National Institute of Justice have found that 30 to 78 percent of arrestees have illicit drugs in their urine, suggesting that drug use played some role in their crimes.[8] Cocaine is the most commonly detected, but heroin, phencyclidine (PCP), marijuana, and amphetamines are also found in significant fractions of arrestees.[9] Surveys of prison inmates indicate similarly high levels of drug use.[10] Furthermore, drug possession or use

is now a contributing factor in 64 percent of the cases in which California parolees are returned to prison for parole violations.[11]

Only a small proportion of the nation's criminals receive treatment for their drug problems while they are in contact with the criminal justice system (CJS). In 1979, a survey by the National Institute on Drug Abuse found 160 prison treatment programs serving about 10,500 inmates, or roughly 5 percent of the prisoners in need of such treatment.[12] By 1987, according to Chaiken,[13] 11.1 percent of U.S. inmates in need, about 51,500, were in drug treatment programs—a sizable increase, but one that still leaves the preponderance of inmates with histories of drug abuse outside treatment programs. A 1991 study of federal prisons by the General Accounting Office found that only 364 inmates were receiving treatment in corrections-based intensive residential programs and that less than half of the treatment slots purportedly available were filled.[14]

6. Collins, Hubbard, and Rachal, "Expensive Drug Use and Illegal Income"; Harry K. Wexler, Douglas S. Lipton, and Bruce D. Johnson, *A Criminal Justice System Strategy for Treating Cocaine-Heroin Abusing Offenders in Custody*, document NCJ 108560 (Washington, DC: Department of Justice, National Institute of Justice, 1988).

7. Chaiken and Chaiken, *Varieties of Criminal Behavior*; Wexler, Lipton, and Johnson, *Criminal Justice System Strategy for Treating Cocaine-Heroin Abusing Offenders*; Christopher A. Innes, *Profile of State Prison Inmates* (Washington, DC: Department of Justice, 1986).

8. U.S., Department of Justice, National Institute of Justice, *1989 Drug Use Forecasting Annual Report: Drugs and Crime* (Washington, DC: National Institute of Justice, 1990).

9. Ibid.

10. Innes, *Profile of State Prison Inmates.*

11. California Blue Ribbon Commission, *Growth and Its Influence on Corrections: Perspectives on the Report of the Blue Ribbon Commission* (Berkeley, CA: Guggenheim Criminal Justice Program, 1990).

12. National Institute on Drug Abuse, *Drug Abuse Treatment in Prisons*, Treatment Research Report Series, DHHS pub. no. (ADM) 81-1149 (Rockville, MD: National Institute on Drug Abuse, 1981).

13. Marcia R. Chaiken, *In-Prison Programs for Drug-Involved Offenders* (Washington, DC: Department of Justice, National Institute of Justice, 1989).

14. U.S., General Accounting Office, *Drug Treatment: Despite New Strategy, Few Federal Inmates Receive Treatment*, GAO/HRD-91-116, Sept. 1991; idem, *Drug Treatment: State Pris-*

The use of drugs among probationers, inmates, and parolees could be sharply reduced—and the incarcerated population and the need for new facilities minimized—given the will to adopt an appropriate program of drug treatment. A growing body of evidence now indicates that intervention by entering offenders into community-based or corrections-based treatment can reduce drug use, criminal behavior and recidivism, even when the addicts do not participate in the program voluntarily.

The next section will provide an overview of the current drug treatment system, particularly as it serves heroin and cocaine users. The efficacy of various treatment modalities is described, including supporting findings from existing research literature. The subsequent section examines the effectiveness of drug treatment for offenders, focusing on studies of corrections-based treatment. Next we propose strategies that are considered essential in the development of successful interventions for offenders. Finally, we present conclusions and suggestions for further research and policy development.

AN OVERVIEW OF TREATMENT FOR DRUG USE

The four major drug treatment modalities are inpatient and outpatient detoxification, outpatient methadone maintenance, therapeutic communities, and outpatient drug-free programs. These modalities account for more than 90 percent of all clients in treatment as of 1987.[15] Given the historical concern with heroin use, it is not surprising that two of these—methadone maintenance and one form of detoxification using methadone—are oriented exclusively toward the opiate-dependent client.

Detoxification typically involves the short-term use of licit drugs—such as antidepressants, methadone, or buprenorphine—to allow a tolerable withdrawal from illicit drugs and the medical management of symptoms. Most detoxification programs focus on narcotics dependence and use methadone to establish a staged withdrawal, typically over 21 days, that provides systematic relief from the opioid-abstinence syndrome. Detoxification programs usually provide no subsequent therapeutic services. The long-term effectiveness of detoxification has not been evaluated often, but it is thought to be minimal.[16]

Methadone maintenance involves the administration of the synthetic opiate methadone to a narcotics-dependent individual at stable dosage levels as an oral substitute for heroin or other opioid drugs. Because methadone is itself addictive, under federal guidelines, clients must have a documented history of addiction and have little expectation of being able to function normally without

15. National Association of State Alcohol and Drug Abuse Directors, *State Resources and Services Related to Alcohol and Drug Abuse Problems, Fiscal Year 1987* (Rockville, MD: Department of Health and Human Services, 1988).

16. Douglas S. Lipton and Michael J. Maranda, "Detoxification from Heroin Dependency: An Overview of Method and Effectiveness," *Advances in Alcohol and Substance Abuse*, 2:31-55 (1982).

chemotherapeutic support.[17] Most programs are in outpatient settings and include explicit rules for behavior, mandatory counseling sessions, routine urine testing, and the taking of medication under direct supervision.

Treatment goals typically do not require complete opiate abstinence but include rehabilitation or improvement in social functioning so as to promote a return to productive community living. Positive outcomes have been reported in most studies of methadone maintenance, including the Drug Abuse Reporting Program (DARP), the Treatment Outcome Prospective Study (TOPS), and other individual program evaluations. Several recent reviews conclude that the evidence consistently shows significant decreases in opioid use and in criminality, as well as improvements in general behavior and health for many addicts.[18]

Anglin and his colleagues, for example, have shown that methadone maintenance decreased the percentage of nonincarcerated time during which addicts engaged in daily narcotics use from about 70 percent—averaged across several studies—to about 12 percent and increased the percentage of nonincarcerated time abstinent from narcotics use from about 12 percent to about 26 percent.[19] Involvement in property crime decreased from about 18 percent of nonincarcerated time when not in treatment to about 11 percent during treatment. Maddux and Desmond found that community crime rates in the San Antonio, Texas, area decreased as methadone treatment rates increased in the local addicted population, then climbed again when cutbacks in funding caused the premature discharge of patients.[20] In a study of 617 clients in New York City, Philadelphia, and Baltimore, Ball et al. found that the average number of days per person during which criminal behavior occurred was reduced from 307 in the year before treatment to 18 to 24 after the clients had been in treatment for six months.[21]

17. Vincent P. Dole and Marie E. Nyswander, "A Medical Treatment of Diacetylmorphine (Heroin) Addiction," *Journal of the American Medical Association*, 193:646-50 (1965).

18. James R. Cooper et al., *Research on the Treatment of Narcotic Addiction: State of the Art*, National Institute on Drug Abuse Research Monograph, DHEW pub. no. (ADM) 83-1281 (Rockville, MD: Department of Health and Human Services, 1983); Frank M. Tims and Jacqueline P. Ludford, eds., *Drug Abuse Treatment Evaluation: Strategies, Progress, and Prospects*, National Institute on Drug Abuse Research Monograph no. 51 (Rockville, MD: Department of Health and Human Services, 1984); Edward C. Senay, "Clinical Implications of Drug Abuse Treatment Outcome Research," in ibid.

19. M. Douglas Anglin and William H. McGlothlin, "Outcome of Narcotic Addict Treatment in California," in *Drug Abuse Treatment Evaluation*, ed. Tims and Ludford, pp. 106-28; idem, "Methadone Maintenance in California: A Decade's Experience," in *The Yearbook of Substance Use and Abuse*, ed. Leon Brill and Charles Winick (New York: Human Sciences Press, 1985), 3:219-80; Yih-Ing Hser, M. Douglas Anglin, and Chih-Ping Chou, "Evaluation of Drug Abuse Treatment: A Repeated Measure Design Assessing Methadone Maintenance," *Evaluation Review*, 12:547-70 (1988).

20. James F. Maddux and David P. Desmond, "Crime and Drug Abuse Behavior: An Area Analysis," *Criminology*, 19:281-302 (1979).

21. John C. Ball et al., "The Reduction of Intravenous Heroin Abuse, Non-Opiate Abuse and Crime during Methadone Maintenance

Therapeutic communities are residential facilities in which treatment involves personality and behavioral rehabilitation within a highly structured environment, focusing on development of social relationships. Examples include the early Synanon program and successors like Daytop Village,[22] Phoenix House, and Gateway House.[23] The primary treatment approach includes group therapy, tutorial learning sessions, remedial and formal education classes, residential job duties, and, in later stages, conventional occupations for live-in/work-out clients.[24] Some therapeutic communities require stays as short as six months, but the optimal period is at least 15 months in residence.[25] Success is defined as a change to a life-style that is drug free, economically productive, and free from antisocial behavior.

Both DARP and TOPS, as well as other reviews of therapeutic communities, have shown significant improvements in clients' immediate and long-term behavior.[26] Drug use and criminality declined while measures of prosocial behavior, such as employment and school involvement, increased.[27] The degree of improvement is directly linked to the amount of time the client spends in the program.[28]

Outpatient drug-free treatment programs were begun in the 1970s, designed mainly for youthful users of drugs other than opiates. Subsequently, almost as many opiate addicts have entered outpatient drug-free programs as methadone programs. Whether treating addiction to opiates or to other drugs, similar services are typically provided.

The primary treatment approach relies on counseling and training in social skills. The outpatient drug-free programs vary widely, ranging from highly demanding nonresidential communities to relaxed programs of recreational activities. The planned duration usually is short, and referral is made to community agencies for health, mental health, educational, vocational, legal, housing, financial, family, and other required services. This treatment emphasizes abstinence from both licit and illicit drugs, with attention paid to circumstances that foster drug use.

Comparisons of the three long-term modalities (including therapeutic communities and methadone maintenance but excluding detoxifi-

Treatment: Further Findings" (Paper delivered at the meeting of the Committee on Problems of Drug Dependency, Philadelphia, PA, June 1987).

22. D. Vincent Biase, *Daytop Miniversity: Advancement in Drug-Free Therapeutic Community Treatment*, Evaluation Report no. 1-H81-DA-01911-01A1 (Rockville, MD: Department of Health and Human Services, National Institute on Drug Abuse, 1981).

23. George DeLeon, "The Therapeutic Community: Status and Evolution," *International Journal of the Addictions*, 20:823-44 (1985).

24. Saul B. Sells, ed., *Evaluation of Treatment*, vols. 1 and 2 (Cambridge, MA: Ballinger, 1974).

25. Ibid.

26. George DeLeon, "Program-Based Evaluation Research in Therapeutic Communities," in *Drug Abuse Treatment Evaluation*, ed. Tims and Ludford.

27. M. Douglas Anglin and Yih-Ing Hser "Treatment of Drug Abuse," in *Drugs and Crime*, ed. Michael Tonry and James Q. Wilson (Chicago: University of Chicago Press, 1990), pp. 393-460.

28. Ibid.

cation) indicate that outpatient drug-free clients were most likely to leave treatment in the first one (21 percent) to four weeks (36 percent).[29] By three months in treatment, more than 60 percent had dropped out, transferred, or completed treatment. Outpatient drug-free clients were also the least successful in reducing their drug use and criminal behavior.[30] As previously noted, methadone maintenance was generally the most effective in reducing drug use and criminal behavior in heroin-dependent clients.

Despite evidence for differential outcomes, the primary criteria for choosing a treatment program, whether for heroin, cocaine, or other drug use, are availability and affordability. In many cases, a client may receive inappropriate or insufficient treatment and pass through several programs before finding one that is ultimately effective. The National Institute on Drug Abuse is now sponsoring research programs to develop protocols to more effectively match treatment services with client needs.

Emerging treatment for cocaine users

Data on drug use among arrestees indicate that cocaine is the drug most commonly used by offenders. These use levels are echoed in the general population. Of approximately 5.2 million U.S. users of cocaine in the mid-1980s, 1 to 3 million were estimated to be in need of treatment,[31] as many as six times the number of heroin addicts. Current prevalence estimates reflect little change in the overall number of users, but the number of abusers in need of treatment has increased because of the greater prevalence, and consequences, of smoking crack cocaine. Many dependent users come into contact with the criminal justice system.

Most of the information now available about treatment for cocaine users comes from studies of narcotics addicts who also used cocaine. From the DARP study, for example, Simpson et al. reported that 38 percent of their sample of narcotics abusers had used cocaine prior to treatment. Only 18 to 22 percent used it one to six years after treatment, but 39 percent used it in the twelfth year after treatment.[32] This increase in the proportion of users may reflect the in-

29. Robert L. Hubbard et al., "Treatment Outcome Prospective Study (TOPS): Client Characteristics and Behaviors before, during, and after Treatment," in *Drug Abuse Treatment Evaluation*, ed. Tims and Ludford.

30. Anglin and Hser, "Treatment of Drug Abuse."

31. George DeLeon, "Cocaine Abusers in Therapeutic Community Treatment," in *Advances in Cocaine Treatment*, ed. Frank M. Tims and Carl G. Leukefeld (Rockville, MD: National Institute on Drug Abuse, forthcoming); Frank H. Gawin, "Cocaine Addiction: Psychology and Neurophysiology," *Science*, 251: 1580-86 (1991); Frank H. Gawin and Herbert D. Kleber, "Cocaine Abuse: Abstinence Symptomatology and Psychiatric Diagnosis," *Archives of General Psychiatry*, 43:107-13 (1986); J. F. Jekel et al., "Epidemic Free-Base Cocaine Abuse: Case Study from the Bahamas," *Lancet*, 1:459-62 (1986). Edward H. Adams and Nicholas J. Kozel, eds., *Cocaine Use in America: Epidemiological and Clinical Perspectives*, National Institute on Drug Abuse Research Monograph 61 (Rockville, MD: National Institute on Drug Abuse, 1985).

32. Dwayne D. Simpson et al., "Addiction Careers: Etiology, Treatment, and 12-year Fol-

creased popularity of cocaine more than a decaying impact of treatment. Nonetheless, several studies found that outpatient treatment was less effective than residential treatment in reducing cocaine abuse.[33] Siguel[34], however, found that most cocaine users were treated in the drug-free modalities.

Studies of the TOPS data indicate that one-fourth of all narcotics addicts in treatment were regular cocaine users in the year before entering treatment[35] and more than 60 percent had used it at some time during that year. For those regular cocaine users who stayed in treatment at least three months, 47 percent of residential community graduates were abstinent in the year after treatment, as were 40 percent of outpatient methadone clients and 42 percent of outpatient drug-free clients.

Because the problem of severe cocaine use is so recent, few treatments targeted specifically at it are available. Instead, clinicians have tended to adapt approaches designed for other forms of drug abuse, such as the 28-day inpatient programs developed for alcohol abuse and the therapeutic communities designed for opiate addiction. Also because of the recent onset of the problem, there have been few short-term studies of the efficacy of these treatments, and virtually no long-term follow-up studies. A growing body of evidence, however, is leading researchers to the conclusion that substance abuse and dependence represent manifestations of a behavioral motif more than syndromes related exclusively to the nature of the substance being used. If that is the case, then treatments that do not rely on chemical intervention should be similarly effective for most types of abusive behavior.

The 28-day inpatient programs for chemical dependency were originally established for the treatment of alcoholism. By the mid-1980s, however, more than half of the patients in many private programs were cocaine abusers.[36] In most cases, the alcohol programs were applied directly to cocaine abusers with few modifications. These facilities typically have a campuslike setting, and most or all of the staff are recovering addicts or alcoholics.[37] The goal is to remove the addict from the environment that trig-

low-Up Outcomes," *Journal of Drug Issues*, 16:107-21 (1986).

33. Burt Associates, *Drug Treatment in New York City and Washington, DC: Follow-Up Studies* (Washington, DC: Government Printing Office, 1977); Thomas R. Kosten et al., "Cocaine Abuse among Opioid Addicts: Demographic and Diagnostic Effects in Treatment," *American Journal of Drug and Alcohol Abuse*, 12:1-16 (1986); Thomas R. Kosten, Bruce J. Rounsaville, and Herbert D. Kleber, "A 2.5-Year Follow-Up of Cocaine Use among Treated Opioid Addicts: Have Our Treatments Helped?" *Archives of General Psychiatry*, 44:281-84 (1987).

34. Eduardo N. Siguel, "Characteristics of Clients Admitted to Treatment for Cocaine Abuse," in *Cocaine: 1977*, ed. Robert C. Peterson and R. C. Stillman, National Institute on Drug Abuse Research Monograph no. 13 (Rockville, MD: National Institute on Drug Abuse, 1977).

35. Robert L. Hubbard et al., eds., *Drug Abuse Treatment: A National Study of Effectiveness* (Chapel Hill: University of North Carolina Press, 1989).

36. Richard A. Rawson, "Inpatient Treatment Programs in the Western United States: A Survey" (Manuscript, Matrix Institute on Addictions, 1986).

37. Richard A. Rawson, "Chemical Dependency Treatment: The Integration of the Alco-

gered dependence and to encourage clients to break through their defenses and confront their denial using techniques based on the Alcoholics Anonymous 12-step program.

Several different studies are evaluating the efficacy of 28-day programs, and there is some follow-up information on one sample of cocaine abusers. Rawson et al. conducted one-year follow-up interviews with a group of 65 cocaine abusers treated at the Sierra Tucson center in Arizona.[38] The population consisted primarily of single, male, white cocaine abusers with relatively short drug histories. Overall, 45 percent of the cocaine abusers treated in the program gave self-reports of achieving one year of abstinence successfully, compared to 75 percent of the alcoholics graduating from the program.

Therapeutic communities have never oriented their treatment approach to any one particular type of drug user; their concern is the person, not necessarily the drug. In fact, they encourage acceptance of the view that abstinence from all drugs is a primary treatment goal. DeLeon has shown that cocaine-related admissions to therapeutic communities had increased from less than 10 percent in 1980 to about 40 percent by 1986.[39] Unfortunately, there is virtually no evaluation available of the

effectiveness of therapeutic communities specifically serving cocaine or crack users, although studies are currently under way.[40]

Outpatient psychotherapy techniques are extremely varied in their approach to the treatment of cocaine abuse. Several reports have indicated that some approaches have significant value in assisting recovery.[41] In all of these psychotherapeutic approaches, the clearly defined goal of therapy is the elimination of cocaine use. More general therapeutic gains in other behavioral or emotional areas are desirable and important for long-term improvement, but they are viewed as secondary to the discontinuation of drug use. Some proponents of in-depth psychotherapy with cocaine users believe that therapy needs to extend more deeply than issues of abstinence and that dealing with these underlying issues is essential to good long-term outcome.[42]

40. George DeLeon, personal communication, 1991.

41. R. M. Kertzner, "Individual Psychotherapy of Cocaine Abuse," in *Cocaine Abuse: New Directions in Treatment and Research*, ed. H. I. Spitz and J. S. Rosecan (New York: Brunner/Mazel, 1987); Robert Millman, "Considerations of the Psychotherapy of the Substance Abuser," *Journal of Substance Abuse Treatment*, 3:103-10 (1986); Marc Galenter, "Psychotherapy for Alcohol and Drug Abuse: An Approach Based on Learning Theory," *Journal of Psychiatric Treatment Evaluation*, 5:551-56 (1983); Bruce J. Rounsaville, Frank H. Gawin, and Herbert D. Kleber, "Interpersonal Psychotherapy Adapted for Ambulatory Cocaine Abusers," *American Journal of Drug and Alcohol Abuse*, 11:171-91 (1985).

42. F. Schiffer, "Psychotherapy of Nine Successfully Treated Cocaine Abusers: Techniques and Dynamics," *Journal of Substance Abuse Treatment*, 5:131-38 (1988).

holism and Drug Addiction Systems," *International Journal of the Addictions*, in press.

38. Richard A. Rawson, Jean L. Obert, and Michael J. McCann, "The Treatment of Cocaine Addiction and Alcoholism at Sierra Tucson: Treatment Outcome Issues" (Manuscript, Matrix Institute on Addictions, 1990).

39. DeLeon, "Cocaine Abusers in Therapeutic Community Treatment."

Arnold Washton has developed a structured outpatient treatment approach that combines behavioral techniques, cognitive strategies, information, family involvement, self-help groups, and urine testing.[43] Washton reports that this combination of procedures appears to provide middle-class patients with a set of tools that allows them to stop cocaine use and initiate positive life-style changes, which in turn promote continued abstinence. In a study of 127 middle-class patients who entered treatment, for example, he found that 65 percent completed the 6- to 12-month program and 75 percent were drug-free at one- to two-year follow-up.[44]

Another approach has been developed by the Matrix Center, a Los Angeles-based institute that was established in 1983 to design a model of outpatient treatment specifically for cocaine abusers. The treatment model, called the neurobehavioral model, integrates structured information and strategies derived from clinical research on addiction into an appropriate treatment approach. The treatment materials have evolved by applying concepts from theoretical and applied psychotherapy research

to the needs of cocaine users attempting to stop their cocaine use.[45]

The neurobehavioral approach to cocaine addiction is intended to address the types of dysfunction that exist when cocaine users enter treatment. No presumptions have been made about underlying psychopathology. The needs of the clients have been determined by a behavioral analysis of the types of problems encountered by cocaine abusers as they proceed through a period of cocaine abstinence. Over 1000 cocaine users have been treated with the methodology.

The neurobehavioral model has been implemented by the Matrix Center in a standardized manner in Southern California since 1985. In two of the four Matrix Center offices, Beverly Hills and Rancho Cucamonga, a large-scale open trial involving 486 patients has been conducted to provide a foundation for future systematic studies of the model.[46] Drug and alcohol histories of both groups were very similar, except that the majority of the Beverly Hills group used cocaine intranasally while the majority of the Rancho Cucamonga group smoked crack. Both groups of subjects had substantial histories of cocaine and other drug use, and about two-thirds of both groups used alcohol three or more times per week. Of those subjects who completed the six-month phase, similar proportions in

43. Arnold M. Washton, "Outpatient Treatment Techniques," in *Cocaine: A Clinician's Handbook*, ed. Arnold M. Washton and Mark S. Gold (New York: Guilford, 1987); idem, *Cocaine Addiction: Treatment, Recovery and Relapse Prevention* (New York: Norton, 1989); Arnold M. Washton and Nanette S. Stone-Washton, "Abstinence and Relapse in Outpatient Cocaine Addicts," *Journal of Psychoactive Drugs*, 22:135-47 (1990).

44. Arnold M. Washton, Mark S. Gold, and A. C. Pottash, *Treatment Outcome in Cocaine Abusers*, National Institute on Drug Abuse Research Monograph no. 67 (Rockville, MD: National Institute on Drug Abuse, 1986).

45. Richard A. Rawson, "Chemical Dependency Treatment: The Integration of the Alcoholism and Drug Addiction Systems," *International Journal of the Addictions*, in press.

46. Richard A. Rawson et al., "Neurobehavioral Treatment for Cocaine Dependency," in *Advances in Cocaine Treatment*, ed. Tims and Leukefeld.

both sites had no cocaine use detected by urinalysis or self-report: 44 percent in Beverly Hills; 40 percent in Rancho Cucamonga.

Other approaches to cocaine abuse treatment include behavioral strategies; 12-step programs similar to Alcoholics Anonymous; nontraditional methods that may include acupuncture, nutritional supplements, and exercise; and pharmacological approaches to block craving for cocaine. None of these has yet had enough study for an adequate evaluation of their efficacy.

A particularly encouraging finding common to most studies of treatment efficacy to date is the heterogeneity of populations in which treatment has been found effective, including incarcerated populations. Successful treatment has been achieved with both sexes, with a broad variety of ethnic groups, with a wide spectrum of age groups, and in every region of the country. (The present discussion is restricted to adults as data on juvenile offenders are rare. See the article by Dembo et al. in this volume for a discussion of issues relating to drug-using juvenile offenders.) These nearly uniform findings suggest that treatment results can be generalized to virtually all population groups.

EFFECTIVENESS OF
CORRECTIONS-BASED
DRUG INTERVENTION

Although there is wide consensus that treatment is an effective way to reduce drug use and its consequences, much less agreement attends the idea that treatment is useful in addressing drug dependence among CJS populations. Indeed, the view is widely held among CJS personnel themselves that rehabilitation efforts aimed at such individuals are ineffective.[47] Some researchers have also argued that cocaine and heroin abusers derive little benefit when they are forced into treatment by the CJS.[48]

Results from extensive research, however, indicate that coerced involvement in community-based programs and/or corrections-based treatment can have a substantial impact on the behavior of chronic drug-abusing offenders.[49] Both reviews of the

47. Robert M. Carter and Malcolm W. Klein, eds., *Back on the Street* (Englewood Cliffs, NJ: Prentice-Hall, 1976); Douglas S. Lipton, Robert Martinson, and Judith Wilks, eds., *The Effectiveness of Correctional Treatment: A Survey of Treatment Evaluation Studies* (New York: Praeger, 1975).

48. B. J. Bullington, D. K. Sprowls, and M. Phillips, "A Critique of Diversionary Juvenile Justice," *Crime & Delinquency*, 24:59-71 (1978); Malcolm W. Klein, "Deinstitutionalization and Diversion of Juvenile Offenders: A Litany of Impediments," in *Crime and Justice*, ed. Norval Morris and Michael Tonry (Chicago: University of Chicago Press, 1979); Robert C. Newman, "Diversion of Addicts from the Criminal Justice System to Treatment" (Paper delivered at the National Conference on Standards, Ethics and Practice, New York, NY, 1983).

49. Marcia R. Chaiken, *In-Prison Programs for Drug-Involved Offenders* (Washington, DC: Department of Justice, National Institute of Justice, 1989); Paul Gendreau and Robert R. Ross, "Revivification of Rehabilitation: Evidence from the 1980s," *Justice Quarterly*, 4(3):359-407 (1987); William H. McGlothlin, M. Douglas Anglin, and Bruce D. Wilson, *An Evaluation of the California Civil Addict Program*, National Institute on Drug Abuse Research Monograph Series, DHEW pub. no. (ADM) 78-558 (Washington, DC: Government Printing Office, 1977).

literature and empirical evidence support this conclusion. Empirical findings come from three areas: (1) long-standing research on the California Civil Addict Program and related programs; (2) outcome research on community-based methadone maintenance and therapeutic community programs, which have shown effective results with clients having extensive criminal histories;[50] and (3) studies by Narcotic and Drug Research, Incorporated (NDRI) that compared outcomes for drug-abusing offenders in several prison-based programs to those who received no treatment.[51] New research findings will be emerging as recently funded studies are completed.

The consistency in consecutive assessments of the benefits of treatment for offenders is compelling. In a 1979 review of the literature,

McGlothlin concluded that, despite less favorable pre-admission characteristics, CJS clients benefited from treatment as much as other clients did, and their addiction-related behaviors improved markedly after treatment.[52] Other studies also suggest that CJS coercion brings addicts into their first treatment episode earlier in their addiction careers than would otherwise have occurred and that they are retained in treatment longer.[53] Later support for this finding was provided by two studies of clients of methadone programs.[54] Individuals receiving treatment were divided into three groups: those entering treatment under low, moderate, or high legal coercion. All three groups showed virtually identical results: markedly decreased daily heroin use—20 percent of the pretreatment level—during treatment, and sustained improvement—50 percent of the pretreatment level—after treatment discharge. Furthermore, heroin addicts who are introduced to methadone treatment while incarcerated

50. George DeLeon, "Program-Based Evaluation Research in Therapeutic Communities"; George DeLeon et al., "Therapeutic Community Dropouts: Criminal Behavior Five Years after Treatment," *American Journal of Drug and Alcohol Abuse*, 6:253-71 (1979); Saul B. Sells and Dwayne D. Simpson, eds., *The Effectiveness of Drug Abuse Treatment*, vol. 3, *Further Studies of Drug Users, Treatment Topologies, and Assessment of Outcomes during Treatment in the DARP* (Cambridge, MA: Ballinger, 1976); ibid., vol. 4, *Evaluation of Treatment Outcomes for 1971-1972 DARP Admission Cohort* (1976); ibid., vol. 5, *Evaluation of Treatment Outcomes for 1972-1973 DARP Admission Cohort* (1976).

51. Wexler, Lipton, and Johnson, *Criminal Justice System Strategy for Treating Cocaine-Heroin Abusing Offenders*; Harry K. Wexler, Douglas S. Lipton, and K. Foster "Outcome Evaluation of a Prison Therapeutic Community for Substance Abuse Treatment: Preliminary Results" (Paper delivered at the annual meeting of the American Society of Criminology, San Diego, CA, Nov. 1985).

52. William H. McGlothlin, "Drugs and Crime," in *Handbook on Drug Abuse*, ed. R. L. DuPont, A. Goldstein, and John A. O'Donnell (Washington, DC: Government Printing Office, 1979).

53. Anglin and Hser, "Treatment of Drug Abuse"; M. Douglas Anglin, Mary-Lynn Brecht, and Ebrihim Maddahian, "Pretreatment Characteristics and Treatment Performance of Legally Coerced Versus Voluntary Methadone Maintenance Admissions," *Criminology*, 27(3):537-57 (1988).

54. James J. Collins and Margaret Allison, "Legal Coercion and Retention in Drug Abuse Treatment," *Hospital and Community Psychiatry*, 34:1145-49 (1983); Robert L. Hubbard et al., "Differential Effectiveness of Drug Abuse Treatment for Types of Heroin Abusers" (Manuscript, Research Triangle Park, 1987).

are more likely to enter and remain in methadone treatment in the community when they are released from custody.[55]

Given that coerced treatment is generally effective for addiction to heroin, cocaine, and other abused drugs, the question then becomes how best to involve drug-using offenders in treatment programs. Several different approaches have been attempted during the last seventy years. One of the earliest efforts was civil commitment, which proved to be extremely practical.

Civil commitment is a legal procedure that allows the commitment of narcotics addicts or other drug users, especially those arrested for criminal activity, to a compulsory drug treatment program that usually includes a residential period and a community-based aftercare period. Provisions are often included for helping clients with education and employment needs and for responding promptly to signs of readdiction— usually detected by regular urinalysis. This approach is particularly attractive because it provides the benefits of rehabilitation for the user while simultaneously reducing demand for drugs during both the treatment and the aftercare phases.

Civil commitment as it was applied in the California Civil Addict Program is discussed next, followed by descriptions of the Treatment Alternatives to Street Crime effort and other less comprehensive programs.

California Civil Addict Program

Several studies of the California Civil Addict Program (CAP) illustrate the effectiveness of in-prison and follow-up treatment. The first study compared narcotics addicts who were admitted to the program and were subsequently released into the community under supervision with addicts who were discharged from the program after a short period because of legal errors in the commitment procedures.[56] During the seven years after commitment, the program group reduced daily narcotics use by an average of 21.8 percent while the discharged group reduced daily use by only 6.8 percent. Furthermore, criminal activities in the program group were reduced by 18.6 percent, while the discharged group reported a reduction of only 6.7 percent.

A second evaluation[57] examined only the program group and identified three subsamples according to drug use and treatment status at the time of the interview, some 12 years after admission to the program: a "maturing out" sample,[58] a "subsequent treatment" sample, and a "chronic street addict" sample. The maturing-out sample, about 40 percent of the program group, had steadily reduced daily narcotics consumption during the average five-year commitment period and did not re-

56. McGlothlin, Anglin, and Wilson, *Evaluation of the California Civil Addict Program.*
57. Anglin and McGlothlin, "Methadone Maintenance in California."
58. Charles S. Winick, "Maturing out of Narcotic Addiction," *Bulletin on Narcotics,* 14:1-7 (1962).

55. Wexler, Lipton, and Johnson, *Criminal Justice System Strategy for Treating Cocaine-Heroin Abusing Offenders.*

sume addicted use after discharge. At the time of the interview, many subjects in this sample occasionally used narcotics, but few were addicted.

The subsequent-treatment sample, approximately 30 percent of the program group, showed a large decrease—approximately 20 to 25 percent—in daily drug use during the commitment period. After discharge, however, addicted use rapidly increased. Three years after discharge, addicted use by this group had reached precommitment levels. Addicted use continued at that resumed level until the group reentered long-term treatment, this time with methadone maintenance.

The chronic street-addict sample, approximately 30 percent of the program group, showed a moderate reduction—7 to 10 percent—in daily narcotics use during the commitment period. After discharge, addicted use rose to levels exceeding those reported in the precommitment period and was still high in the year preceding interview. For that year, the chronic street addicts described themselves as being addicted 55 percent of their nonincarcerated time, as compared to approximately 4 percent of the maturing-out sample and 8 percent of the methadone-maintenance sample.

These studies have two important findings. First, civil commitment as implemented in the California CAP reduced daily narcotics use and associated property crime by program participants to one-third the levels displayed by similar addicts who were not in the program. Second, while the program's effects differed across three types of addicts, narcot-

ics use and crime were suppressed in all three groups.

Unfortunately, these results were not available to California corrections planners in a timely fashion. During the 1970s, budgetary pressures led not only to a cutback in the number of convicts enrolled in the program but also to cutbacks in or the removal of some of the most effective elements of the program, including training of personnel, time spent in the program, and monitoring of clients by urinalysis.

Similar positive results have been obtained by other programs involving criminal justice clients. A study of a therapeutic community in a New York state prison, for example, found that only 27 percent of the subjects in the therapeutic community were rearrested while on parole, compared to 40 percent of those not treated.[59] Furthermore, for those who were arrested, the time until arrest was significantly longer for those treated in the therapeutic community. One meta-analysis of 80 different studies showed that appropriate treatment for drug use in prisons was associated with a significantly lower rate of recidivism than was found in those receiving no treatment or inappropriate treatment. Treatment was found to be effective in both adults and juveniles, in studies before and after 1980, in studies using randomized and nonrandomized designs, and in diversionary, community, and residential programs.[60]

59. Wexler, Lipton, and Foster, "Outcome Evaluation of a Prison Therapeutic Community."
60. Don A. Andrews et al., "Does Correctional Treatment Work? A Clinically-Relevant

*Treatment Alternatives
  to Street Crime*

Some state counties have developed coordinated programs to refer drug-using offenders to community-based treatment programs in lieu of prosecution or probation revocation. One such program, called Treatment Alternatives to Street Crime (TASC), was initiated in 1972 as a community-based treatment for drug-dependent individuals who otherwise might become progressively more involved with the criminal justice system. To motivate drug offenders to enter and remain in treatment, TASC employs diversionary dispositions such as deferred prosecution, creative community sentencing, and pre- and post-trial intervention. Dropping out of treatment or other noncompliance is treated by the courts as a violation of the conditions of release.

Evaluations of the impact of TASC have been limited.[61] Most TASC programs, however, are believed to have performed the treatment-outreach function successfully. Sells, for example, reports that 50 percent of TASC referrals entered treatment for the first time.[62] Although no detailed supportive data are available, some independent local evaluations have concluded that local TASC programs effectively intervened with clients to reduce drug abuse and criminal activity.[63]

The only available evaluations of the impact of TASC or similar programs are based on the Treatment Outcome Prospective Study.[64] These studies compared CJS-involved clients —in TASC and under other forms of CJS supervision—to voluntary drug-treatment clients in terms of demographic characteristics, treatment retention, treatment progress, and predatory behavior in the year following treatment termination. TASC clients improved as much as the voluntary clients with respect to drug use, employment, and criminal behavior during the first six months of treatment. TASC clients also tended to remain in both residential and outpatient drug-free modalities six to seven weeks longer than did voluntary clients or those under other CJS referrals, a finding usually associated with better treatment outcomes.[65]

Unfortunately, budgetary pressures have taken their toll on TASC as they did on the California CAP. At the height of its implementation in the early 1980s, TASC programs were operating in 39 of the 50 states. By 1988, withdrawal of government funds had reduced the number of programs to just over 100 in only 18 states.[66] More

and Psychologically Informed Meta-Analysis," *Criminology*, in press.

61. Anglin and Hser, "Treatment of Drug Abuse."

62. Saul B. Sells, "Treatment and Rehabilitation," in *Encyclopedia of Crime and Justice*, vol. 2, ed. S. H. Kadish (New York: Free Press, 1983).

63. L. Foster Cook et al., "Treatment Alternatives to Street Crime," in *Compulsory Treat-*

ment *of Drug Abuse: Research and Clinical Practice*, ed. Carl G. Leukefeld and Frank M. Tims, National Institute on Drug Abuse Research Monograph no. 86, DHHS pub. (ADM) 88-1578 (Washington, DC: Government Printing Office, 1988).

64. James J. Collins and Margaret Allison, "Legal Coercion and Retention in Drug Abuse Treatment"; Robert L. Hubbard et al., "Role of Drug-Abuse Treatment in Limiting the Spread of AIDS," *Review of Infectious Disease*, 10:377-84 (Mar.-Apr. 1988).

65. Anglin and Hser, "Treatment of Drug Abuse."

66. Cook et al., "Treatment Alternatives to Street Crime."

recently, the increasingly severe impact of drug-using offenders on the criminal justice system has promoted a greater policy interest in TASC as an alternative to incarceration. The 1990s may see an increased utilization of this type of intervention.

Other assessments of CJS populations in treatment

Other studies have shown that legal pressure increases rates of admission to treatment programs and may promote better retention in treatment, consequently improving the overall results of the program. McFarlain et al., for example, found that legal pressure increased retention during the first 30 days after admission, but not long-term retention.[67] Similarly, Schnoll et al. found that legal pressure increased retention in an inpatient treatment program and that clients admitted immediately after release from prison were most likely to complete the program.[68]

Longitudinal data from DARP indicate that coercion does not impair the effectiveness of treatment programs. Sells and associates and Simpson and Friend examined the relationship between admission man-

dated by the criminal justice system and length of stay in treatment, as well as client performance during and after treatment. These studies found that clients entering treatment with some legal involvement performed as well as those who entered voluntarily. The studies also showed, however, that legal status itself was not necessarily a significant contributor to retention, as indicated by multivariate discriminate functions estimated separately for the three major treatment approaches of methadone maintenance, outpatient drug-free programs, and short-term therapeutic community programs.[69]

More recently, Anglin and Powers studied 202 methadone-maintenance clients who had experienced each of four different treatment regimens during their addiction careers: methadone maintenance alone, legal supervision (probation or parole) alone, both interventions simultaneously, and neither intervention. Overall, legal supervision was better than no intervention in improving the drug-related behavior of narcotics addicts, and methadone maintenance was better than legal supervision. The combination of methadone maintenance and legal supervision was at least as good as methadone maintenance alone, and was better with regard to abstinence from narcotics use. The study also showed no differences in the effectiveness of the ther-

67. R. A. McFarlain et al., "Psychological Test and Demographic Variables Associated with Retention of Narcotics Addicts in Treatment," International Journal of the Addictions, 12(2-3):399-410 (1977).

68. S. H. Schnoll et al., "The Impact of Legal Involvement on Substance Abusers in a Residential Treatment Setting," Corrective and Social Psychiatry and Journal of Behavior Technology, Methods, and Therapy, 26:21-28 (1980).

69. Sells and Simpson, eds., Effectiveness of Drug Abuse Treatment, vol. 3; ibid., vol. 4; ibid., vol. 5; Dwayne D. Simpson and J. Friend, "Legal Status and Long-Term Outcomes for Addicts in the DARP Follow-Up Project," in Compulsory Treatment of Drug Abuse, ed. Leukefeld and Tims.

apies with respect to gender or ethnicity, suggesting that the combination of legal supervision and methadone maintenance should be effective for most demographic groups.[70]

STRATEGIES FOR DEVELOPMENT OF EFFECTIVE INTERVENTIONS FOR OFFENDERS

That treatment for drug use is effective and that its effectiveness is not diminished when users are coerced into programs by the criminal justice system has been convincingly established. A similar conclusion is warranted for corrections-based treatment. But the results from many different studies indicate that despite similarities between clients, program outcomes can vary widely. In constructing an optimum treatment program, therefore, we must select the best aspects of each program, combine them for optimum efficacy, and consider suitability of elements when implementing programs in particular communities. The recommendations presented here are drawn from clinical experience, from relevant research literature, and from guidelines based on extensive studies of treatment outcomes conducted under the auspices of the National Institute of Justice.[71] These guidelines are particularly important given that many

federal and state agencies will significantly increase the funds devoted to treating drug-using offenders in 1992 and beyond.[72]

Several integral steps are involved in setting up an effective program for the treatment of drug use, but the most important initial step is the development of the institutional will to implement the program, thereby overcoming a number of entrenched attitudes within the CJS. Many members of the CJS have not been educated to the potential benefits of community- or corrections-based interventions in conjunction with legal supervision; a substantial number may believe that drug treatment is ineffectual or coddles the drug-using offender. Such attitudes can adversely affect any program, no matter how well designed. Because of underfunding and bureaucratic and political constraints resulting from errant attitudes toward treatment, many developing or existing criminal-justice-based programs are severely restricted from their inception.[73]

Many of the misunderstandings surrounding criminal-justice-based treatment programs arise because communication between the CJS and the community treatment system has been almost nonexistent. Members of these systems need to move out of their traditionally adversarial

---

70. M. Douglas Anglin and Keiko I. Powers, "Individual and Joint Effects of Methadone Maintenance and Legal Supervision on the Behavior of Narcotics Addicts," *Journal of Applied Behavioral Science*, in press.

71. Wexler, Lipton, and Johnson, *Criminal Justice System Strategy for Treating Cocaine-Heroin Abusing Offenders*.

72. General Accounting Office, *Drug Treatment: Despite New Strategy, Few Federal Inmates Receive Treatment*; idem, *Drug Treatment: State Prisons Face Challenges in Providing Services*.

73. Wexler, Lipton, and Johnson, *Criminal Justice System Strategy for Treating Cocaine-Heroin Abusing Offenders*; Chaiken, *In-Prison Programs for Drug-Involved Offenders*.

stance and toward the realization that, by collaborating to produce the desired behavior changes, they can significantly improve outcomes for individuals under their care and for society as a whole.

Important considerations in the development and implementation of CJS-based programs are delineated below. Several guidelines for identifying and treating drug-using offenders are provided, based on relevant evaluation results that have supported the view that interventions can be effective with CJS populations. Special features may be necessary to maximize the chance of success with CJS populations, however, and certain program structures are required to achieve optimum results. The following recommendations and guidelines are grouped in three categories—preincarceration, in-prison programs, and community aftercare—which broadly reflect the three phases of involvement of offenders with the CJS when various levels and types of coercion may be used to bring drug-using offenders into treatment.

Preincarceration

To reduce crime, strain on the CJS, and risk of acquired immune deficiency syndrome (AIDS), the focus should be on chronic users of heroin, cocaine, and injected drugs. Abuse of amphetamines may merit special attention in selected localities, but the majority of arrests are related to either heroin or cocaine.

All persons who are arrested should be tested for use of drugs, especially heroin and cocaine. Many chronic drug users have contact with the criminal justice system about once per year,[74] usually through arrest, and this contact should be seized as an opportunity to detect and assess any drug use and to present treatment options.[75] Records of urinalyses should be maintained in court and corrections files along with other pertinent information, and they should be used in determining suitability for pretrial release as well as sentencing if the arrestees are convicted.

All arrestees who test positive in urinalyses and show other indications of substance abuse should be targeted for further assessment and should be required to attend orientation and preliminary intake procedures while they are in detention as a first step toward placing them in treatment, either while in prison or on their return to the community.[76]

Full corrections-based treatment programs should not be initiated, however, for those offenders who will be freed from custody in less than three months. It is neither cost effective nor therapeutically wise to begin such programs when there is little expectation that treatment can be

74. Wexler, Lipton, and Johnson, *Criminal Justice System Strategy for Treating Cocaine-Heroin Abusing Offenders.*

75. Mary A. Toborg et al., *The Washington, D.C. Urine Testing Program for Defendants Awaiting Trial: A Summary of Interim Findings* (Washington, DC: Toborg Associates, 1986).

76. Collins, Hubbard, and Rachal, "Expensive Drug Use and Illegal Income"; Mary A. Toborg et al., eds., *Treatment and Alternatives to Street Crime (TASC): An Evaluative Framework and State of the Art Review* (Washington, DC: Lazar Institute, 1975).

completed.[77] Rather, such drug-using offenders should be linked to community-based programs. When possible, those arrested primarily for drug abuse or possession should be considered for community-based sentencing and intervention programs rather than prison. To prepare prerelease drug-using offenders for reentry into society, they should be counseled on participation in community-based programs as a means of avoiding recidivism.

Long-term economic benefits accrue from treatment, not from incarceration. If chronic drug use is considered to be a form of illness, prison terms seem an inappropriate cure. Regardless of the philosophical position on that point, community-based programs are much cheaper. Each new bed in a minimum-security prison in California now costs $100,000 in capital outlay,[78] and the average cost of incarceration in California state prisons is about $920 per month.[79] In contrast, the average monthly cost of drug treatment in California is about $250 for publicly supported methadone maintenance and $690 for therapeutic communities. The cost of probation with urine testing is about $50

per month. Prison parole with testing is about $165 per month.[80]

These costs can be largely offset, furthermore, by a reduction in crimes committed by individuals undergoing treatment.[81] The average heroin abuser generates economic consequences to society of almost $34,000 per year, including $14,000 worth of money and goods taken during non-drug crimes.[82]

In-prison programs

Chronic users of cocaine and heroin who are sentenced to prison should be enrolled in treatment programs, either voluntarily or on a compulsory basis. Prisoners should be enrolled in treatment programs about 9 to 12 months prior to their eligibility for parole. Such enrollment should be a condition for parole or early release. Most authorities agree that earlier enrollment in treatment programs is fruitless because the prisoners will remain in an environment—the prison—that can erode the gains made in treatment and that is conducive to relapse.[83] For the same reasons, the prisoners enrolled in therapeutic programs should be kept separate from the general prison population.[84]

77. Wexler, Lipton, and Johnson. *Criminal Justice System Strategy for Treating Cocaine-Heroin Abusing Offenders.*

78. California Blue Ribbon Commission, "Growth and Its Influence on Corrections."

79. Elizabeth P. Deschenes, M. Douglas Anglin, and George R. Speckart, "Narcotics Addiction: Related Criminal Careers, Social, and Economics Costs," *Journal of Drug Issues,* in press; Joan Petersilia, Peter W. Greenwood, and Mark Lavin, *Criminal Careers of Habitual Felons* (Washington, DC: Government Printing Office, 1978).

80. Deschenes, Anglin, and Speckart, "Narcotics Addiction."

81. M. Douglas Anglin and Yih-Ing Hser, "Legal Coercion and Drug Abuse Treatment: Research Findings and Social Policy Implications," in *Handbook of Drug Control in the United States,* ed. James A. Inciardi (Westport, CT: Greenwood Press, 1989).

82. Johnson et al., *Taking Care of Business.*

83. Wexler, Lipton, and Foster, "Outcome Evaluation of a Prison Therapeutic Community."

84. Wexler, Lipton, and Johnson, *Criminal Justice System Strategy for Treating Cocaine-Heroin Abusing Offenders.*

The total period of supervision must be a lengthy one, certainly no less than five years. Dependence on opiates and other drugs is a chronically relapsing condition. Except in a minority of cases, several cycles of treatment, aftercare, and relapse may be expected. The typical successful intervention achieves longer periods in which the dependence is controlled and shorter periods of relapse.

The CJS-based program must be conducted in two phases, carried out in corrections and in the community. The first phase should include placement of the drug user in a living unit with other recovering offenders. At the beginning of this period, a program plan should be instituted. The client's behavior should be regularly observed, with objective means for monitoring drug use, such as urine testing. If the program plan for the opiate-dependent individual includes methadone or naltrexone treatment, then treatment participation should be monitored and the individual should be tested often and randomly for drug use.

Other services—such as job training—that might be useful in preventing relapse after the inmate is paroled should be effected on an individual basis. For many addicts, the personal benefits gained from educational and vocational training are important over the long term in preventing or reducing relapse.[85]

The corrections-based phase of the program, as well as the community-release phase, must be flexible. Some level of continued drug use may be expected from the majority of those in such programs.[86] Flexibility in dealing with such infractions is a key ingredient of success in keeping clients in a treatment program, as shown in a study of three methadone programs in Southern California.[87] Of the two flexible programs, the one with the more adaptive policy on client interactions retained 77 percent of admissions after two years, while the program with the more punitive orientation retained only 42 percent. The third program, with the most inflexible policies—and also an average dosage level half that of the other two—retained only about 23 percent of its admissions after two years.

Authority to deal with program infractions should reside with the staff members directly responsible for supervising the addict. Intermittent drug use that does not seriously disrupt the individual's program plan, as well as other program infractions, should be dealt with on an individual basis in the context of the addict's overall adjustment. Any detected readdiction, however, would require immediate placement of the addict under strict control, either into a de-

85. M. Douglas Anglin et al., "An Empirical Study of Maturing Out: Conditional Factors," *International Journal of the Addictions,* 21:233-46 (1986).

86. Anglin and McGlothlin, "Methadone Maintenance in California"; McGlothlin, Anglin, and Wilson, *Evaluation of the California Civil Addict Program.*

87. Dennis G. Fisher and M. Douglas Anglin, "Survival Analysis in Drug Program Evaluation: Part I. Overall Program Effectiveness," *International Journal of the Addictions,* 22(2):115-34 (1987); William H. McGlothlin and M. Douglas Anglin, "Long-Term Follow-Up of Clients of High- and Low-Dose Methadone Programs," *Archives of General Psychiatry,* 38:885-92 (1987).

toxification or residential program or —in the case of opiate dependence— into a methadone or naltrexone program.

An incentive system should be adopted to tie socially desirable behavior goals in the treatment program to rewards for inmates. One potential approach might be to establish a system of restitution points in which a prisoner would be required to earn a set number of points, depending on his or her crime, before being released from field supervision. Points could be acquired by any type of desirable social behavior, such as meeting quantifiable steps in treatment programming or a clean urine test, and they could be deducted for each offense, such as losing a job or having a positive urine test. The final incentive for release from custody would thus be clearly in front of each offender, along with the cost of each infraction and the reward for success.[88]

Prisoners making good progress in treatment and those who have successfully graduated from the program should be co-opted into leadership roles both to increase their own success and to provide role models for others. Many addicts have never been given the opportunity to assume authority or positions of responsibility, and the changes produced in them by such opportunities are often remarkable.

Supervisors and staff should be rewarded for success in reducing recidivism. At present, no rewards are tied to such success, and, thus, there is no sustaining force promoting this goal.[89] The rewards might include increased pay or longer vacations.

The importance of high-quality staff cannot be overemphasized. Joe, Simpson, and Sells, for example, found that positive outcomes for treatment were associated with the higher quality of the professional specialty of the staff involved in diagnosing clients at admission and designing treatment plans.[90] Ball and Ross have described similar findings in a study of six methadone programs in three cities.[91]

Community aftercare

Upon completion of the in-prison portion of their rehabilitation programs, probationers and parolees should be enrolled in community-based treatment programs. Even a year of treatment at the end of a prison term is insufficient to ensure successful rehabilitation. With very few exceptions, studies have shown that the longer an individual is retained in a treatment program providing a continuity of care, the more that drug use and associated criminal activities are reduced and the greater the likelihood of successful

88. Wexler, Lipton, and Johnson, *Criminal Justice System Strategy for Treating Cocaine-Heroin Abusing Offenders.*

89. Wexler, Lipton, and Johnson, *Criminal Justice System Strategy for Treating Cocaine-Heroin Abusing Offenders.*

90. George W. Joe, Dwayne D. Simpson, and Saul B. Sells, "Treatment Process and Relapse to Opioid Use During Methadone Maintenance," *American Journal of Drug and Substance Abuse,* in press.

91. John C. Ball and Alan Ross, *The Effectiveness of Methadone Maintenance Treatment: Patients, Programs, Services, and Outcomes* (New York: Springer-Verlag, 1991).

employment.[92] Unfortunately, pressures have forced the CJS to continually shrink the client's time in treatment, often to less than the critical threshold of 90 days required for minimum efficacy.[93]

Measures must be taken to assure retention in programs. Because programs can exert influence only when patients are enrolled, retention has been viewed as a crucial aspect of all treatment. Unfortunately, factors that prolong retention have not been thoroughly studied. Some research suggests that a broad definition of retention may be needed. Simpson et al. report that 39 percent of methadone-program clients and about 25 percent of outpatient drug-free clients return to treatment within a year.[94] This raises the question of whether repeated exposure to treatment is more effective than one

episode—at least for some drug abusers.[95] The total time in treatment may be more important, when accrued across treatment episodes, than retention in a single program.

All offenders previously determined to be drug users who are on probation and parole should be given frequent urine tests for drugs, whether they are enrolled in a therapeutic program or not. Considerable evidence points to the effectiveness of urine monitoring when linked to immediate sanctions such as those applied by CJS programs.[96] Such combinations have been shown to be more effective than supervision without testing in reducing daily narcotics use and criminal activity in the California CAP. This finding has been replicated in later work with methadone clients.[97] Other researchers have also found that effective monitoring of urinalysis results will help to interrupt relapse to daily heroin and cocaine use and thus to reduce the rate of criminality.[98]

92. Ball et al., "Reduction of Intravenous Heroin Abuse"; Wexler, Lipton, and Foster, "Outcome Evaluation of a Prison Therapeutic Community"; William H. McGlothlin and M. Douglas Anglin, "Effects of Closing the Bakersfield Methadone Clinic," in *Problems of Drug Dependence*, National Institute on Drug Abuse Research Monograph no. 47, ed. L. S. Harris (Rockville, MD: National Institute on Drug Abuse, 1979); Dwayne D. Simpson, "The Relation of Time Spent in Drug Abuse Treatment to Posttreatment Outcome," *American Journal of Psychiatry*, 136(11):1449-53 (1979); idem, "Treatment for Drug Abuse: Follow-Up Outcomes and Length of Time Spent," *Archives of General Psychiatry*, 38:875-80 (1981).

93. Simpson, "Relation of Time Spent."

94. Dwayne D. Simpson et al., *Evaluation of Drug Abuse Treatments Based on the First Year after DARP: National Follow-Up Study of Admission to the Drug Abuse Treatments in the DARP during 1969-72*, DHEW pub. no. (ADM) 78-701 (Washington, DC: Government Printing Office, 1978).

95. A. Thomas McLellan and Keith A. Druley, "Responsiveness to Treatment in Court-Referred vs. Voluntary Drug Abuse Patients," *Hospital and Community Psychiatry*, 28:238-41 (1977).

96. McGlothlin, Anglin, and Wilson, *Evaluation of the California Civil Addict Program*.

97. M. Douglas Anglin, Elizabeth P. Deschenes, and George R. Speckart, "The Effect of Legal Supervision on Narcotic Addiction and Criminal Behavior" (Paper delivered at the annual meeting of the American Society of Criminology, Montreal, Canada, Nov. 1987).

98. Toborg et al., *Washington, D.C. Urine Testing Program*; Jay A. Carver, *Drugs and Crime: Controlling Use and Reducing Risk through Testing*, National Institute of Justice Reports, (SNI) 199 (Washington, DC: Department of Justice, 1986).

Heroin addicts on parole or probation should be considered for effective narcotics antagonist treatment to reduce the probability that they will use heroin. Naltrexone is an easily administered drug that, taken daily, produces almost immediate withdrawal symptoms in addicts when they use an opiate but that is harmless to nonaddicts.[99] It is most effective with heroin-addicted offenders who have a high level of community integration.

If parolees on methadone maintenance are arrested, they should continue to be maintained on methadone while they are in custody previous to conviction and possible reincarcerations. In this manner, return to their methadone program after release from jail would be facilitated.[100] Those who are convicted upon their rearrest and sentenced to longer prison terms should be given the option to remain on methadone or to enter a detoxification program and then enroll in an in-prison therapeutic community.

The surveillance and treatment functions of field supervision officers should be separated to increase confidentiality and trust among those supervised. Trust and confidentiality are essential to the effectiveness of the treatment or counseling relationship, and they cannot be achieved if the parolee fears that he or she may be sent back to jail for admitting to drug use or other criminality. Surveillance and rehabilitation should

be handled by staffs who work separately but cooperatively to avoid role confusion for both officer and offender.[101]

There should be provisions for an early discharge from the program for good behavior. Post-discharge participation in long-term self-help groups such as Alcoholics Anonymous may be a condition of early discharge. Follow-up interviews and random urine tests may also ensure adherence to conditions of release. Early discharge should not occur before a minimum period, however; at least two years of community supervision should be completed without relapse to addicted use and with progress in employment and in adequately meeting other social responsibilities.

All programs must undergo regular evaluation to determine the level of effectiveness. Programs must be assessed to determine the need for compensatory adjustments because of unacceptable treatment outcomes, changes in client characteristics, or new developments in the treatment of drug dependence that might be appropriate.

CONCLUSION

The preceding recommendations are derived from conclusions that are amply supported by research findings and have been accepted within the field for a long time.[102] Their inclusion in treatment strategies has been difficult, however, and can only

99. Wexler, Lipton, and Johnson, *Criminal Justice System Strategy for Treating Cocaine-Heroin Abusing Offenders.*
100. Ibid.

101. Ibid.
102. Saul B. Sells, ed., *Evaluation of Treatment* (Cambridge, MA: Ballinger, 1974), vols. 1 and 2.

be expected to become more so when the criminal justice system is involved. Treatment programs exist in the context of competition for resources with other social programs, a lack of adequately trained staff, and, perhaps most important, a history of shifting and unstable funding. Problems of funding are partially attributable to conditions fostered by the "war on drugs," which has resulted in an unfortunate internecine battle for resources between "branches of the service" that should be cooperating rather than competing.

By the mid-1980s, societal concerns with cocaine- and crack-related crime and human immunodeficiency virus (HIV) infection in intravenous drug users began to promote greater policy attention. Increased enforcement activities and stiffer penalties for drug possession and sales drove prison and jail crowding to unprecedented heights. Concomitantly, enforcement and corrections costs began taking a larger and larger share of resources, so less costly alternatives have been sought. Diverting drug-abusing offenders from incarceration into treatment has shown great potential for reducing crime, improving health, and lowering corrections costs.

Recognition of those potential benefits by legislators and others may lead, in effect, to a shotgun marriage of the CJS and drug treatment based more on the hope of decreased costs and reduced prison congestion than on the known reality of drug treatment success. But such a forced union, without adjustments in both CJS and treatment-provider attitudes about collaborative treatment

viability, may result in disappointment. The more successful treatment outcomes cited by researchers and endorsed by legislators have been obtained in the programs where funding is at least adequate, personnel are well trained and emotionally involved, and treatment programs are carefully planned and implemented. If treatment programs are forced on the CJS during a time when budgets are tight and personnel overworked, the odds are greater that their implementation will be much less effective than programs operating under better conditions.

Already, some evidence indicates such ineffective implementation. Tight budgets in some regions, for example, have forced some CJS-related programs below the critical threshold of three-month retention in treatment. Similarly, there is a vast gap in philosophy and perception between the treatment community and the CJS. Even though methadone maintenance is viewed by many researchers as the most effective form of treatment for heroin addiction, it is strongly resisted by a large segment of the CJS, where it is viewed as coddling the addict or contributing to his or her continued drug use. This gulf must be bridged if the CJS is to obtain the maximum benefit from new treatment evaluations. Existing and ongoing research is useful to policymakers only when the findings are considered in policy development.

The criminal justice system is already subject to disparate policy input concerning everything from offenders' civil rights to the ultimate goals of rehabilitation. Complex social and behavioral problems have been dealt with using complex, expensive, corrections-based approaches that are proving less than effective in most cases and especially so regarding drug use and its consequences. Coping with continuing drug problems will require changes in the mission of the CJS, and the process will be resisted as a further complication. Treatment of drug use is not a simple matter, but the techniques for treating drug use among offenders have been demonstrated to be effective—and implementing them on a wider scale should be well within the realm of possibility. We can and must implement treatment programs within the criminal justice system if we are to make a significant impact on the level of drug abuse and criminality in our society and the costs associated with enforcement, adjudication, and corrections.

ANNALS, *AAPSS*, 521, May 1992

Operation Tripwire Revisited

By ROBERT L. DuPONT and ERIC D. WISH

ABSTRACT: A major new proposal to refocus national efforts on heroin addicts in the criminal justice system, called Operation Tripwire, was announced on 1 October 1977. The proposal called for the universal testing of offenders in the criminal justice system for drugs, and the establishment of sustained drug-free status, confirmed by repeated drug testing, as a condition of release to the community. Despite its being grounded in a large body of solid research evidence and meeting vital social needs, Tripwire was never implemented. Today, with the introduction of the Drug Use Forecasting program, we have a more convincing indication of the enormous drug abuse problems in the criminal population. It may be time to dust off and update the original Tripwire idea. If that is to happen, it will require the convergence of many political, media, and fiscal forces, all based on research. The potential beneficiaries of such a development are many, but the odds against it remain long.

Robert L. DuPont was the first director of the National Institute on Drug Abuse, from 1973 to 1978, and the second White House drug czar, from 1973 to 1975. He is currently the president of the private, nonprofit Institute for Behavior and Health, Inc.

Eric D. Wish is director of the Center for Substance Abuse Research at the University of Maryland in College Park. As a visiting fellow at the National Institute of Justice from 1986 to 1990, he supervised the development of the Drug Use Forecasting program.

IN the fall of 1977, Robert L. Du-
Pont, then director of the National Institute on Drug Abuse (NIDA),
proposed a major new initiative to
test the urine of all parolees and probationers in the country for heroin
use, making clean urines a condition
of continued release to the community. This was called "Operation Tripwire," to signify that the urine test
was to trigger imprisonment as a
sanction for heroin use.

The Tripwire idea was never implemented, and, in fact, the proposal
itself was one of the factors that led
to the request by the secretary of the
Department of Health, Education and
Welfare for the resignation of DuPont
as NIDA director a few months later.
The climate of the times was hostile
to this proposal as federal drug abuse
officials were then promoting decriminalization of marijuana and cocaine,
not new ideas to reduce heroin use
among criminal offenders.

The first part of this article rekin-
dles the memory of that period and
explores what was then known about
drug abuse and crime, as it related to
drug testing within the criminal justice system, and the factors that led
to the rejection of this idea.

Today we have a wider definition
of the problem of illicit drug abuse.
Urine-testing technology and practices have developed substantially.
We also have hard data on drug use
by arrestees provided by the National
Institute of Justice's Drug Use Forecasting system, which was conceived
and implemented in 1987 by Eric
Wish, Paul Cascarano, John Speva-
cek, and Joyce O'Neil, with the strong
support of James K. Stewart, the director of the National Institute of
Justice.

The second section of the article
dusts off the Tripwire proposal, suggests that it now include all illicit
drugs, and puts it at the center of the
criminal justice system (CJS) efforts
in the 1990s to cut the link between
illicit drug use and crime. The potential beneficiaries are many, including
drug-abusing criminal offenders
themselves, their families, and communities. In addition, an updated
Tripwire proposal offers hope to the
criminal justice system, which is now
being crushed by the load of drug-involved offenders. Most important of
all, a new Tripwire proposal offers
hope to the communities hardest hit
by illicit drug abuse, communities
made unlivable by drugs, especially
poor urban communities.

The social institutions having the
broadest and most powerful impact
in these communities are the schools,
Aid to Families with Dependent Children, and the criminal justice system. If these communities are to rid
themselves of the modern plague of
drug abuse, these institutions offer
the greatest hope. Because of the higher
levels of controversy surrounding the
schools and Aid to Families with Dependent Children, when it comes to
effective antidrug efforts,[1] the last best
chance for these communities to end
the two-decade-long drug abuse epidemic lies with the CJS. The CJS has
the most direct impact on the youths

1. Robert L. DuPont, "Should Welfare
Mothers Be Tested for Drugs?" in *Winning the
Drug War: New Challenges for the 1990s*, ed.
Jeffrey A. Eisenach (Washington, DC: Heri-
tage Foundation, 1991), pp. 83-95.

at highest risk, teenagers and young adults engaging in criminal behavior. The Tripwire proposal is powerful medicine to help solve this problem in these besieged communities.

Finally, the third section of the article focuses on the general problems of research and policy in the criminal justice system, using the issue of drug testing in the criminal justice system as a model for this broader perspective.

DRUGS AND CRIME, 1977

The modern American experience with drugs and crime dates from the late 1960s, when there was a dramatic upsurge in the rates of crime and illicit drug use throughout the country, despite the widespread economic prosperity at the time and despite the major funding then taking place for community development and poverty programs.[2] Washington, D.C., at a time when it was a federal city not yet governed by home rule, was a focus of unique concern. The city was labeled in the 1968 presidential election as the "crime capital" of the nation.

Hallucinogens were widely used by American youths for the first time in the late 1960s, especially on the nation's most prestigious campuses, with their effects being glorified as "consciousness expansion" by Timothy Leary, the Harvard professor, and other pied pipers of drug abuse. Marijuana use soon surpassed hallucinogen use as illicit drug use spread to all segments of America's youths.[3]

The federal role in drug abuse at that time was more or less limited to research on opiates and to law enforcement targeted on drug trafficking.[4] The federal research interest was centered in Lexington, Kentucky, where the government's small research-oriented treatment program for addicts had been located since the 1930s on the remarkable assumption that taking addicts out of large cities into the fresh air of the "narcotics farm" would help them kick their habits. The Addiction Research Center (ARC) at Lexington was not only the source for virtually all non-law-enforcement federal drug abuse activities but a major foundation on which the National Institute for Mental Health, the National Institute on Alcohol Abuse and Alcoholism, and the NIDA were built. Until the late 1960s, ARC was virtually the only place in the world where biological research on addiction took place.

ARC was the place where a distinguished physician-researcher, George E. Vaillant, got his start by establishing, with a follow-up of 100 addicts released from Lexington, that the best prognosis for addicts' achieving prolonged abstinence occurred not with prolonged incarceration but with short periods of incar-

2. James Q. Wilson and Robert L. DuPont, "The Sick Sixties," *Atlantic Monthly*, Oct. 1973, pp. 91-98.

3. Robert L. DuPont, *Youth and Drugs: Society's Mixed Messages*, DHHS pub. no. (ADM) 90-1689 (Rockville, MD: Department of Health and Human Services, Office for Substance Abuse Prevention, 1990), pp. 1-3.

4. Robert L. DuPont, "The Drug Abuse Decade," *Journal of Drug Issues*, 8:173-87 (1978).

ceration followed by intensive and prolonged supervision in the community with reincarceration being the swift consequence of return to illicit drug use.[5] This pioneering research supported the development of the civil commitment programs in New York and California and a much smaller program in the federal government, created by the Narcotics Addiction Rehabilitation Act, begun in 1967.[6]

In August 1969, a group of college students working within the District of Columbia Department of Corrections tested the urine of people recently incarcerated. They found that 45 percent tested positive for heroin use. A self-report questionnaire administered to these arrestees showed that their heroin use had begun within the previous three years and that the rate of new heroin use was directly correlated with the rate of serious crime in the city.[7]

From 1965 on, methadone maintenance treatment became more widely used in New York City under the leadership of physician-researchers Vincent Dole and Marie Nyswander. In Chicago, a brilliant young research physician, Jerome Jaffe, created the multimodality drug abuse treatment concept in which a central publicly funded treatment program offered a spectrum of treatment options, including both methadone detoxification and methadone maintenance, as well as a variety of drug-free treatments, especially the therapeutic community.[8]

The newer forms of treatment for addiction, therapeutic communities and methadone maintenance, focused on heroin addicts. Neither approach was primarily dependent on civil commitment, an idea that was eclipsed, even in California and New York, where it was most fully developed, by the early 1970s. Civil commitment programs were found to be expensive and difficult to administer. They were overwhelmed by the rising rates of heroin addiction, which pumped ever larger numbers of addicts into already underfunded facilities. By the early 1970s in the United States, drug abuse treatment meant a combination of voluntary treatment —mostly methadone treatment—

5. George E. Vaillant, "A Twelve Year Followup of New York Narcotic Addicts: I. The Relation of Treatment to Outcome," *American Journal of Psychiatry*, 122:727-37 (1966); idem, "A 20 Year Followup of New York Narcotic Addicts," *Archives of General Psychiatry*, 20:237-41 (1973).

6. William H. McGlothlin, M. Douglas Anglin, and B. D. Wilson, *Narcotic Addiction and Crime* (Los Angeles: University of California, Los Angeles, 1977).

7. Robert L. DuPont, "Profile of a Heroin-Addiction Epidemic," *New England Journal of Medicine*, 285:320-24 (1971); Nicholas J. Kozel, Robert L. DuPont, and Barry S. Brown, "Narcotics and Crime: A Study of Narcotic Involvement in an Offender Population," *International Journal of the Addictions*, 7:443-50 (1972); Urbane F. Bass, V. W. Brock, and Robert L. DuPont, "Narcotic Use in an Inmate Population at Three Points in Time," *American Journal of Drug and Alcohol Abuse*, 3:375-86

(1976); Nicholas J. Kozel and Robert L. DuPont, *Criminal Charges and Drug Use Patterns of Arrestees in the District of Columbia*, National Institute on Drug Abuse Technical Paper (Rockville, MD: National Clearinghouse on Drug Abuse Information, 1977).

8. National Commission on Marihuana and Drug Abuse, "History of the Treatment of Opiate Dependence," in *Drug Use in America: Problem in Perspective* (Washington, DC: Government Printing Office, 1973), pp. 305-42.

and treatment linked to the criminal justice system—mostly therapeutic communities.

Leaders of each of these innovative treatment approaches were physicians and other health professionals personally committed to research. The early 1970s were the Camelot of publicly funded drug abuse treatment. It was an incredibly fertile period of activity led by a handful of scientists who possessed creativity and charisma. They were supported by both political parties without obvious partisanship, from the local and state levels to the federal level.[9]

Innovations in drug abuse treatment at this time were primarily taking place in Washington, D.C., New York, and Chicago. The Narcotics Treatment Administration, Washington, D.C.'s citywide comprehensive drug abuse treatment agency, was created on 18 February 1970. The country's first court-based universal drug testing was begun in the newly created Superior Court on 1 April of that year.[10] These efforts in Washington formed the basis for the modern federal efforts in the drug abuse field, including the White House Special Action Office for Drug Abuse Prevention (SAODAP) and Treatment Alter-

natives to Street Crime.[11] The Washington experience began with research in the D.C. Jail and led to the publication of more than 100 research papers during the National Treatment Administration's first three years of operation. The Washington program, headed by Robert L. DuPont, grew out of the D.C. Department of Corrections and was closely linked to the rehabilitation components of the local criminal justice system, including pretrial release, probation, parole, and halfway-house programs.[12]

The first White House drug czar, appointed on 17 June 1971, was Jerome Jaffe, the country's most distinguished innovator in the drug abuse field.[13] His first assignment from the President was to go to Vietnam to deal with the explosive problem of heroin addiction among American military personnel. Jaffe's response to this problem was definitive: test the urine of all servicemen before they returned to the United States, making a clean urine a condition for release at home. This approach was known informally in military jargon as "Operation Golden Flow."

The White House drug office was a consistently friendly home for drug

9. Jerome H. Jaffe, "The Swinging Pendulum: The Treatment of Drug Users in America," in Handbook on Drug Abuse, ed. Robert L. DuPont, Avram Goldstein, and John A. O'Donnell (Washington, DC: Government Printing Office, 1979), pp. 3-16.

10. Robert L. DuPont and Richard N. Katon, "Development of a Heroin Addiction Treatment Program: Effect on Urban Crime," Journal of the American Medical Association, 216:1320-24 (1971); Robert L. DuPont and Mark H. Greene, "The Dynamics of a Heroin Addiction Epidemic," Science, 181:716-22 (1973).

11. Strategy Council on Drug Abuse, Federal Strategy for Drug Abuse and Drug Traffic Prevention 1973 (Washington, DC: Strategy Council on Drug Abuse, 1973).

12. Robert L. DuPont, "How Corrections Can Beat the High Cost of Heroin Addiction," Federal Probation, 35:43-50 (1971); idem, "Heroin Addiction Treatment and Crime Reduction," American Journal of Psychiatry, 128:856-60 (1972).

13. David F. Musto, The American Disease—Origins of Narcotic Control (New York: Oxford University Press, 1987).

abuse researchers of all kinds. Not only was Treatment Alternatives to Street Crime the first national program to link the criminal justice system to substance abuse treatment, but it was an early product of SAODAP,[14] as were the major national drug abuse epidemiological studies, including the Drug Abuse Warning Network, which collected data from emergency rooms and medical examiners around the country; the Client Oriented Drug Abuse Program, which gathered data about drug abusers in all federally funded treatment programs; the National Drug Abuse Treatment Utilization Survey; and the National Household Survey on Drug Abuse. In 1975, SAODAP began support for the Monitoring the Future Project of the Institute for Social Research at the University of Michigan, Ann Arbor, which annually conducts the National High School Survey for the National Institute on Drug Abuse. This survey remains the nation's largest and most frequently administered drug use survey.[15]

One of the many brilliant researchers who worked with SAODAP in that era was John A. O'Donnell, who had worked for years at the ARC. He and his young colleague, Richard R. Clayton, studied drug use among American young men and established the linkage between the use of gateway drugs and the risk for subsequent heroin use, and many of the most fundamental characteristics of modern American drug abuse epidemiology.[16]

The nation's most distinguished black physician in the drug abuse field was Beny J. Primm, who in the late 1960s founded the comprehensive methadone treatment program in Brooklyn called the Addiction Rehabilitation and Treatment Center. When Dr. Jaffe was sent by the President to Vietnam in June of 1971, he took Dr. Primm with him.

Since the end of the first American drug abuse epidemic in about 1920, heroin addiction had been the central drug problem that preoccupied both law enforcement and treatment officials.[17] One of the many surprising aspects of the modern drug abuse epidemic was that heroin use, an end-stage drug habit, increased sharply in the very early stages of the modern American drug epidemic, peaking in 1971, long before marijuana and cocaine use reached their peaks in 1978 and 1987, respectively.[18] In the United States from about 1910 to about 1977, serious drug abuse was equated all but universally with heroin addiction.[19]

14. McGlothlin, Anglin, and Wilson, *Narcotic Addiction and Crime*.

15. U.S., Department of Health and Human Services, *Drug Abuse and Drug Abuse Research: The Third Triennial Report to Congress from the Secretary, Department of Health and Human Services*, DHHS pub. no. (ADM) 91-1704 (Rockville, MD: Department of Health and Human Services, National Institute on Drug Abuse, 1991).

16. John A. O'Donnell et al., *Young Men and Drugs—A Nationwide Survey*, DHEW pub. no. (ADM) 76-311 (Washington, DC: Superintendent of Documents, U.S. Government Printing Office, 1976).

17. Musto, *American Disease*.

18. Robert L. DuPont, "Prevention of Adolescent Chemical Dependence," *Pediatric Clinics of North America*, 34:1-11 (1987).

19. National Commission on Marihuana and Drug Abuse, *Drug Use in America*.

These experiences in the evolution of the national response to drug abuse shaped the Tripwire proposal.[20] This brief review of the history of the early years of the drug abuse epidemic makes clear that heroin was the drug that mattered most and that urine testing and compulsory treatment, including both civil commitment and the use of the criminal justice system, were at the center of drug abuse policy.[21] It is also important to recall that these early efforts to respond to the drug abuse epidemic focused on crime and poverty areas of large cities.

As the nation's heroin problems worsened in the early 1970s and the opposition to the war in Vietnam intensified, it became commonplace to blame the returning veterans for the heroin addiction problems in the nation's cities. The single most dramatic example of research at the highest scientific level affecting national drug abuse policy in a highly politicized area was the study by Lee N. Robins of returning servicemen.[22]

Dr. Robins, not surprisingly, found that the rates of heroin use by servicemen while in Vietnam vastly exceeded the rates for a carefully matched control group of young men. What was revolutionary in her results was the finding that three years after their release from military service, whether they had received drug abuse treatment or not, the rates of heroin use for subjects who had served in Vietnam were not significantly different from those of the matched control group who had never served in the military or gone to Vietnam. This finding, which was so convincing that it left no room for doubt, effectively ended that highly political explanation for America's heroin epidemic.

Robins found that 88 percent of the servicemen who had been addicted to heroin while in Vietnam had not been addicted at any time during the three years after their return. Furthermore, even among those who reported heroin addiction during their first year back in the United States after leaving Vietnam, 70 percent were not addicted at any time during the following two years. These stunning findings went to the heart of two other common misconceptions in the drug abuse field: (1) that most people who were once addicted to heroin stayed addicted for the rest of their lives; and (2) that the only way to end heroin addiction was by using drug abuse treatment.[23] This study raised

20. Robert L. DuPont, "Operation Trip-Wire: A New Proposal Focused on Criminal Heroin Addicts" (Paper delivered at the convention of the Federal Bar Association, Washington, DC, 1 Oct. 1977).

21. McGlothlin, Anglin, and Wilson, Narcotic Addiction and Crime; William H. McGlothlin, "Criminal Justice Clients," in Handbook on Drug Abuse, ed. DuPont, Goldstein, and O'Donnell, pp. 203-9; William H. McGlothlin, M. Douglas Anglin, and B. D. Wilson, An Evaluation of the California Civil Addict Program (Rockville, MD: National Clearinghouse on Drug Abuse Information, 1977).

22. Lee N. Robins, The Vietnam Drug User Returns (Rockville, MD: National Clearinghouse on Drug Abuse Information, 1974); idem, "Addict Careers," in Handbook on Drug Abuse, ed. DuPont, Goldstein, and O'Donnell, pp. 325-36.

23. Lee N. Robins et al., "Vietnam Veterans Three Years after Vietnam: How Our Study Changed Our View of Heroin," in Problems of Drug Dependence, ed. L. Harris (Richmond, VA: Committee on Problems of Drug Dependence, 1977).

serious questions about the relevance of these assumptions for other populations and for the policies based on them. This historic and influential study by Dr. Robins required the active leadership of the White House drug czar because it involved timely and substantial funding for the nation's top longitudinal epidemiological researchers and the active participation of major government agencies, including the understandably skittish Department of Defense and Veterans Administration.

In the formative years of the contemporary federal drug abuse prevention program, the link between drug use and serious crime was a controversial issue. While the first focus of national concern about drugs was on heroin addiction and related inner-city crime, the drug issue rapidly evolved to focus on the unprecedented rises in marijuana use within the far larger middle class. Pot smoking was not obviously crime related. In the 1970s there was a broadly based effort to normalize the use of marijuana, seeking to treat it similarly to alcohol and tobacco. For this pro-pot movement to prosper, it was essential to unhook illicit drug use and crime except to the extent that marijuana sale and use were themselves criminal offenses. In the logic of those years, the application of criminal penalties to marijuana use was seen as a miscarriage of justice.

In the early 1970s, the most effective form of drug treatment appeared to be methadone maintenance for heroin addiction. In the 1975 federal drug strategy, attempting to respond to the already waning public support for government-sponsored drug programs, there was a commitment to accommodating the conflicting forces then shaping federal policy by refocusing federal efforts on those aspects of illicit drug use that created the greatest social costs.[24] This meant focusing on overdose deaths and serious crime and ignoring marijuana and cocaine. The latter were then widely considered to be soft drugs, in contrast to heroin, the prototypical hard drug. The heart of this strategy was to focus on crime and heroin addiction, the bedrock of the support for the federal drug program.[25] A central programmatic expression of this strategy was Operation Tripwire, proposed 1 October 1977 by the director of the National Institute on Drug Abuse, Robert L. DuPont, in a speech at the annual meeting of the Federal Bar Association in Washington, D.C.

The larger objective of the Tripwire proposal was to help heroin addicts themselves overcome their deadly habit by using the power of the criminal justice system. The proposal established a systematic link between the criminal justice system and drug abuse treatment. Tripwire was also designed to relieve the crushing cost to the criminal justice system caused by the heroin epidemic, and, even more important, it was intended to help reclaim families and communities being torn apart by

24. Strategy Council on Drug Abuse, *Federal Strategy for Drug Abuse*.

25. James F. Maddux, "History of the Hospital Treatment Programs, 1935-74," in *Symposium on Drug Addiction and the U.S. Public Health Service*, DHHS pub. no. (ADM) 77-434, ed. W. R. Martin and H. Isbell (Washington, DC: Government Printing Office, 1978), pp. 217-50.

the crime and sickness directly caused by heroin addiction.

The Tripwire proposal can be divided into three areas: screening, supervision, and the consequences for positive drug tests. The screening area had two parts. First, all parolees and probationers, regardless of their conviction offense or history of drug or alcohol abuse, would have their urine tested for heroin use on an unannounced basis "once or twice a year." Second, all offenders released from incarceration would be given physical examinations looking for track marks indicating past intravenous drug use, and they would be interviewed and their records reviewed for evidence of past heroin use.

In terms of supervision, offenders identified by either means, routine screening or screening at release from a correctional institution, as having a history of heroin use would be subject to regular urine monitoring, with clean urines being a requirement for continued freedom in the community. They would all be subject to monthly or more frequent unannounced drug testing.

As to consequences for positive drug tests, offenders producing a positive drug test for heroin while under routine CJS supervision would be placed in more intensive supervision with "weekly or more frequent urine tests." If a second urine drug test were positive, the offenders would be required to enter treatment but would be left free to select the modal-ity of treatment they preferred. Repeated failure of the drug test while under supervision would lead to "prompt reincarceration" that would be for "three to six months," followed by release to the community with continued intensive supervision including regular unannounced urine tests. The Operation Tripwire proposal noted that, based on the Vaillant and Robins findings, "some heroin addicted offenders will be able to refrain from regular heroin use as a result of close supervision, even without treatment."

A pilot phase for Operation Tripwire was envisioned with the ultimate cost of the program projected to be about $12-$14 million a year. The Tripwire program was to be initially funded cooperatively by NIDA and the Department of Justice and operated by single state agencies for drug abuse prevention.

Tripwire never got started. The argument that dominated the proposal focused not on the vital practical implementation issues—which are the focus today of proposals to extend the use of drug testing in the criminal justice system—but on the fundamental assumptions that heroin use caused crime, that close supervision with strict consequences could reduce heroin use, and that reducing heroin use would lead to reduced criminal activity. These conclusions, now largely taken for granted, were hotly debated in 1977 with many influential academics at the time expressing skepticism and even hostility on all three points.[26] Tripwire could go nowhere if these fundamental assumptions were not accepted.[27]

In an attempt to diffuse some of the controversies that arose in reaction to the original proposal, a scaled-down pilot project, Paroled Addicts in Treatment for Heroin, was developed. A recent review[28] of the link between the criminal justice system and drug abuse treatment has refocused on the long-neglected Tripwire and Paroled Addicts in Treatment for Heroin proposals:

In October 1977 Robert L. DuPont, then Director of the National Institute on Drug Abuse, presented a paper titled "Operation Trip-Wire: A New Proposal Focused on Criminal Heroin Addicts" to the Federal Bar Association Convention. . . .[29] Using the findings of McGlothlin and colleagues, . . .[30] he proposed setting up a "tripwire" in the form of urine testing that would identify daily heroin users who were on probation and parole. If an addicted probationer or parolee did not stop his or her daily drug use, the user would be referred to compulsory drug abuse treatment; if treatment was re-fused or daily heroin use maintained, the addict would be reincarcerated. Even though the proposal was changed to a research study called Paroled Addicts in Treatment for Heroin (PATH), the study never got under way because of the controversy. Criticism focused on three areas: (1) the image problem created when a health agency proposed a mechanism for behavioral control using the criminal justice system, (2) the violation of probationers' civil rights when tested, and (3) the inadequacy of the urine testing technology. . . .[31] However, in spite of the controversy, practitioners and researchers interested in the relationship between drugs and crime supported the PATH concept, not only because of their clinical experience but also because of the large number of crimes committed by addicts.[32]

The Tripwire proposal fell on deaf ears in the criminal justice system, the drug abuse treatment community, and the federal government. The heroin epidemic that had so rattled the country at the end of the 1960s was clearly diminishing by 1977.[33] The Special Action Office for Drug Abuse Prevention was closed in 1975 as the initial political focus on the drug problem waned. While there

26. National Commission on Marihuana and Drug Abuse, *Drug Use in America*.

27. For a friendlier review of the thinking about drugs and crime at the time of the original Tripwire proposal, see William H. McGlothlin, "Drugs and Crime," in *Handbook on Drug Abuse*, ed. DuPont, Goldstein, and O'Donnell, pp. 357-64.

28. Carl G. Leukefeld, "Opportunities for Enhancing Drug Abuse Treatment with Criminal Justice Authority," in *Improving Drug Abuse Treatment*, DHHS pub. no. (ADM) 91-1754 ed. Roy W. Pickens, Carl G. Leukefeld, and Charles R. Schuster (Washington, DC: Government Printing Office, 1991), pp. 328-37.

29. DuPont, "Operation Trip-Wire."

30. McGlothlin, Anglin, and Wilson, *Evaluation of the California Civil Addict Program*.

31. Carl G. Leukefeld, "The Clinical Connection: Drugs and Crime," *International Journal of the Addictions*, 20(6,7):1049-64 (1985).

32. John C. Ball et al., "The Criminality of Heroin Addicts: When Addicted and When Off Opiates," in *The Drugs-Crime Connection*, Sage Annual Reviews of Drug and Alcohol Abuse, vol. 5, ed. James A. Inciardi (Beverly Hills, CA: Sage, 1981), pp. 39-65; David N. Nurco et al., "A Comparison by Ethnic Group and City of the Criminal Activities of Narcotic Addicts," *Journal of Nervous and Mental Disease*, 174:112-16 (1986).

33. Mark H. Greene and Robert L. DuPont, "The Epidemiology of Drug Abuse," *American Journal of Public Health*, pt. 2, 64:1-56 (1974).

has been a White House drug czar every year since 1971, SAODAP was unique. It was a large office with substantial funding. SAODAP was a home for researchers; it was not a political operation but a social policy laboratory. Later drug chiefs lacked the scientific staff and the budget that SAODAP, thanks to the vision of Jerome Jaffe and others who developed the office in 1971, had.

By 1977, crime rates had fallen, as had budgets in both the criminal justice system and the drug abuse field. A logical response to a program that was working, as the original federal heroin addiction program clearly was in 1977, would have been to increase its support. This is precisely the opposite of the way the political process worked. As soon as there was even the slightest evidence that the country had turned the corner on heroin addiction, the support from both political parties for any effort to deal with the drug problem virtually vanished.[34]

This political thinking is similar to what psychiatrists call primary process thinking, the primitive thinking associated with dreams and with psychosis. If something is growing, it is out of control and justifies almost any action. If the problem is shrinking, then it not only does not justify action, but it is treated as if it does not exist. In this maladaptive thinking, the size and importance of the problem are ignored while only the change in the size of the problem is considered to be important. Unfortu-

nately, much media-driven political thinking about health and social problems has these same qualities.

The ebb and flow of support for public funding of drug abuse prevention bears eloquent and painful witness to primary process thinking at work in the contemporary United States. When the heroin problem was worsening in the late 1960s and early 1970s, there appeared to be almost no limits to federal funding for antidrug efforts. As soon as the heroin indicators turned down in the mid-1970s, the public support virtually evaporated. More recently, when the cocaine problem dramatically worsened during the crack epidemic in the late 1980s, an even larger run-up of public funding occurred. As soon as the cocaine indicators began to fall, the political and media support for public funding or antidrug efforts eroded.

On a more purely political front, the new administration that came into Washington in 1977 was devoted to decriminalizing marijuana use. It took a remarkably benign view of cocaine use. Reform in 1977 meant including drug addiction as a handicapping illness under federal law in order to protect the drug addict from discrimination. This attitude was part of a generally permissive approach to illicit drug use in the government at that time. There was more concern for preventing authorities, including those in the criminal justice system, from infringing on the rights of convicted criminal offenders than there was for reducing their criminal activity.[35] Tripwire was 6 years too late to catch the political

34. Robert L. DuPont, "The Future of Drug Abuse Prevention," in *Handbook on Drug Abuse*, ed. DuPont, Goldstein, and O'Donnell, pp. 447-52.

35. Musto, *American Disease*.

winds that propelled the drug abuse field when heroin addiction was public enemy number one and 10 years too soon to catch the even more potent political winds of the crack epidemic.

In late 1977, the head of the Department of Health, Education and Welfare asked for the resignations of all institute directors in the Alcohol, Drug Abuse, and Mental Health Administration, including the director of NIDA who had a few months earlier proposed Operation Tripwire in the belief that it was the most important new idea in the drug abuse field at the time. Here was an idea that could build on the solid foundations of the previous decades of drug abuse research and contribute significantly to bringing to an end the drug plague in America's cities. A few months after the secretary of health, education, and welfare received the resignation of the NIDA director, the President sacked this secretary, showing once again the short life span of those who swim with sharks.

The drug field took a dramatic turn in the decade after Tripwire was proposed. Innovation shifted away from publicly funded drug abuse treatment as many of the brilliant young leaders left the field entirely. The Parents' Movement, focusing on marijuana use by middle-class teenagers, took hold beginning in 1976 in Atlanta, Georgia. The Parents' Movement became, by the end of the decade, the engine driving the entire drug abuse effort. This was a movement that was not centered on heroin use or on publicly funded treatment. It was a movement that saw experts in the drug abuse field, including researchers, as preoccupied with heroin addiction and as dangerously permissive on the use of marijuana. Because the leaders of the Parents' Movement controlled the political process, drug czars after 1980 had to pass the political litmus test of this movement to be selected by the White House.[36]

Meanwhile, a quiet revolution was taking place in drug abuse treatment. As local, state, and federal funding fell for public treatment programs, which had been dominated since the late 1960s by methadone treatment and therapeutic communities, the initiative for innovation shifted to the private sector. The Minnesota Model was developed in the 1970s and was widely applied throughout the nation in the 1980s. This was a privately funded 28-day residential treatment program using the disease concept of addiction and relying heavily on the 12-step programs based on Alcoholics Anonymous.[37] This movement revolutionized drug abuse treatment, making it far more successful than it had ever been before. Like the Parents' Movement, the Minnesota Model was largely unconnected to governmental activities, to research, or to the urban underclass.[38]

36. Robert L. DuPont, "Commentary: NIDA's Role in Applied Research," in *Drugs in the Workplace: Research and Evaluation Data*, DHHS pub. no. (ADM) 91-1730 ed. Steven W. Gust et al. (Washington, DC: Government Printing Office, 1991), 2:225-30.

37. U.S., White House, Office of National Drug Control Policy, *Understanding Drug Treatment* (Washington, DC: Government Printing Office, 1990).

38. Robert L. DuPont and John P. McGovern, ed., "A Bridge to Recovery—An Intro-

TRIPWIRE IN THE 1990s

The striking and completely unpredicted rise in the use of cocaine in the early 1980s, followed by the devastating impact of the crack cocaine epidemic in the United States in 1986 and 1987, occurred when the political climate had changed dramatically from that of the early 1970s. The prison population and crime rate, which had declined or stabilized in the 1970s, rose menacingly in the late 1980s. Attitudes toward drugs in general and toward marijuana and cocaine in particular, after the impact of the Parents' Movement, became progressively harder. Support for legalization, or even for decriminalization, had peaked in 1978 and was on a long-term downward trend characteristic of the end of drug epidemics. The national attention on illicit drug use focused not on heroin, as it had from the late 1960s until about 1977, or on marijuana, as it had from 1977 until 1985, but on cocaine.

Each of the two times there has been a large increase in the public attention to the drug issue, first from about 1969 to 1972 and then from 1986 to 1990, there was a flurry of media attention to the alternative option to the policy of prohibition of illegal drug use. This alternative approach calls for the legalization of currently illicit drugs. In both of these episodes, there was little popular support for the legalization of drugs, but the media and certain relatively small but excessively vocal segments of the intellectual community found these ideas attractive. A few highly visible attorneys, economists, and some politically liberal academics have been attracted to the idea of legalizing drugs as have, somewhat paradoxically, a few conservative market-oriented opinion leaders. Television coverage, especially during these two episodes of intense national focus on illicit drug use, gave the appearance that there was wide and growing support for the legalization of drugs. Polls taken for the last thirty years have made clear that there has never been substantial support for making drugs such as cocaine and marijuana, to say nothing of heroin, phencyclidine (PCP), and LSD, as freely available as we now make alcohol and tobacco. These same polls show that the support for legalization has declined steadily for over a decade.

Those who favor legalization of currently illegal drugs have had the most success when their audience was young people and when the drug was marijuana, the illegal drug that came closest to being legalized in the United States during the last twenty years. The percentage of American high school seniors who believed marijuana use should be entirely legal peaked in 1977 at 33.6 percent and fell steadily thereafter to 16.6 percent in 1989.[39] A statewide telephone poll conducted in Maryland in the fall of 1990 is typical of the findings among American adults. In this

duction to 12-Step Programs" (Manuscript, Institute of Behavior and Health, 1991).

39. Lloyd D. Johnston, Patrick M. O'Malley, and Jerald G. Bachman. *Trends in Drug Use and Associated Factors among American High School Students, College Students, and Young Adults: 1975-1989* (Ann Arbor, MI: University of Michigan, Institute for Social Research, 1991), p. 144.

survey, 15.0 percent of the 968 respondents answered "yes" to the question, "Should adults be able to possess small quantities of marijuana for personal use without legal penalty?" "No" was the answer of 82.3 percent while 2.7 percent said they had no opinion on this question. The question in this poll was phrased to elicit the maximum support for the concept of legalization of drugs, as it focused on private marijuana use by adults.[40]

In the heroin phase of the American drug epidemic, the public policy score was kept by counting overdose deaths. That is how the nation kept track of whether we were winning or losing the war on drugs. In the marijuana phase, the score was kept by monitoring the percentage of high school seniors who smoked marijuana daily. The cocaine phase of the contemporary drug epidemic was scored by counting the rates of murder and of the births of cocaine-addicted babies. The tragic increase in the use of marijuana and cocaine that occurred after the mid-1970s made clear the dangers of defining some illicit drug use as soft or trivial. It was precisely the policy position that focused on heroin addiction and rejected marijuana and cocaine use as serious drug problems, which had seemed so forward-looking in 1975, that set the stage for marijuana and cocaine to become the primary epidemic drugs of the following 15 years.[41]

In 1981, there was a tragic crash on the aircraft carrier *Nimitz*. Investigation subsequently showed that nearly half of all sailors on the ship had recently used marijuana, cocaine, or other illicit drugs. This led to a new initiative in the military, labeled Zero Tolerance, focused on regular, random drug testing of all service personnel. This effort led to prompt and profound reductions in drug use in the military. The civilian labor force followed suit with drug testing in the workplace.[42] These efforts captured the initiative in the private sector and the focus on marijuana and cocaine, the two illicit gateway drugs.[43] These new initiatives in the civilian workplace were associated with improvements in drug-testing technology and a new level of standardization in the urine drug-testing process.[44] The new testing technology and processes were far cheaper, far more accurate, and far more sensitive than the testing that was available in 1977, when Tripwire was proposed.

40. "Poll Finds Most Marylanders against Drug Legalization," *CESAR Reports*, 1:1 (Spring 1991).

41. Strategy Council on Drug Abuse, *Federal Strategy for Drug Abuse.*

42. Robert L. DuPont, "Never Trust Anyone under 40: What Employers Should Know about Drugs in the Workplace," *Policy Review*, 48:52-57 (Spring 1989); idem, "Drugs in the American Workplace: Conflict and Opportunity, Part I: Epidemiology of Drugs at Work," *Social Pharmacology*, 3:133-46, (1989); idem, "Drugs in the American Workplace: Conflict and Opportunity, Part II: Controversies in Workplace Drug Use Prevention," ibid., 3147-64 (1989).

43. Robert L. DuPont, *Getting Tough on Gateway Drugs: A Guide for the Family* (Washington, DC: American Psychiatric Press, 1984).

44. U.S., Department of Health and Human Services, "Mandatory Guidelines for Federal Workplace Drug Testing Programs," *Federal Register*, 11 Apr. 1988, pp. 11979-89.

In 1987, the first new national data system since the original SAODAP programs was begun when the Drug Use Forecasting (DUF) system began testing booked arrestees. Today there are 24 DUF sites across the United States. This historic program not only for the first time peeled back the curtain of denial from the criminal justice system about the full extent of current illicit drug use among arrestees, but it provided a new window on the extent of drug use in the underclass that had been systematically undercounted by earlier national drug use surveys.[45] Unlike the surveys of households and high school students which had, until DUF, been the basis for the way the nation estimated the number as well as the trends of users of various illicit drugs, the DUF system included not only self-report of drug use but also urine testing. The following section describes the DUF program and the search for a powerful sponsor to launch the first new national drug use monitoring program in the United States in twenty years.

*Development of
the DUF program*

The National Institute of Justice initiated the DUF program in 1987. Findings from a number of research projects had suggested that following drug use trends of criminals was a valuable indicator of illicit drug use in the population at large. The influential work of John C. Ball and David N. Nurco had demonstrated that heroin addicts in Baltimore committed six times as many crimes while using the drug frequently than when they used the drug infrequently.[46] McGlothlin and Anglin's careful study of persons admitted to the California Civil Addict Program also documented the association between drug use and crime rates. These studies showed that criminals were at very high risk of using illicit drugs.[47]

In 1983, the National Institute of Justice funded two research studies on drug-testing programs for arrestees. The first project evaluated the existing program in Washington, D.C., which was begun in 1970. All persons arrested in the District of Columbia and charged with a criminal offense had their urine tested for drugs of abuse. The court used the test results at arraignment to determine who should be sent to urine-monitoring or drug abuse treatment programs during the period of pretrial release. The research study was designed to assess the impact of the drug-testing program on the criminal justice system and the arrestee's pretrial misbehavior.[48]

The second study funded by the National Institute of Justice was de-

45. Eric D. Wish, "U.S. Drug Policy in the 1900s: Insights from New Data from Arrestees," *International Journal of the Addictions*, 25(3A):377-409 (1990-91); Eric D. Wish and Bernard A. Gropper, "Drug Testing by the Criminal Justice System: Methods, Research, and Applications," in *Drugs and Crime*, ed. Michael Tonry and James Q. Wilson (Chicago: University of Chicago Press, 1990), 13:321-91.

46. Ball et al., "Criminality of Heroin Addicts."

47. McGlothlin, Anglin, and Wilson, *Evaluation of the California Civil Addict Program.*

48. Mary A. Toborg et al., *Assessment of Pretrial Urine Testing in the District of Columbia* (Washington, DC: Department of Justice, National Institute of Justice, 1989).

signed to set up a drug-testing program for arrestees processed in Manhattan Central Booking. Because no pretrial drug-testing program was operating in New York City, the testing had to be set up as part of a confidential research study. The urine test results were retained and analyzed solely by the researchers. The primary focus of the research was on the ability of drug use at arrest to predict pretrial misbehavior.[49]

These two studies produced startling results. More than one-half—54 percent—of the booked arrestees in Washington, D.C., and Manhattan in 1984 tested positive for a drug at arrest.[50] These findings showed the high level of recent drug use, especially of cocaine, among persons arrested for a variety of crimes. The results were used to prepare testimony before the President's Panel on Organized Crime in 1984 to show that cocaine had become a common street drug in Manhattan.[51] Of equal importance was the finding that it

49. Eric D. Wish, Mary Cuadrado, and Stephen Magura, "Drug Abuse as a Predictor of Pretrial Failure-to-Appear in Arrestees in Manhattan" (Final report submitted to U.S., Department of Justice, National Institute of Justice, Jan. 1988); Douglas A. Smith, Eric D. Wish, and G. R. Jarjoura, "Drug Use and Pretrial Misconduct in New York City," *Journal of Quantitative Criminology*, 5:101-26 (1989).

50. Eric D. Wish, Mary A. Toborg, and John P. Bellassai, "Identifying Drug Users and Monitoring Them during Conditional Release" (National Institute of Justice Briefing Paper, Department of Justice, National Institute of Justice, 1988).

51. Eric D. Wish, "Cocaine Use in Arrestees in New York City, Washington, D.C.," in *Report to the President and the Attorney General: America's Habit: Drug Abuse, Drug Trafficking and Organized Crime* (Washington, DC: Government Printing Office, 1986).

was feasible to obtain voluntary urine specimens from arrestees being processed in a hectic urban booking facility—Manhattan—as part of a research study.

In an auspicious happenstance, Eric D. Wish, the director of the Manhattan pretrial testing research project, on an airplane discussed with James K. Stewart, director of the National Institute of Justice, the possibility of establishing a national system of tracking drug use by arrestees by obtaining periodic, voluntary, and anonymous interviews and urine specimens from new samples of booked arrestees in the largest cities of the United States. The discussion with Stewart came after a succession of similar discussions with staff of other federal agencies. Only Stewart, however, was willing to support the project and to provide the continuing leadership needed to implement a new national drug monitoring program. In November 1986, Eric Wish became a visiting fellow at NIJ to help design and establish what was to become the Drug Use Forecasting program.

As was found in the study of arrestees in Manhattan, a majority of the arrestees in each DUF city were willing to provide a voluntary and anonymous interview and urine specimen to the DUF interviewers. In every major city where the DUF program was initiated, 50 percent or more of the booked arrestees tested positive for at least one drug. In most cities, cocaine was the most prevalent drug, sometimes found in 60 percent or more of the arrestees. In no other segment of the population, except perhaps for persons admitted to drug treatment programs, were such high rates of drug use found by urinalysis.

The tremendous amount of drug use found in arrestees, together with the fact that two to four times more drug use was found in arrestees by urinalysis than through their voluntary and anonymous self-reports of drug use, showed the magnitude of the drug problem in offenders that was going undetected by traditional criminal justice assessments.

The national response

There was a growing recognition by policymakers that drug testing should become a routine and universal function of the criminal justice system. Testing could be used to identify illicit drug users at arrest as well as to monitor persons released to the community before trial and after conviction. The endorsement of this approach is best exemplified by the requirement of the policy plan for 1990 of the White House Office of National Drug Control Policy that the states of the nation begin to plan for the establishment of urine testing in all segments of the criminal justice system.[52] Thus it had taken almost 15 years for policymakers to begin to realize the benefits of the strategy envisioned by the Operation Tripwire proposal in 1977.

In 1988, the Office of National Drug Control Policy was the new White House drug office and was under the leadership of the most visible drug czar the nation had ever

52. U.S., White House, Office of National Drug Control Policy, *National Drug Control Strategy* (Washington, DC: Government Printing Office, 1990).

had, William Bennett. Like the early 1970s, when the first White House drug office, SAODAP, was created, the bonanza of money and political support to deal with drugs was short-lived. Today, the second director of the Office of National Drug Control Policy, Governor Bob Martinez, faces, as did the second head of SAODAP, Robert L. DuPont, the demoralizing problems of declining political and budgetary support. Of the nation's eight drug czars, the first four held office during the heroin phase, the next two during the marijuana phase and the Parents' Movement, and the most recent two czars during the cocaine or, more accurately, the crack phase of the nation's drug abuse epidemic. The first six were all health care professionals and researchers. The last two are the first drug czars to be politicians with no prior experience in drug abuse treatment, prevention, or research.

As the 1980s ended, the nation's prisons were bursting under the load of incarcerated offenders. Whatever the politics of longer sentences and more efficient criminal justice processing, the long-term costs of drugs and crime were unsustainable at the local, state, and national levels. It became fashionable once again to look for new ideas that could cut the cost of the vicious cycle of drugs and crime.

An updated Tripwire proposal would cover all illicit drugs and take advantage of the new immunoassay drug tests to do far more testing than was done in the past. The application of the new drug-testing technology to hair, instead of urine, would offer the opportunity to extend the surveillance window from the 1-3 days provided by urine for most drugs to 90 days as provided by hair.[53] An updated Tripwire would also involve wider use of the 12-step programs that have revolutionized the private sector drug treatment field in the last decade.

The Tripwire proposal calls for universal, routine, and frequent tests for illicit drug use, with incarceration being the swift response to continued drug use. Treatment must be linked to the CJS not as a way of covering up continued use of drugs but as a way of helping offenders stop their drug use. The testing program needs to be universal because of the great power of denial. The period of incarceration need not be prolonged, but it must be repeated as often as the offender returns to illicit drug use. There is a powerful resistance to drug testing on one hand and reincarceration as a predictable response to positive drug tests on the other. Nevertheless, only a systematic approach, such as Tripwire, can help the majority of criminal offenders, their families, and their communities who are now being destroyed by drug abuse.

IMPLICATIONS OF TRIPWIRE FOR DRUG ABUSE RESEARCH AND PUBLIC POLICY

Science and policy are always uneasy allies. Neither is a certain beacon for navigation through complex and controversial issues. This has been true with every aspect of the

connection between criminal justice and drug abuse. There have always been scientists, and policy experts, on all sides of every subject, and this is true today of drug testing for conditionally released offenders.

Tripwire was a solid idea that fit well with the needs of the time. It built on an extensive body of research and on the initial federal efforts in the drug abuse field. It focused on the most socially disruptive segment of the illicit-drug-using population and on those with the greatest need. Tripwire used the knowledge that most heavy users only stop illicit drug use when they have compelling reasons to stop and when those reasons are applied repeatedly over a long period of time.[54] Tripwire also harnessed the powerful political process unleashed by the downturn in political support for drug abuse as the first evidence of the drop in heroin trends became apparent.

So what went wrong? Why was Tripwire not adopted in 1977, and why in 1992 does it seem like a good, new idea for some time in the future? A combination of unfortunate developments undermined the potential support for Tripwire. Within the criminal justice system in the late 1970s there was little enthusiasm for drug testing, which used a new and unfamiliar technology. There was a well-established inertia for doing things as they had always been done. Most people in the criminal justice system thought they knew who was using drugs and what to do about it. Drugs were seen as a relatively un-

53. See Tom Mieczkowski, "New Approaches in Drug Testing: A Review of Hair Analysis," this issue of *The Annals* of the American Academy of Political and Social Science.

54. Vaillant, "20 Year Followup of New York Narcotic Addicts."

important part of the crime problem. Therefore, most CJS leaders at that time did not perceive a need for a new and potentially expensive program based on urine testing and compulsory mechanisms for reincarceration of drug-using offenders to ensure that they stopped illicit drug use. Within drug treatment, there was then a growing interest in outpatient, nonmethadone treatment for abusers of drugs other than heroin. Methadone maintenance treatment for heroin addicts had been a controversial treatment that generated little political support, especially within the drug treatment community. Nonmethadone treatments did not work well with these difficult patients, so many in the drug-free treatment community were eager to stop treating criminal heroin addicts and to start treating occasional marijuana and cocaine users, or what were called at the time "polydrug abusers."

More directly, the fall of 1977 saw the election of Jimmy Carter as president and his appointment of a new secretary of health, education, and welfare, Joseph Califano. Califano wanted new heads of all his institutes. The incumbent head of NIDA, who conceived the Tripwire proposal, was a holdover from the Ford administration in Califano's mind. Califano got rid of the heads of the mental health and alcohol institutes in the summer of 1978, before he axed the director of NIDA, the most visible patron of the Tripwire idea.

Tripwire did not fit the more permissive approach to drugs of the Carter administration. Carter and his White House drug czar were supporting the decriminalization of marijuana. They were also tolerant of the recreational use of cocaine. A tough approach to criminal heroin addicts did not find favor with either Carter or Califano. Since the Tripwire proposal lacked a powerful political constituency and came at a time when the media had grown tired of drug stories, the Tripwire idea died at birth. The drug budget in those years was shrinking, not expanding, so a new and potentially expensive idea was not quickly adopted. This same situation is occurring today as the drug budgets are looked at increasingly to reduce costs rather than to add new programs. The fact that Tripwire promised to cut costs in the CJS profoundly over the long haul held little appeal to executive and legislative staffs attuned to the impact of a proposal on the current year's budget. In the late 1970s, after the exaggerated claims for social programs in the 1960s, they had grown cynical about promises of long-term returns on social program investments.

Can Tripwire now be revived in a new, updated form? Earlier experience suggests this will be a difficult sale, regardless of the research evidence that this targeted approach within the criminal justice system is the right thing to do from many points of view, including both budgetary and humanitarian concerns. There are today, as there were in 1977, many good reasons to support the Tripwire idea. It helps those drug abusers who are the neediest and those creating the highest social costs. A revived Tripwire would be especially beneficial to the communities hardest hit by the current drug epidemic, the poorest urban communities. A revived Tripwire offers the best hope of cutting the size of CJS populations, including those in expensive jails and prisons. Tripwire harnesses the newly improved technology and lowered cost of drug testing. Especially were a new Tripwire to be linked to hair testing, with the latter's 90-day surveillance window, compared to the 3-day window for urine testing, it could be a powerful new weapon in the war against drugs.

But the resistance to the Tripwire concepts are many and enduring. There are two primary reasons for pessimism, the first being the lack of high-level sponsorship. The Tripwire idea would have to be picked up by the drug czar or even the President to be certain of getting a trial. Alternatively, the secretary of health and human services or the attorney general could provide effective sponsorship, and the heads of the National Institute on Drug Abuse and the National Institute of Justice could be effective parents as well. Lower-level sponsorship is unlikely to move the largely immobile bureaucracies in either the criminal justice or the drug abuse fields. Congressional sponsorship of a new Tripwire would be useful but a double-edged sword at any time, given the inescapable conflicts between the legislative and executive branches of government. These conflicts are virtually insurmountable when the two branches of government are controlled by different political parties. If a powerful Democratic committee chairperson were to pick up the Tripwire idea during the administration of a Republican President, it would meet with little enthu-

siasm and much resistance from all executive branch officials.

One possible solution to this dismal problem can be gleaned from the experience of SAODAP twenty years ago. Under the leadership of Jerome Jaffe, a scientist with impeccable credentials, that agency made great strides in the use of research to guide national drug policy. Perhaps a return to the tradition of appointing scientists experienced in substance abuse research to lead the country's drug policy agency would help promote new, more effective ideas. Such a person could marshal the resources to launch a revised Tripwire program and other innovative programs.

The experience with Jerome Jaffe at SAODAP and with James K. Stewart at the National Institute of Justice, as well as with many other leaders who initiated major new programs in the drug and crime field, demonstrates that successful leaders may or may not be scientists but must be open to the lessons of science and then have the personal qualities necessary to organize these lessons into coherent, practical programs. Successful leaders identify personally with these new programs and carry them through the long, painful, and uncertain gauntlet of politics, budget review, and bureaucratic resistance to become, ultimately, the new foundation on which future innovation can be built. Such leaders are rare and precious in this and in other fields. Whether scientists themselves or not, it is clear today that leaders are most likely to succeed when they marshal a convincing body of scientific evidence and a substantial number of scientific leaders to help them build, sell, and sustain their new programs.

The second major barrier to the implementation of a new Tripwire proposal, after the lack of high-level sponsorship, is budgetary constraints. In times of generally rising government spending, promising new ideas are swept up quickly and enthusiastically. When the overall budget is constrained, as the federal budget has been for over a decade now, new ideas are hard to fund. The ubiquitous naysayers in the bureaucracy have an easy time stopping new ideas when they ally themselves with the powerful forces of fiscal restraint.

So what hope is there for the basic Tripwire idea of universal, systematic drug testing of all criminal justice subjects and for continued illicit drug use to be linked to incarceration? Surely, the Tripwire idea needs to be refined and pilot tests conducted. The Tripwire idea needs to be widely discussed in the professional literature with an openness to the public media. During such an incubation period, the Tripwire idea must wait for a high-level patron who will adopt it as his or her own idea, for a time when there is a receptiveness to the link between drugs and crime, and for a willingness to spend additional money on the new program. Such a moment may be a few months off, or many years.

It is probable that the basic Tripwire concepts will be adopted into wide practice within a decade, even without a major programmatic initiative. The last 15 years have seen growing use of urine tests for nonmedical drug use within the criminal justice system. The question, in our view, is less whether the Tripwire ideas will be widely adopted than how and when drug testing will become a matter of routine and universal practice within the criminal justice system. Science is a useful precondition for such an adoption, but it is not a sufficient basis for it to occur. For Tripwire, or any other research-based programmatic idea, to become a reality it will require a confluence of political, media, and economic forces far beyond mere science.

ANNALS, *AAPSS*, **521**, May 1992

Pretrial Drug Testing: Panacea or Pandora's Box?

By CHRISTY A. VISHER

ABSTRACT: Pretrial drug testing of arrestees and defendants released before trial is increasingly being implemented in state and local criminal justice agencies. The federal courts are also considering whether pretrial drug testing should be initiated in each district. But researchers and policymakers are currently engaged in a vigorous debate about the merits and drawbacks of pretrial drug-testing programs. Critics contend that the programs are difficult to implement, are too expensive, and have little real impact on criminal behavior and illegal drug use. Proponents argue that pretrial drug testing enables criminal justice officials to reliably detect drug use and improve release decisions, to effectively supervise drug-involved offenders before trial, and to encourage these offenders to seek treatment. This article reviews state and local experience with pretrial drug testing, discusses the evaluations that have been conducted, and offers some suggestions as to the role of pretrial drug testing in our nation's drug control policy.

Christy A. Visher is currently senior research associate at the National Institute of Justice, the principal research agency of the U.S. Department of Justice. She received her M.A. (1980) and Ph.D. (1982) in sociology from Indiana University. Dr. Visher conducts research on issues related to criminal justice policy and provides advice and support to Institute management on research issues. Her recent research interests include drug testing, the relationship between illegal drug use and criminal behavior, violent offending, and criminal careers.

NOTE: Points of view expressed in this article do not necessarily represent the official position of the National Institute of Justice or the U.S. Department of Justice.

IN the 1980s, rising public awareness of the drug abuse problem in all sectors of society led to a variety of strategies for reducing and controlling illicit drug consumption. A principal strategy in the workplace, the military, and the criminal justice system has been an increased emphasis on the detection of persons who use illegal drugs. Since drug users may not show any overt symptoms of use and will often conceal illegal drug use if asked about it directly, urinalysis technologies have emerged as a convenient tool for identifying users of illegal drugs.

Drug testing has been used for decades in drug abuse treatment programs to monitor clients' drug use during treatment. Drug testing also has a long history in the military and in professional sports. Probation and parole agencies in a few states—notably California—and in the federal system have had drug-testing programs in place for more than a decade. In the last several years, drug testing has become a common requirement for persons convicted of drug offenses or suspected of using drugs who are placed on probation or parole. Drug testing is also gaining the attention of national policymakers. The President's Office of National Drug Control Policy has recommended that states implement comprehensive drug-testing programs—from arrest through post-conviction supervision—as part of their criminal justice programs.[1]

Pretrial drug testing of suspected offenders at arrest and during the period before trial, however, is a relatively new practice. After the arrest and arraignment of suspected offenders, judges must make bail and pretrial-release determinations and set any conditions of release. The principal concern in this decision-making process is the defendant's risk of flight and potential danger to the community, which are the only statutory reasons for deciding whom to release before trial. In 1984, the Federal Bail Reform Act urged that a defendant's drug involvement be considered in these risk assessments. Washington, D.C., has put this suggested policy into practice and operates the most comprehensive pretrial drug-testing program in the country. Arrestees are asked to submit to a drug test at arrest, and those testing positive for illegal drugs may be released before trial with the condition that they enter a monitoring or treatment program involving regular drug testing.

Both state and federal criminal justice systems are now debating the merits and drawbacks of establishing similar pretrial testing programs. Among the concerns raised about pretrial drug testing are the utility of the program in minimizing the risk of releasing drug-using defendants by reducing pretrial rearrests and increasing court appearances, the accuracy of the testing procedures, possible constitutional challenges to drug testing at the pretrial stage, and the costs associated with operating a pretrial testing program.

A series of studies funded by the National Institute of Justice and the

1. U.S., Office of National Drug Control Policy, *National Drug Control Strategy* (Washington, DC: Government Printing Office, 1989), p. 26.

Bureau of Justice Assistance of the U.S. Department of Justice provides empirical and practical information about the utility of pretrial drug testing. Drawing on these studies, this article discusses the current debates within research and policy on pretrial drug testing. First, it describes the Washington, D.C., pretrial testing program, the longest-running such program in the country, and several studies of that program. Second, it reviews additional research on the use of drug-testing results as a predictive indicator of pretrial misconduct. Third, it relates the experiences and findings of six other jurisdictions that attempted to replicate the District of Columbia program. Finally, it considers the future of pretrial drug testing and whether pretrial testing programs have a place in our national drug policy.

PRETRIAL DRUG TESTING IN WASHINGTON, D.C.

Pretrial drug testing has existed in Washington, D.C., since the 1970s. The early phase of the program referred suspected drug-involved offenders to a local treatment agency for testing, and results were delivered to the courts. But in 1984, this testing program was transferred to the criminal justice system, and the Pretrial Services Agency (PSA) of Washington, D.C., launched an expanded, comprehensive program for all arrestees and released drug-involved offenders.[2] The basis for the new program arose from research that has

consistently shown that the most frequent, serious offenders are also the heaviest drug users.[3] Moreover, for many drug-involved offenders, criminal activity appears to rise or decline with level of drug use.[4] In practical terms, the identification of drug-involved offenders and the potential control of their drug use appeared to be a useful approach to managing high-risk defendants at the earliest stage of the criminal justice process.

The pretrial testing program in the District of Columbia has two components: (1) drug testing of arrestees prior to the initial court appearance and release decision,[5] and (2) regular monitoring of drug use through testing as a condition of release. Testing is completed before arraignment in a facility within the courthouse and results are made available to the judge before the initial court appearance. The PSA uses the EMIT (enzyme

2. John Carver, "Drugs and Crime: Controlling Use and Reducing Risk through Testing," *NIJ Reports*, no. 199 (Sept.-Oct. 1986).

3. Jan Chaiken and Marcia Chaiken, *Varieties of Criminal Behavior* (Santa Monica, CA: RAND, 1982); Eric Wish and Bruce Johnson, "The Impact of Substance Abuse on Criminal Careers," in *Criminal Careers and "Career Criminals,"* vol. 2, ed. A. Blumstein et al. (Washington, DC: National Academy Press, 1986).

4. J. C. Ball et al., "The Criminality of Heroin Addicts When Addicted and When off Opiates," in *The Drugs-Crime Connection*, ed. J. A. Inciardi (Beverly Hills, CA: Sage, 1981); Bruce Johnson et al., *Taking Care of Business: The Economics of Crime by Heroin Users* (Lexington, MA: Lexington Books, 1985); Ko-lin Chin and Jeffrey Fagan, "Impact of Crack on Drug and Crime Involvement" (Paper delivered at the annual meeting of the American Society of Criminology, Baltimore, MD, 1990).

5. Arrestees who are charged with minor crimes—for example, misdemeanors and traffic violations—are often released at a district police station. Since they are not brought to the central booking facility, they are not tested for drug use.

multiplied immunoassay test) to screen arrestees for five drugs: cocaine; opiates—primarily heroin; phencyclidine (PCP); methadone; and amphetamines. The initial drug test is voluntary, but high compliance is achieved because, before granting nonfinancial release, judges will often order testing of those who refuse. Test results are not used in prosecution or adjudication decisions.

In most state and federal courts, judges may set release conditions to minimize the safety threat posed by high-risk defendants and to ensure appearance at trial. The second component of the Washington, D.C., testing program, drug monitoring during release, provided judges with a new option for handling drug-involved offenders who were thought to pose increased risk if released. Arrestees who test positive for drugs at arrest are placed in a regular drug-testing or treatment program as a condition of release. Defendants must report at least weekly for testing; all tests are recorded in an automated information system. Violations—positive test results or nonappearance for testing—are met with a system of graduated sanctions, including more frequent testing, detention for three to five days, and, in extreme cases, being held in jail until trial. Some judges use performance in the monitoring program in sentencing convicted defendants.

Evaluation of the Washington, D.C., testing program

It was hoped that the Washington, D.C., program would provide local criminal justice officials with objective information about drug use. Such information would then be used in pretrial-release decisions as a possible risk factor for assessing defendant suitability for release. Legally, the likelihood of rearrest before trial and failure to appear for scheduled court appearances (FTA) are the primary concerns. District of Columbia officials also hoped that a pretrial monitoring program might help control drug use among released defendants, which in turn might lead to reductions in pretrial misconduct—either rearrest or FTA—in this high-risk group. One comprehensive evaluation and several other analyses examined whether the program was accomplishing these two objectives in its first two years of operation by the D.C. PSA.

Persons who tested positive for drugs at arrest were more likely to be rearrested and miss scheduled court appearances than those who did not test positive for drugs, according to data from the program.[6] Indeed, the risk of rearrest in the early weeks after release was about four times higher for drug users than nonusers, even after taking into account defendant attributes usually associated with pretrial rearrest.[7] Moreover, the results of the drug test at arrest appeared to add significantly to the as-

6. Mary Toborg et al., *Assessment of Pretrial Urine Testing in the District of Columbia* (Washington, DC: National Institute of Justice, 1989); Christy A. Visher and Richard L. Linster, "A Survival Model of Pretrial Failure," *Journal of Quantitative Criminology*, 6:153-84 (1990).

7. Visher and Linster, "Survival Model of Pretrial Failure," p. 167, tab. 5.

sessment of pretrial risk, over and above the typically collected information on defendant's employment, prior convictions, and pending case status.[8] In particular, multiple drug use increased the risk of pretrial misconduct.

Thus, in Washington, D.C., drug test results seem to improve a judge's ability to reliably assess defendant risk of pretrial misconduct. But does regular testing reduce rearrest and FTA rates for all released drug users? An evaluation of the monitoring component of the program indicated that about two-thirds of the defendants assigned to drug monitoring during release stayed with the program for at least three tests. These defendants had lower rates of rearrest and FTA than did those who never showed up for testing or who dropped out of the program before the third test.[9] But an experimental evaluation of the effects of the monitoring program, in which eligible defendants were randomly assigned to either regular drug testing, community drug treatment, or a control group, found no differences between the three groups in rearrest or FTA rates.[10] Implementation problems, however, may have compromised the experimental design.

8. Toborg et al., "Assessment of Pretrial Urine Testing," p. 10.

9. Ibid., pp. 13-14. Surprisingly, this finding was independent of whether those who showed up for testing were positive or negative for illegal drugs.

10. Ibid., pp. 23-24. This type of evaluation is the strongest statistical test of whether regular drug testing during release might reduce pretrial misconduct. Such experiments, however, are difficult to carry out successfully in an actual criminal justice environment, and implementation problems usually occur.

Taken together, evaluations of the Washington, D.C., program indicate that some drug users were better risks than others and that a monitoring program may help to sort out the good and bad risks. A small group of drug users did not comply with the program, and their noncompliance was a strong indicator of their high risk for pretrial rearrest and FTA. In another study of the program, defendants who did not report for their first post-release test had a much greater risk of rearrest and FTA than those who reported for the test.[11] In summary, in the Washington, D.C., program, a large group of released drug users who were regularly tested for drug use had lower than average rearrest and FTA rates, actually similar to those who did not use drugs. It is difficult to determine, however, whether regular testing encouraged good behavior or whether this group of released drug users would have been low risks without the testing program.

Drug tests and risk management

Independent research conducted in Manhattan and in Dade County, Florida, provides additional information on whether drug tests at arrest might improve judges' assessments of defendant risk for pretrial rearrest or FTA if the defendant is released before trial. Pretrial testing programs were not operational at these sites, but both jurisdictions were con-

11. Christy A. Visher, "Using Drug Testing to Identify High-Risk Defendants on Release: A Study in the District of Columbia," *Journal of Criminal Justice*, 18:321-32 (1990).

sidering the implementation of testing programs and allowed researchers to gather data on defendants being considered for release, including the results of voluntary drug testing at arrest. Since these were exploratory studies, judges were not informed of the drug test results, and defendants were assured that the results would be used only for research purposes.

At both sites, released defendants who tested positive for illegal drugs had higher rates of pretrial misconduct than did defendants similar in all respects but who had not tested positive. In Manhattan, both pretrial rearrest and FTA rates were higher among those testing positive, especially for those testing positive for more than two drugs.[12] But a separate analysis of the Manhattan data concluded that urine testing was not a feasible policy alternative because assessment of individual risk of failure to appear was not measurably improved by drug test results.[13] In Dade County, drug test results were

statistically related to the risk of pretrial rearrest, especially rearrest for serious crimes, but not to FTA.[14] Some drug-specific results—for example, that PCP use affected rearrest, but not FTA, in Manhattan—also existed, but no clear patterns emerged in the two jurisdictions.[15]

Drita analyzed only failure to appear and did not adjust for sample-selection effects or time at risk.

14. John Goldkamp, Michael Gottfredson, and Doris Weiland, "Pretrial Drug Testing and Defendant Risk," *Journal of Criminal Law and Criminology*, 81:585-652 (Fall 1990). The Dade County study appears to be seriously flawed, however. It is difficult to interpret the results because of the simultaneous inclusion of four measures of the drug test results—namely, positive for marijuana, positive for cocaine, positive for either, and positive for both—in the logit analysis. Ibid., p. 624 (tab. 7), p. 626 (tab. 9). These measures are likely to be highly correlated—one did not pass tolerance—which would cause unstable and unreliable coefficient estimates. These problems raise serious doubts about substantive conclusions based on this analysis.

15. Comparisons of empirical studies carried out by different investigators in different jurisdictions are inherently difficult. These two studies had many important differences: they were carried out in different years—1984 in Manhattan and 1987 in Dade County—during a period when illegal drug use was experiencing rapid change; they measured variables differently, especially the drug test results; and they used dissimilar analytic techniques. The overall rearrest rate in Manhattan was 25 percent compared to 15 percent in Dade County; the FTA rates were 33 percent and 9 percent in Manhattan and Dade County, respectively— these differences are probably related, in part, to the length of the follow-up period in the two studies. Opiate use, a characteristic of serious drug use and criminal behavior, was practically nonexistent in Dade County, whereas 21 percent of the Manhattan sample tested positive for opiates. Finally, 56 percent tested positive for drugs in general in Manhattan compared to 80 percent in Dade County.

12. Douglas A. Smith, Eric Wish, and G. Roger Jarjoura, "Drug Use and Pretrial Misconduct in New York City," *Journal of Quantitative Criminology*, 5:101-26 (1989); Eric Wish, Mary Cuadrado, and Stephen Magura, "Drug Abuse as a Predictor of Pretrial Failure-to-Appear in Arrestees in Manhattan" (Final report submitted to the National Institute of Justice, U.S. Department of Justice, 1988).

13. S. Belenko and I. Mara-Drita, "Drug Use and Pretrial Misconduct: The Utility of Prearraignment Drug Tests as a Predictor of Failure-to-Appear" (Manuscript, Criminal Justice Agency, New York, 1988). These results were based on a slightly different sample and different analytic methods from those of the analysis reported in the published study of the Manhattan data by Smith, Wish, and Jarjoura, "Drug Use and Pretrial Misconduct in New York City." The study by Belenko and Mara-

The issue of whether drug test information is a strong indicator of pretrial misconduct or whether the statistical relationship is substantively significant is addressed in all reports, albeit using different approaches that are difficult to compare. But other defendant characteristics used in predicting pretrial misconduct, such as community ties, have rarely, if ever, been held to this rigorous standard to justify their predictive utility in judges' pretrial-release decisions. In any event, a statistical relationship between drug test results and pretrial misconduct is only one of many factors involved in debates about the merits of a pretrial drug-testing program in a particular jurisdiction.

In summary, drug test results appear to improve the classification of defendants according to the risk of pretrial misconduct in three sites—Washington, D.C., Manhattan, and Dade County—but the improvement by drug test results of individual predictions of risk is not necessarily guaranteed. In illustrating this concept, the Manhattan study used the example of releasing 100 defendants testing positive for PCP and 100 defendants who tested negative for PCP but who were similar to the first group on all other characteristics. The analysis showed that 37 would be expected to be rearrested in the first group, but among the defendants who had not used PCP, only 25 would be expected to be rearrested.[16] Choosing which PCP user would be rearrested is a much more difficult task, and determining whether drug

test results would in fact improve such individual predictions requires a different type of analysis from that used in existing studies.[17]

REPLICATIONS OF THE WASHINGTON, D.C., PROGRAM

In an effort to gain further insight into whether pretrial testing programs would be useful in other jurisdictions, the Bureau of Justice Assistance funded six sites to implement programs modeled on the one in the District of Columbia. The six jurisdictions were Prince George's County, Maryland, a suburb of Washington, D.C.; Milwaukee County, Wisconsin; Multnomah County, Oregon, the county that includes Portland; Pima and Maricopa counties, Arizona, the counties that include, respectively, Tucson and Phoenix; and New Castle County, Delaware, which includes Wilmington.[18] The Bureau of Justice

16. Smith, Wish, and Jarjoura, "Drug Use and Pretrial Misconduct in New York City," p. 119.

17. The statistical determination of whether specific information predicts individual criminal behavior is a two-step analytic task. Initially, a prediction instrument using the information is developed, and then a second analysis, with a different sample or with the same sample at a later point in time, is used to confirm the instrument's accuracy. The analyses reported here are only the first step in this process. For further discussion, see, for example, Don Gottfredson and Michael Tonry, eds., Prediction and Classification: Criminal Justice Decision Making (Chicago: University of Chicago Press, 1987), esp. pp. 21-52, 201-48.

18. The federal court system also implemented a demonstration pretrial testing program in several sites without the monitoring component, but an evaluation of its effectiveness was not conducted. See U.S., Administrative Office of the United States Courts, The Demonstration Program of Mandatory Drug Testing of Criminal Defendants (submitted to the U.S. Congress, 1991).

Assistance funded evaluations of four of these programs, and the National Institute of Justice funded evaluations of the two programs in Arizona. The evaluations were to address the two questions raised in the previous studies: (1) are the results of drug tests at arrest significantly related to pretrial rearrest and FTA? and (2) does regular drug testing during pretrial release reduce pretrial rearrest and FTA among released drug users?[19]

Implementing
pretrial drug testing

The six demonstration sites experienced varying levels of difficulty in the implementation of a pretrial

19. The implementation issues and evaluation results of the six sites are discussed in a series of reports to the funding agencies: Stefan Kapsch and Louis Sweeny, "Multnomah County DMDA Program Evaluation Final Report" (Final report, Bureau of Justice Assistance, U.S. Department of Justice, 1990); idem, "Multnomah County DMDA Project Implementation Report" (Final report, Bureau of Justice Assistance, U.S. Department of Justice, 1990); John S. Goldkamp, Peter Jones, and Michael Gottfredson, "Measuring the Impact of Drug Testing at the Pretrial Release Stage: Pretrial Drug Testing in Milwaukee County, New Castle County and Prince George's County, Preliminary Report" (Report, Bureau of Justice Assistance, U.S. Department of Justice, 1989); idem, "Measuring the Impact of Drug Testing at the Pretrial Release Stage: Experimental Findings from Prince George's County and Milwaukee County, Final Report" (Report, Bureau of Justice Assistance, U.S. Department of Justice, Nov. 1990); Michael Gottfredson, Chester L. Britt, and John Goldkamp, "Evaluation of Arizona Pretrial Services Drug Testing Programs, Final Report" (Report, National Institute of Justice, U.S. Department of Justice, 1990). Additional reports on the pretrial demonstration programs are available

drug-testing program, and these difficulties had implications for the evaluations. In two sites—Multnomah County and New Castle County—the severity of the problems meant that a reasonable evaluation of the program could not be conducted during the time allotted for the evaluation by the funding agency. Table 1 summarizes both the implementation problems and the results of the evaluations. Among the most serious implementation problems occurring at the six sites were

- inability of two sites to test the majority of defendants at arrest for illegal drug use;
- the lack of support among pretrial staff in recommending eligible defendants—usually those with positive test results—for the monitoring program;
- the failure to provide the arraignment judge with initial drug test results before the hearing;
- the arraignment judge's low rate of referring eligible defendants to the monitoring program;
- high rates of noncompliance—not showing up—for testing among the released defendants in the monitoring program;
- the inability of some sites to randomly assign defendants to experiment, or monitoring, and control groups without bias;
- difficulty in maintaining current information about test results, sanctions pending, and so

in seven issues of the *Pretrial Reporter*, the newsletter of the National Association of Pretrial Services Agencies (Oct., Dec. 1988; Feb., Apr., June, Aug. 1989; Feb. 1991).

TABLE 1

IMPLEMENTATION ISSUES AND EVALUATION RESULTS FOR THE SIX DEMONSTRATION SITES

Program Site	Implementation Issues	Evaluation Results
Prince George's County, Maryland	40 percent of the defendants eligible for monitoring program were assigned cash bail. Pretrial staff did not recommend the monitoring program. Test results were not reported to the arraignment judge. Testing center was inconveniently located. There was a high no-show rate for monitoring program. Only 17 percent of eligible defendants were referred to program. Sanctions were not applied as proposed. The information system for tracking defendants was delayed.	Drug test results did not improve assessment of risk of pretrial rearrest or FTA. Monitoring program did not reduce rearrests or FTAs.
Pima County, Arizona	There were low rates of rearrest or FTA during evaluation. There was a very small number of cases for monitoring experiment ($n = 222$). 30 percent of the monitored group was never tested.	Drug test results did not improve assessment of risk of pretrial rearrest or FTA. Monitoring program reduced rearrests, especially for drug crimes, but not FTAs.
Maricopa County, Arizona	Target sample ($n = 500$) of tested arrestees could not be achieved; final sample = 284. Randomization into experiment was faulty. Number of cases in experiment was small ($n = 234$). 30 percent of the monitored group was never tested.	Drug test results improved assessment of risk of pretrial rearrest, but not of FTA. Monitoring program modestly reduced FTAs, but not rearrests.
Milwaukee County, Wisconsin	50 percent of arrestees were not tested. Only 19 percent of eligible defendants were referred to monitoring program. There was weak support for program among pretrial staff and judges. Sanctions were not applied as proposed.	Drug test results improved assessment of risk of FTA, but not of rearrests. The monitoring program did not reduce rearrests or FTAs.

| Multnomah County, Oregon | Only 30-50 percent of arrestees were tested. There was a low program referral rate— 10-40 percent of eligible defendants—by judges. The structure of pretrial release system impeded coordination. 54 percent of the monitored group was never tested. The testing center was inconveniently located. The information system did not permit adequate tracking of released defendants. | Insufficient data were collected to assess the effect of drug test results on pretrial misconduct. Evaluation of the monitoring experiment was unreliable because of implementation problems. |
| New Castle County, Delaware | Lengthy delays were encountered in logistical planning for the program. Initial lack of community support for the program existed. There was a lack of support from pretrial services staff for implementing program. The information system did not permit adequate collection of data for evaluation. There was lack of support among judiciary. Funding was terminated by the federal agency before evaluation. | No data were collected to assess the effect of drug test results on pretrial misconduct. There were insufficient cases in monitoring program for evaluation. |

SOURCES: Stefan Kapsch and Louis Sweeny, "Multnomah County DMDA Program Evaluation Final Report" (Final report, Bureau of Justice Assistance, U.S. Department of Justice, 1990); idem, "Multnomah County DMDA Project Implementation Report" (Final report, Bureau of Justice Assistance, U.S. Department of Justice, 1990); John S. Goldkamp, Peter Jones, and Michael Gottfredson, "Measuring the Impact of Drug Testing at the Pretrial Release Stage: Pretrial Drug Testing in Milwaukee County, New Castle County and Prince George's County, Preliminary Report" (Report, Bureau of Justice Assistance, U.S. Department of Justice, 1989); idem, "Measuring the Impact of Drug Testing at the Pretrial Release Stage: Experimental Findings from Prince George's County and Milwaukee County, Final Report" (Report, Bureau of Justice Assistance, U.S. Department of Justice, 1990); Michael Gottfredson, Chester L. Britt, and John Goldkamp, "Evaluation of Arizona Pretrial Services Drug Testing Programs, Final Report" (Report, National Institute of Justice, U.S. Department of Justice, 1990); Pretrial Reporter (Oct., Dec. 1988; Feb., Apr., June, Aug. 1989; Feb. 1991).

forth for defendants in the monitoring program; and
- the lack of judicial support for the sanctioning plan, a lack that led to high violation rates—no-shows and positive tests—among defendants in the testing program.

Some sites were able to correct most of these problems as the programs continued—in some cases, after the evaluation was completed—but the quality of the data collected during the early phase of the programs was clearly affected by the implementation problems. The impact of these problems on the evaluation results will be discussed shortly. In general, the practical problems of implementing pretrial drug-testing programs were related to support for the program within the local criminal justice community and the cognizant agencies and were also related to the logistical capability of the jurisdiction to implement the program. Legal considerations arose in the planning stage at several demonstration sites, although none seriously impeded the implementation of the programs.

Implementation of a pretrial testing program modeled after the Washington, D.C., program demands the involvement of all agencies within a local criminal justice system. The pretrial services agency often must coordinate its efforts with the police or sheriff's department responsible for detaining the arrestees until testing can take place. In Milwaukee, implementation of the program was delayed until the police department consented to drug testing of arrestees being held until arraignment. In Prince George's County, bail magistrates at local police stations released 40 percent of eligible defendants on cash bail with no other release conditions before testing could occur. These defendants were not considered for release supervised by the pretrial services agency, hence they were not placed in the monitoring program.

Other problems surfaced when private agencies with important roles in the pretrial release system were involved in the demonstration program. Initially in Maricopa County, few arrestees agreed to be tested; it was later determined that a private agency, the Treatment Assessment Screening Center, not previously involved with interviewing arrestees, was not correctly explaining the nature of the pretrial testing program. In Multnomah County, one private agency interviewed and tested arrestees before the release hearing, and three other agencies—public and private—supervised released defendants. Difficulties in coordinating the efforts of these organizations led to considerable interagency diversity in the implementation of the monitoring program and to problems in tracking defendants during release.

Support from the judiciary was particularly crucial to the implementation of the program. Judges were supposed to use drug test results in determining pretrial release, assigning eligible drug users to the drug-monitoring program, and imposing sanctions on defendants who failed to comply with the monitoring program. Although the chief judge or magistrate at all demonstration sites had indicated support for the program before federal funding, individual judges at some sites apparently did not support the program's goals. Thus, at some sites, relatively few eligible defendants were referred to the monitoring program, and sanctions for program violations were not consistently carried out. In Multnomah County, when it became apparent that judges were not using the program as a release condition, the chief judge issued a court order directing referral to the monitoring program as a condition of release for eligible defendants, and program referral rates improved dramatically.

Logistical problems in implementing the pretrial testing program at a few sites proved as serious as did system support problems. Among the most common problems were (1) integrating the program within an existing structure of pretrial-release procedures; (2) creating a computerized information system that would allow the efficient tracking of defendants and the collection of data for the evaluation; (3) locating a testing facility that was accessible to defendants during release; (4) informing new and rotating pretrial personnel and judges about the testing program and its operations; and (5) scheduling court hearings for defendants who did not comply with the testing program. Solving logistical issues surrounding the day-to-day operation of a pretrial drug-testing program requires the involvement of many different agencies, whose actions must be coordinated.

At most sites, one or more of these implementation problems seriously affected the collection of the data necessary for an adequate evaluation of the pretrial testing program. The interpretation of these data is addressed in the next section. But in New Castle County, the problems encountered in commencing and managing the program were so profound that the program was never fully implemented and federal funds for program operation and evaluation were terminated.[20] In Multnomah County, the program eventually overcame most of the implementation problems, but data for one portion of the evaluation were never collected and faulty procedures during the experimental phase of the evaluation raise serious doubts about the available data.

Results of the evaluations

In four of the six sites, the evaluators were able to collect the necessary data for an assessment of whether the program was meeting its stated goals. Recall that the two questions at issue were (1) whether drug abuse detection—using urinalysis—at arrest might provide additional information about the risk of pretrial rearrest or FTA for released defendants, and (2) whether drug use monitoring—regular urinalysis—during release might reduce pretrial rearrest and FTA.

At two of these four sites, defendants who tested positive for illegal drugs at arrest were at significantly greater risk of pretrial rearrest or FTA, after taking into account factors

20. Goldkamp, Jones, and Gottfredson, "Measuring the Impact of Drug Testing at the Pretrial Release Stage: Pretrial Drug Testing," pp. 81-96.

usually considered by the arraignment judge. In Milwaukee and Maricopa counties, positive drug test results increased risk of FTA and re-arrest, respectively. As to the experimental evaluation of the drug-monitoring component, again, two of the four sites—Pima and Maricopa counties—concluded that the program significantly reduced, respectively, rearrest and FTA for released drug-involved defendants. The impact of the program was not large at these sites, however, and the evaluators concluded that the program had only modest effects on pretrial misconduct.[21]

Interpreting these evaluation results is difficult, and caution is urged for a number of reasons. First, the implementation problems discussed earlier reduced the quality of the evaluation data at several sites. Consider those sites that tested only half of the eligible defendants at arrest. If, for example, the defendants who refused the test were at greater risk of pretrial misconduct than those who agreed to be tested, then the evaluation results were based on a relatively low-risk group and it is not surprising that the drug tests results did not add to the risk assessment of pretrial misconduct. As another example, for sites that had low referral rates of eligible defendants to the monitoring program—referred defendants may have differed in important respects from defendants not referred—the experimental evaluation cannot effectively assess the program's impact on pretrial misconduct for the total eligible population. Also, for sites where many monitored defendants did not appear for testing or were not sanctioned for violations, the evaluation is not of the program that was planned.

Second, and equally important, were serious anomalies in some of the statistical analyses, which make valid interpretation of the results highly questionable.[22] Small sample sizes, especially for the experimental evaluation, also hindered convincing analyses at several of the sites. Moreover, it is difficult to compare the evaluation results across sites because of different analytic procedures, especially the measurement of drug test results. For example, the number of drugs for which an arrestee tested positive increased the likelihood of pretrial rearrest and FTA in the earlier studies in Washington, D.C., and Manhattan. Unfortunately, the evaluations of the dem-

21. In the Pima County experiment, 4 percent of the drug-monitored group was rearrested compared to 12 percent of the control group ($p = .06$). In the Maricopa County experiment, the drug-monitored group had a 29 percent FTA rate whereas the control group had a 39 percent FTA rate ($p = .11$). Sample sizes in both analyses were small, which reduced the likelihood of finding large statistically significant differences between the groups.

22. In particular, the analyses of the release decisions in Prince George's County and Milwaukee (Goldkamp, Jones, and Gottfredson, "Measuring the Impact of Drug Testing at the Pretrial Release Stage: Experimental Findings," p. 27, tabs. 2.7 and 2.8) suffer from the problems raised earlier about the Dade County study (Goldkamp, Gottfredson, and Weiland, "Pretrial Drug Testing and Defendant Risk," n. 12). The simultaneous inclusion of multiple measures of drug test results—namely, positive for any drug, positive for cocaine, and number or positive test results—in the multivariate analysis confounds any substantive interpretation of the results.

onstration sites did not always include this measure.

In summary, the serious implementation problems encountered at some demonstration sites coupled with analytic problems in the evaluation analyses complicate our understanding of whether pretrial testing programs might be beneficial for release decisions or as a supervisory tool in those sites. A review of the evaluation results published in the *Pretrial Reporter* concluded that "the question of pretrial drug testing should not be considered answered," largely because of the implementation issues.[23] That review also suggested that a more current evaluation of existing programs be undertaken now since many of the problems have been overcome and some sites report clear benefits of the programs.

ASSESSING THE UTILITY OF PRETRIAL DRUG TESTING

Studies from nine jurisdictions—Washington, D.C.; Dade County; Manhattan; and the six demonstration sites—have examined the practical utility of pretrial drug testing for release decisions or pretrial supervision of drug-involved offenders. At five of the seven sites that collected data on release decisions, drug test results provided additional information about the defendant's potential risk of rearrest or FTA but not always about both types of miscon-

duct. Thus drug tests at arrest are likely to be useful in pretrial-release decision making, but drug test results may not be equally predictive of rearrest and FTA in all jurisdictions.

The drug-monitoring program for released drug users, however, reduced rearrests or FTAs—and these were modest effects—in only two of the five jurisdictions that implemented the monitoring experiment, in Pima and Maricopa counties. Even though regular drug testing during release may not decrease pretrial misconduct for all released drug users, some types of drug-involved offenders appear to benefit. At three demonstration sites—Pima County, Prince George's County, and Milwaukee—a reasonable minority of released drug users consistently tested negative while in the monitoring program: one-third or more of those assigned to regular drug testing during pretrial release had no positive tests.[24] This group of drug-involved offenders may have been infrequent drug users, or the enforced nature of the program may have deterred them from illegal drug use while awaiting trial.

Other data suggest that compliance with drug-monitoring programs may serve as an early-warning system for pretrial misconduct among released drug users. This signaling effect, described by the evaluators of

23. National Association of Pretrial Services Agencies, "Pretrial Drug Testing: A Review of Three Evaluations," *Pretrial Reporter*, Feb. 1991, p. iv.

24. Specifically, in Pima County, 29 percent of the defendants in the monitoring program had no positive tests during monitoring, in Prince George's County 36 percent had no positive tests, and in Milwaukee 32 percent had no positive tests. Similar data from Maricopa County and Washington, D.C., are not presented in available sources.

TABLE 2

**DEFENDANT BEHAVIOR IN DRUG-MONITORING PROGRAMS,
PRETRIAL REARRESTS, AND FAILURE TO APPEAR**

Site	Percentage of Scheduled Drug Tests Missed by Defendants	N	Percentage of Defendants Who Were Rearrested	Percentage of Defendants Who Failed to Appear
Prince George's County, Maryland	0 - 25	43	4.6	2.3
	26 - 50	80	11.2	35.0
	51 - 75	87	13.8	32.2
	76+	69	14.5	27.5
Milwaukee County, Wisconsin	0 - 25	132	10.6	8.3*
	26 - 50	62	21.3	19.4
	51 - 75	71	23.9	45.1
	76+	67	22.3	56.7

SOURCES: Adapted from data presented in John S. Goldkamp, Peter Jones, and Michael Gottfredson, "Measuring the Impact of Drug Testing at the Pretrial Release Stage: Experimental Findings from Prince George's County and Milwaukee County, Final Report" (Report, Bureau of Justice Assistance, U.S. Department of Justice, Nov. 1990), pp. 92, 114, tabs. 5.15, 6.9.

*The rates of failure to appear (FTA) for Milwaukee include failure to appear for scheduled drug tests, which complicates the interpretation of whether noncompliance with the drug-testing program— here, percentage of scheduled drug tests missed by defendants—was related to other FTAs.

the Washington, D.C., program,[25] appeared to have some support from three sites that reported detailed data on defendant performance in the monitoring program (see Tables 2 and 3). For example, in Prince George's County, defendants who missed less than 25 percent of their tests were much less likely to be rearrested than those who missed more than 75 percent of their tests; 4.6 percent of the former compared to 14.5 percent of the latter were rearrested. A similar pattern was found in Milwaukee County (see Table 2). In Pima County, defendants with few positive tests during monitoring were less likely to be rearrested or to fail to appear than defendants with

more positive tests (see Table 3).[26] Thus a pretrial drug-monitoring program can be a useful strategy for supervising some offenders. Pretrial drug testing may reduce drug use, and perhaps related criminal activity, for one group of released drug-involved offenders, and it provides

25. Toborg et al., *Assessment of Pretrial Urine Testing*, pp. 12-16.

26. Data from Prince George's County and Milwaukee on positive test results and pretrial misconduct are difficult to interpret because of analytic problems. The analysis unfortunately combined defendants who had no positive tests with those who missed all tests, the latter being a group likely to comprise drug users. Thus the reported high FTA rates for those with no positive tests in Prince George's County and Milwaukee are not surprising since many of the defendants in that group had missed all tests. See Goldkamp, Jones, and Gottfredson, "Measuring the Impact of Drug Testing at the Pretrial Release Stage: Experimental Findings," p. 92 (tab. 5.15), p. 114 (tab. 6.9).

TABLE 3

**PRETRIAL MISCONDUCT AND DEFENDANT BEHAVIOR
IN THE DRUG-MONITORING PROGRAM, PIMA COUNTY, ARIZONA**

Positive Test Results	N	Percentage of Defendants with Rearrests or FTAs
None	45	8.8
1-2	37	10.8
3-9	35	28.6
10 or more	6	—*
Missed all tests	30	50.0
Total	153	15.0

SOURCE: Tabulated from data presented in Michael Gottfredson, Chester L. Britt, and John Goldkamp, "Evaluation of Arizona Pretrial Services Drug Testing Programs, Final Report," (Report, National Institute of Justice, U.S. Department of Justice, 1990), pp. 41-42.

NOTE: Pretrial misconduct is measured by defendant's positive test results; defendant behavior is measured by number of rearrests or FTAs.

*Too few cases to compute a meaningful percentage.

the courts with information on high-risk releasees who are not complying with the monitoring program.

The pretrial drug-testing program in the District of Columbia faced some of the problems that the demonstration sites experienced, but these problems were eventually resolved. When judges and hearing commissioners in Washington, D.C., were interviewed about their opinions of the program, most responded that they used the information generated by the testing program a great deal and that it represented a substantial improvement over previous practices.[27] Clearly, one key to the success of the pretrial testing program in Washington, D.C., has been the willingness of the judges to impose sanctions on defendants who failed to comply with

the monitoring program.[28] Judges in the District of Columbia believe that accurate information about drug use is vital to their decisions regarding pretrial release and supervision of released drug-involved offenders. The Washington, D.C., program was recently expanded to include testing of juvenile offenders.

In some sense, an overall assessment of the usefulness of both components of a pretrial testing program is akin to interpreting a picture of a partially filled glass of water: is the glass half empty or half full? Opponents of pretrial drug testing view the inconsistent evaluation results as primarily showing small benefits of drug testing at the pretrial stage and propose that decisions about such programs be based on issues of cost and convenience. Proponents of the program minimize the logistical and financial issues and point to the utility of the program in raising commu-

27. Mary A. Toborg and John P. Bellassai, "Assessment of Pretrial Urine Testing in the District of Columbia: The Views of Judicial Officers" (Final report, National Institute of Justice, U.S. Department of Justice, 1988), pp. 4, 10.

28. Ibid., pp. 5-9.

nity awareness about illegal drug use and providing much-needed alternatives, albeit incomplete ones, to assist in the control of drug-involved offenders. Researchers have focused on rearrest and FTA as evaluation outcomes because of the statutory requirements that underlie judges' pretrial-release decisions. But there may be other practical, nonlegal benefits, including the ability to detect drug abusers and send them to treatment.

THE FUTURE OF PRETRIAL DRUG TESTING

Pretrial drug-testing programs present many challenges to jurisdictions considering the implementation of drug testing for detection and supervision of drug-involved offenders at the pretrial stage. At least two obstacles to such programs have largely disappeared, however: concerns about the accuracy of drug tests and legal issues. Despite some claims to the contrary, immunoassay urinalysis technologies are widely regarded as very accurate,[29] and the accuracy of the most commonly used test in criminal justice operations, EMIT, has been upheld in numerous court decisions.[30]

A recent study by the National Institute of Justice evaluated the accuracy of four commonly used drug-testing urinalysis technologies.[31] The study concluded that immunoassays are much more accurate than thin-layer chromatography, which was commonly used in the 1970s. Drug testing using immunoassay methods correctly identifies 98 to 99 percent of negative urine specimens—that is, it yields few false positive results—and correctly identifies about 80 percent of positive urine specimens, that is, it yields a moderate number of false negative results. The study recommended that positive results be confirmed by a highly accurate method if the test result is contested by the defendant and could be used for punitive action.

Several legal issues concerning the constitutionality of pretrial drug testing were discussed at length at most of the demonstration sites. Among the issues raised was whether pretrial drug tests violate Fourth Amendment protections against unreasonable searches, Fifth Amendment guarantees against self-incrimination, or Fourteenth Amendment protections pertaining to equal treatment and

29. See, for example, Kenneth Davis and Richard Hawks, *Urine Testing for Drugs of Abuse*, Research Monograph no. 73 (Rockville, MD: National Institute on Drug Abuse, 1973); David Hoyt et al., "Drug Testing in the Workplace—Are Methods Legally Defensible?" *Journal of the American Medical Association*, 258:504-9 (July 1987).

30. See the review of drug-testing case law in U.S., Department of Justice, Bureau of Justice Assistance, *American Probation and Parole Association's Drug Testing Guidelines and Practices for Adult Probation and Parole Agencies* (Washington, DC: Bureau of Justice Assistance, 1991), pp. 87-108.

31. Christy Visher and Karen McFadden, *A Comparison of Urinalysis Technologies for Drug Testing in Criminal Justice*, National Institute of Justice Research in Action (Washington, DC: Department of Justice, National Institute of Justice, June 1991); Christy Visher, *A Comparison of Urinalysis Technologies for Drug Testing in Criminal Justice* (Washington, DC: Department of Justice, National Institute of Justice, 1991).

substantive and procedural due process requirements.[32] Two recent legal analyses of the existing case law disagree as to whether pretrial drug testing will withstand these constitutional challenges.[33]

Nonetheless, the only formal legal challenge to pretrial drug testing occurred in Washington, D.C., in *Berry v. District of Columbia*.[34] In general, the U.S. Court of Appeals for the District of Columbia upheld the constitutionality of the monitoring program but sent the case back to the lower court for more specific information about its operation before a final ruling. In 1990, the case was dismissed, basically for lack of response by the plaintiff to the appeal court's ruling. The constitutionality of voluntary testing of arrestees before arraignment had not come before the courts in the eight years of the program's operation in Washington, D.C. Hence, as of this writing, there are no pending legal challenges to pretrial drug testing in either state or federal courts.

More serious potential obstacles to pretrial drug testing are the problems that can arise in the actual implementation of a program. As discussed earlier, these problems can spell the difference between a successful program and an unsuccessful one. Internal and external support for pretrial testing is critical to its effectiveness. The introduction of a new operation into an existing system of procedures often meets with resistance from staff, and building support among the staff involved in the implementation of a pretrial testing program is essential to its success. Moreover, in the jurisdictions that have experimented with pretrial drug testing, the judiciary significantly influenced the program's operation. Invariably, lack of support by the judiciary impeded any successful implementation of the program. But, at the same time, judges have individual philosophies about the use of drug test results, and jurisdictions should expect judges to differ in their application of the testing program.

The successful operation of pretrial drug-testing programs is also dependent on other local circumstances. Jurisdictions vary widely in patterns of criminal behavior and drug use, which may affect how such programs are best utilized. For example, jurisdictions with small criminal caseloads, such as New Castle County, Delaware, may not benefit as much from program implementation as would a jurisdiction with a greater caseload. As another example, Pima County experienced very low rates of pretrial misconduct during the evaluation phase of the project. If such low rates are typical, then a large-scale drug-monitoring program may not be able to improve behavior of defendants on release sufficiently to justify its costs. The drug detection component of the program might be

32. National Association of Pretrial Services Agencies, "Pretrial Drug Testing in Six Jurisdictions: Legal Issues in Pretrial Urinalysis," *Pretrial Reporter*, June 1989, pp. i-iv.

33. Cathryn Jo Rosen and John S. Goldkamp, "The Constitutionality of Drug Testing at the Bail Stage," *Journal of Criminal Law and Criminology*, 80:114-76 (1989); Reggie B. Walton, Gary J. Peters, and J. Anthony Towns, "Pretrial Drug Testing—An Essential Component of the National Drug Control Strategy," *Brigham Young University Law Journal*, in press.

34. *Berry v. District of Columbia*, 833 F.2d 1031, 1034-36 (D.C. Cir. 1987).

useful, however, for tracking drug use in the offender population, identifying drug-involved offenders, and encouraging drug-positive arrestees to seek treatment.

Conversely, jurisdictions with high rates of drug use in the arrestee population may find that initial drug test results cannot improve release decisions significantly since the vast majority of arrestees will test positive for drug use. In this situation, the screening component might be used to identify users of multiple drugs—users at highest risk if released—and a drug-monitoring program might help the supervising agency differentiate those drug users who are likely to engage in pretrial misconduct while on release from those who are good risks. Moreover, as some of the demonstration programs showed, 30 to 40 percent of those who tested positive for illegal drugs at arrest had no positive tests while in a drug-monitoring program. For many drug-involved offenders, reductions in drug use may lead to reductions in criminal activity. More research is needed on identifying those drug-involved offenders who might benefit from drug monitoring.

Costs associated with pretrial drug-testing programs also vary with local circumstances. Particular policy and procedural decisions about the program, such as staffing patterns, choice of testing equipment, number of drugs being tested for, and size of target population, can substantially affect operating costs. For example, these types of factors resulted in more than a threefold difference in estimated, first-year costs for operating both components of a pre-

trial testing program in two jurisdictions with the same annual arrestee population.[35]

Policymakers and criminal justice officials must weigh all of these considerations—expected utility, implementation issues, local circumstances, value to the community, and costs—in making decisions about the implementation of pretrial drug-testing programs. Information gained from pretrial testing can also be useful for assessing drug treatment needs, tracking local changes in drug use preferences, and documenting need for state and federal assistance for drug enforcement and treatment programs. Pretrial testing, both at arrest and during release, is also one component of the comprehensive drug-testing program recommended by the President's Office of National Drug Control Policy for state and local criminal justice agencies.

As a first step, the testing of arrestees can provide valuable information about the nature and extent of drug use among the offender population, which can be used in planning both comprehensive drug-testing and treatment programs. This type of approach would probably be a suitable initial stage for most jurisdictions and could be modeled after the National Institute of Justice's Drug Use Forecasting program.[36] Drug testing as a supervision tool, whether

35. U.S., Department of Justice, Bureau of Justice Assistance, *Estimating the Costs of Drug Testing for a Pretrial Services Program* (Washington, DC: Bureau of Justice Assistance, 1989), p. 17.

36. The Drug Use Forecasting program obtains voluntary and anonymous urine specimens and interviews from a sample of arrestees in 24 cities each quarter. For more infor-

during pretrial release or as a post-conviction option, requires considerable additional planning, and favorable outcomes may require a year or more of cooperative effort. Examining and understanding the problem is always much easier than devising solutions to it.

CONCLUSION

At the present time, pretrial drug-testing programs are under considerable scrutiny. As more jurisdictions implement such programs, more will be learned about how and under what circumstances pretrial testing can improve the management of drug-involved defendants in the community. In the meantime, evaluations are needed of established programs, even though these programs may have been studied in the past. A 1990 nationwide survey of state and local pretrial service programs found that 72 programs were conducting pretrial testing at some level, usually selectively as a condition of release.[37] Little is known about these programs, however.

mation about the program, see Joyce Ann O'Neil and Virginia Baldau, *Drug Use Forecasting: 1990 Annual Report* (Washington, DC: Department of Justice, National Institute of Justice, 1991).

37. Discussed in Walton, Peters, and Towns, "Pretrial Drug Testing."

Many criminal justice officials are uncertain about whether pretrial drug testing would be useful for their jurisdiction. But much of this uncertainty is based on misinformation or lack of information about the operations, practicality, and utility of pretrial drug testing. It is hoped that this article has illuminated some of these issues. Nevertheless, it is also apparent that pretrial drug testing will fail when local criminal justice officials have not adequately planned for its implementation. Officials involved in ongoing pretrial testing programs and other experts can provide practical information and technical assistance in designing programs.

Pretrial drug-testing programs can be adapted to local circumstances and can play an important role in the detection and supervision of drug-involved offenders. The utility of specific components of pretrial testing may vary from one jurisdiction to another. What works in one jurisdiction may not work elsewhere. Moreover, these programs do not necessarily lead to a Pandora's box of problems and difficulties, although they do require careful planning and continual attention. With strong internal and external support, pretrial testing programs can form a key element in a jurisdiction's criminal justice policy on drug abuse and drug-related crime.

ANNALS, *AAPSS*, 521, May 1992

New Approaches in Drug Testing: A Review of Hair Analysis

By TOM MIECZKOWSKI

ABSTRACT: This article reviews the development of hair analysis as a drug-screening technology. It compares the advantages and disadvantages of drug screens that employ urinalysis and hair analysis technologies. It reviews the various controversies that have attended the development and implementation of hair analysis. It discusses the role of ideological, sociological, and political factors in the evolution of the technique. Finally, it reviews professional and governmental responses to the technology and recommends future courses of research to resolve the outstanding disagreements.

Dr. Tom Mieczkowski is on the faculty of the University of South Florida in the Department of Criminology. He has been researching drug abuse and crime since the early 1980s. Since 1987 he has been involved in epidemiological research, primarily analyzing self-reported drug abuse using data based on both urinalysis and hair analysis techniques. He has published an edited book of research reports titled Drugs, Crime, and Social Policy *(1991).*

THE process of technical development and scientific research is often conceptualized by nonscientists as an idealized series of events. In this idealized view, scientists do their work with perfect objectivity, and technology and scientific data are evaluated solely on their merits. Rational decision making is the hallmark of the scientific process, and sociological and political dynamics are not elements in the process of discovery.

Philosophers of science have in the course of this century questioned this vision of scientific data and research and have substituted instead a more contentious description of the processes of science.[1] Sociological factors, ideological views, and similar forces are, in fact, central to the development of science. Scientific discovery, especially in an age of "big" and expensive science, is also complicated when one adds to the mix potential large profitability, and the inertia of prior investment and market control of scientific services and technology.

The current wide-ranging concern with illicit-drug epidemiology is an excellent case in point. The field offers numerous empirical questions of interest that also are important for policy. Who uses illicit drugs? What types of drugs are they, and how often are they used and in what dosages? Are there different answers for various relevant categories of users, such as age, gender, ethnicity, and educa-

tion? How does drug use relate to criminality, biological morbidity, or family organization? Our ability to create meaningful drug policy is hostage, at least in part, to our ability to respond to these questions accurately.

Researchers have turned to drug detection technologies to aid them in searching for answers to these questions. The development of immunochemical drug assays has been a major element in advancing epidemiological knowledge of drug use. Yet the development and use of such technology has evoked substantial debate. The introduction and development of urinalysis as a drug research instrument, for example, at its inception engendered considerable controversy although now it is routinely accepted. Recently, hair analysis—and, specifically, radioimmunoassay technology to assay hair—has been introduced, and it has stirred considerable controversy as well.

Technical issues are one aspect of this controversy. Other factors also contribute to it. Drug testing has become big business. Commercial application is well developed and highly competitive, with large financial stakes involved in servicing the drug-testing industry. Likewise, government agencies have become deeply involved in creating standards, certifying laboratories, and expending public funds in a monitoring and regulatory role.

SELF-REPORTED DRUG USE AND URINALYSIS

For a number of years, drug epidemiology estimates have relied almost exclusively upon information coming

1. Thomas Kuhn, *The Structure of Scientific Revolutions* (Chicago: University of Chicago Press, 1970); Karl Popper, *The Logic of Scientific Discovery* (New York: Basic Books, 1969).

from drug use self-report studies. These data were rarely verified by comparison to other indicators of drug use. As a consequence, there was a long-held belief that self-reports of drug use were quite reliable.[2] In recent years, however, this perception has come under strong criticism.[3] It is now recognized that self-reports of drug use, in the absence of any cross-comparator, are not accurate and that the drug use is most likely underreported, probably by substantial amounts.[4] But now drug use surveys can evaluate response validity because they are able to take advantage of a unique circumstance; the biological presence or absence of the drug in question can be detected by chemical assay. In recent years, the development of low-cost immunoassays have made large-scale urine-based drug screening a popular validation method. Studies have measured the concordance of self-reported and urinalysis data in order to measure the reliability of self-reported information. Since the mid-1980s,

most research done employing this approach has reported relatively poor reliability for self-reports, especially for the use of cocaine.[5]

Drug report validation research has employed three urinalysis techniques: enzyme multiplied immunoassay (EMIT), radioimmunoassay (RIA, herein referred to as "RIAH" when hair is the specimen), and fluorescence polarization immunoassay. All three provide high degrees of sensitivity and specificity on a very cost-effective basis. Urine-based techniques, however, are essentially limited to testing for and reporting on the presence or the absence of a drug or series of drugs over a short retrospective period; the period is about two days for cocaine, for example. In addition, while the fluorescence polarization immunoassay provides data on the concentration level of the detected drug in the urine, this information cannot be reliably interpolated to estimate the consumed dosage. All urinalysis tests employ arbitrary cutoff levels. If assay values fall below these cutoffs, the specimens are reported as drug negative. Thus a specimen may have trace amounts of a drug but be reported as negative.[6]

Table 1 provides some critical characteristics of urine-based and hair-based drug assays. The technical issues involved in assaying for drugs of abuse are considerable, and

2. Tom Mieczkowski, "The Accuracy of Self-Reported Drug Use: An Analysis of New Data," in Drugs, Crime and the Criminal Justice System, ed. R. Weisheit (Cincinnati: Anderson, 1989).

3. Eric D. Wish and Bernard Gropper, "Drug Testing by the Criminal Justice System," in Drugs and Crime, ed. Michael Tonry and James Q. Wilson (Chicago: University of Chicago Press, 1990).

4. Eric D. Wish, Mary Cuadrado, and James Martorana, "Estimates of Drug Use in Intensive Supervision Probationers: Results from a Pilot Study," Federal Probation (Dec. 1986); Lana Harrison, "The Validity of Self-Reported Drug Use among Arrestees" (Paper delivered at the annual meeting of the American Society of Criminology, Reno, NV, 24 Nov. 1989).

5. S. Magura et al., "The Validity of Methadone Client's Self-Reported Drug Use," International Journal of the Addictions, 22 (1988).

6. A false positive is a drug-free urine that is recorded as a drug-positive urine. A false negative is a urine that has a drug or drugs present but is recorded as drug free.

TABLE 1

PROPERTIES OF URINE AND HAIR SPECIMENS AS ANALYSIS MEDIA FOR DRUG TESTING

	Urine Specimens	Hair Specimens
Retrospective period	Generally 2-3 days*	Typically several months
Cutoff levels	Arbitrary	Arbitrary
Cross-reactions	Possible or problematic	Possible or problematic
Dosage quantification	Not claimed	Claimed
Assay replication	Not possible for identical sample	Possible for same sample
Evasion or manipulation	Generally easy	Very difficult
Storage or handling	Complex; requires freezing or refrigeration	Simple; stored at normal conditions
Potential for specimen sepsis	High; for example, hepatitis transmission	Low

*For drugs except marijuana, which may be detected generally from 5 to 30 days after use.

a complete review is beyond the scope of this short article. The focus of this analysis will be on the two most important advantages of hair analysis: the long time span, or window, of detection and the potential for estimating the ingested dosage levels of illicit drugs based on assay outcomes. The presence of drugs can be detected in hair for several months after their ingestion, depending on hair length. The detection can be achieved at sensitivity levels comparable to those of urinalysis. The costs are slightly higher for hair-based assays, but since these assays need to be done less frequently than urine assays, hair analysis can be quite cost-effective.

HAIR AS AN ALTERNATIVE TEST MEDIUM

Table 1 indicates that urine lacks certain desirable characteristics as a test medium in some critical areas. Some of these problems can be remedied by using hair instead of urine as the testing medium. Since the basic assaying technologies for hair and urine are similar, however, not all the difficulties are improved. But in those areas where hair offers an advantage, the implications are profound.

Hair analysis has been done by many researchers over the last thirty years.[7] It has been used to test for the presence of toxic substances in forensic settings and to assess exposure to toxic metals in at-risk populations.[8] The earliest date of its use for testing for illicit drugs is 1954.[9] In the inter-

7. M. Harkey and G. Henderson, "Hair Analysis for Drugs of Abuse," in *Advances in Analytical Toxicology*, ed. Randall Baselt (Chicago: Year Book Medical, 1989).

8. A. Chatt et al., "Scalp Hair as a Monitor of Community Exposure to Environmental Pollutants," in *Hair, Trace Elements, and Human Illness*, ed. A. Brown and R. Crounse (New York: Praeger, 1980).

9. R. Goldblum, L. Goldbaum, and W. Piper, "Barbiturate Concentrations in the Skin and Hair of Guinea Pigs," *Journal of Investigative Dermatology*, 22:121-28 (1954).

vening 37 years, a great number of scientists have used various assay techniques to evaluate hair shafts for the presence of illicit drugs, and these efforts have been widely published.[10] As well as detecting the presence of illicit drugs, some researchers have reported correlations between levels of self-reported consumption and hair-

10. T. H. Maugh, "Hair: A Diagnostic Tool to Complement Blood, Serum, and Urine," *Science*, 202:1271-73 (1978); D. Valente et al., "Hair as a Sample in Assessing Morphine and Cocaine Addiction," *Clinical Chemistry*, 27(11): 1952-53 (1981); W. Arnold and K. Puschel, "Experimental Studies on Hair as an Indicator of Past or Present Drug Use," *Journal of the Forensic Science Society*, 21(83)(1981); F. Smith and D. Pomposini, "Detection of Phenobarbital in Bloodstains, Semen, Seminal Stains, Saliva Stains, Perspiration Stains, and Hair," *Journal of Forensic Sciences*, 26:582-86 (1981); O. Suzuki, H. Hattori, and M. Asano, "Detection of Amphetamine and Meth-Amphetamine in a Single Human Hair by Gas Chromatography/Chemical Ionization Mass Spectrometry," ibid., 29:611-17 (1984); J. Sramek et al., "Hair Analysis for Detection of Phencyclidine in Newly Admitted Psychiatric Patients," *American Journal of Psychiatry*, 142(8):950-53 (1985); W. Arnold, "RIA Analysis of Head Hair for Narcotics and Substitutes," *Journal of Clinical Chemistry and Clinical Biochemistry*, 24:797-98 (1986); M. Michalodimitrakis, "Detection of Cocaine in Rats from Analysis of Hair," *Medical Science Law*, 27:13-15 (1987); S. Balabanova and H. Wolf, "Determination of Methadone in Human Hair by Radioimmunoassay," *Z. Rechtsmed*, 102:1-4 (1989); A. Franceschin, L. Morosin, and L. Dell'Anna, "Detection of Morphine in Hair with the Abbot TDX," *Clinical Chemistry*, 31:2125 (1987); N. Haley and D. Hoffman, "Analysis of Nicotine and Cotinine in Hair to Determine Cigarette Smoker Status," ibid., 31:1598-1600 (1985); M. Marigo et al., "Determination of Morphine in Hair of Heroin Addicts by HPLC with Fluorimetric Detection," *Journal of Analytical Toxicology*, 10:158-61 (1986); R. Martz, "The Identification of Cocaine in Hair by GC/MS and MS/MS," *Crime Lab Digest*, 15:67-73 (1988).

assay values.[11] The number of papers reporting the use of assay techniques to evaluate hair shafts for various abused drugs is now substantial.

In the late 1970s, a renewed interest arose in using hair analysis to detect abused drugs, with an emphasis on developing RIA technology for high-volume screening of hair samples. A researcher in this area, Werner Baumgartner, along with a number of colleagues, began to publish a series of reports on their work developing RIA procedures for detecting opiates and cocaine in human hair. They also began to quantify exposure to these drugs based on assay outcomes.[12] In 1987, Baumgartner and several

11. E. Cone, "Testing Human Hair for Drugs of Abuse. I. Individual Dose and Time Profiles of Morphine and Codeine in Plasma, Saliva, Urine, and Beard Compared to Drug-Induced Effects of Pupils and Behavior," *Journal of Analytical Toxicology*, 14:1-7 (1990); G. Graham et al., "Determination of Gestational Cocaine Exposure by Hair Analysis," *Journal of the American Medical Association*, 262(23):3328-30 (1989); Valente et al., "Hair as a Sample in Assessing Morphine and Cocaine Addiction"; S. Magura et al., "The Validity of Hair Analysis for Detecting Cocaine and Heroin Use among Addicts," *International Journal of the Addictions*, in press; R. Welch et al., "Radioimmunoassay of Hair: A Valid Technique for Determining Maternal Cocaine Abuse," *Substance Abuse*, 11(4):214-17 (1990).

12. A. Baumgartner et al., "Radioimmunoassay of Hair for Determining Opiate-Abuse Histories," *Journal of Nuclear Medicine*, 20:748-52 (1979); A. Baumgartner, P. Jones, and C. Black, "Detection of Phencyclidine in Hair," *Journal of Forensic Sciences*, 26(3):576-81 (1981); W. Baumgartner et al., "Radioimmunoassay of Cocaine in Hair: A Concise Communication," *Journal of Nuclear Medicine*, 23: 790-92 (1982); W. Baumgartner, "Hair Analysis for Drugs of Abuse: Solving the Problems of Urinalysis" (Testimony before the U.S., House of Representatives, Subcommittee on Human

associates established the Psychemedics Corporation of California, a laboratory exclusively offering large-scale commercial hair analysis services. It remains today the only commercial laboratory offering large-volume screening of hair for drugs of abuse, although other laboratories have, in the past, offered comparable hair analysis services, and many reference laboratories will perform gas chromatography/mass spectrometry (GC/MS) testing of individual hair samples.

THE BASIS OF HAIR ASSAYS

Both hair and urine assays rely on the same testing technologies, immunoassay techniques. Because of specimen-based time differentials, hair does not offer a short retrospective time frame, while urine does. In fact, each technique offers a complementary time frame. It is estimated that it takes approximately five to seven days before an illicit drug that was ingested is detectable in the hair shaft.[13] On the other hand, ingested drugs appear very rapidly in the urine. This means that the 48 to 72 hours of detectability—the so-called urine memory—make urine an appropriate specimen for incidence testing, to determine immediately after an event if a person had been exposed to drugs within this short time span.

Hair analysis, on the other hand, by examining a much wider time span, can provide information on the long-term drug use history of an individual—for instance, to corroborate a claim of long-term abstinence in a person who tests urine positive.

The basis of hair analysis is that the illicit drugs—or their identifiable metabolites[14]—are absorbed into the hair shaft, where they remain in a fixed state. It appears that these substances are tightly bound in the hair and therefore are very stable over extremely long time periods.[15] Furthermore, Baumgartner and others have reported that the quantitative levels of deposition in the hair correspond to the amount of drug consumed, so one can estimate the degree of use or exposure to the substance or substances analyzed.[16] Any significant amount of material that comes into contact with the hair through external means—such as through passive exposure to smoke or dust—can be removed by appropriate washing and measurement of the wash outcomes.

Hair analysis was developed primarily to provide several specific kinds of information that are un-

Resources, 20 May 1987); W. Baumgartner, V. Hill, and W. Blahd, "Hair Analysis for Drugs of Abuse," *Journal of Forensic Sciences*, 34(6):1433-53 (1989); J. Baer et al., "Hair Analysis for the Detection of Drug Use in Pretrial, Probation, and Parole Populations," *Federal Probation*, Mar. 1991, pp. 3-10.

13. Cone, "Testing Human Hair for Drugs of Abuse."

14. When reference is made to a "drug" test it should be understood that in some cases the assay actually detects a metabolite of a drug, such as benzoylecognine. For the sake of brevity, I will use the term "drug," in that context, to mean drug or drug metabolite.

15. L. Cartmell et al., "The Frequency and Antiquity of Prehistoric Coca Leaf Chewing Practices in Northern Chile: A Radioimmunoassay Study of a Cocaine Metabolite in Human Mummy Hair," *Latin American Antiquity*, in press.

16. Baumgartner, "Hair Analysis for Drugs of Abuse."

available from urinalysis. Table 1 provides a side-by-side comparison of these two techniques. The most important difference is the extended time frame of hair analysis, followed by the potential for the quantification of dosage.

CONTROVERSIES

There are controversies over any type of drug testing. Drug testing that is done on a large scale—screening—and often without the establishment of legal probable cause to test is particularly controversial. Legal concerns of this kind are applicable to all drug testing, regardless of the particular testing technique. These issues, however, to some degree become more pronounced with respect to hair analysis. Hair analysis is more difficult to evade, and, most important, it reveals the use of a drug over a long time axis. Because of these facts, hair analysis adds a more telling urgency to legal and ethical issues associated with drug testing.

The basic scientific analytical processes involved in the hair analysis technique are not themselves controversial. The use of immunoassay and chromatographic/spectroscopic techniques for chemical qualitative and quantitative analysis is very well established science. As previously cited, there are a large number of independent researchers who have confirmed the utility of these processes applied to hair. In fact, in the literature on hair testing there is not any challenge to the basic concept of the hair analysis technique. There is, however, controversy related to the interpretation of hair analysis outcomes

and how these outcomes may or may not be appropriately employed. This controversy involves disputes over some contradictory findings reported for the effectiveness of washing techniques,[17] issues of external contamination,[18] the effects of variations in hair texture and type,[19] establishing standards and cutoff levels, and unknown aspects regarding the incorporation mechanisms at work in drug absorption and how they might affect test interpretation.[20]

17. B. Goldberger et al., "Testing Human Hair for Drugs of Abuse III: Identification of Heroin and 6-Acetylmorphine as Indicators of Heroin Use," *Journal of Analytical Toxicology*, in press; C. Allgood, L. Sniegoski, and M. Welch, "Determination of Drugs of Abuse in Hair by GC/MS" (Paper delivered at the 38th ASMS Conference on Mass Spectrometry and Allied Topics, Tucson, AZ, 3-8 June 1990).

18. E. Cone et al., "Testing Human Hair for Drugs of Abuse II: Identification of Unique Cocaine Metabolites in Hair of Drug Abusers and Evaluation of Decontamination Procedures," *Journal of Analytical Toxicology*, in press.

19. D. Kidwell, "Caveats in Testing for Drugs of Abuse" (Paper delivered at the National Institute on Drug Abuse, Technical Review, 1990).

20. Harkey and Henderson, "Hair Analysis for Drugs of Abuse." The Allgood et al. analyses employed GC/MS. Although some vapor deposition products remained on the hair after washings, Allgood et al. believed the issue was resolvable by relying on ratios of compounds in the hair. They concluded, "It appears that the determination of drugs or their metabolites in the hair is a viable method of analysis and offers several advantages to the commonly used urinalysis." C. Allgood, L. Sniegoski, and M. Welch, "The Analysis of Human Hair for Drugs of Abuse" (Paper delivered at the 39th ASMS Conference on Mass Spectrometry and Allied Topics, Nashville, TN, 19-24 May 1991). Kidwell presents data on several subjects in evaluating the relative comparison of black

The processes by which illicit drugs —or other substances—are incorporated into hair are not well understood, and this fact makes some researchers uneasy about interpreting hair analysis. For example, it may be that substances can be bonded to or deposited on the hair in several different fashions. Some have speculated that, because of these potential complex bondings, assayed compounds may "migrate" along the shaft.[21] If drugs absorbed into hair move within the shaft, they would produce a "smearing effect." This would damage the time analysis capability of the test.

A second issue is that while hair analysis may identify drugs, is it identifying drugs that have been retained in the hair due to passive exposure? Passive exposure is generally taken to mean unconscious, environmental exposure to drugs. Passive exposure and contamination may occur by numerous possible mechanisms—for instance, by simply touching one's hair with one's hands. It is noteworthy that these analytic techniques detect the presence of compounds at extremely low levels. Critics contend, for example, that people living in environments where cocaine or marijuana smoking is relatively common may test positive even though they have not used the substance. Some research has shown that in particular circumstances people may inadvertently but chronically be exposed to small amounts of drugs, for example, bank tellers, due to handling large amounts of contaminated currency. And, certainly, people may live in apartment buildings or family settings where they may be knowingly or unknowingly exposed to illicit drugs. But there is virtually no data from real-world research of such circumstances. Exposure events have been simulated in laboratories, but generally under unrealistic circumstances.

Critics maintain that the ability to clarify the role of passive exposure, mechanisms of incorporation, and chemical-bonding issues with definitive research makes unclear the interpretative guidelines that should be applied to the outcome of hair analysis results. Hair analysis advocates argue that these distinctions can be made and that these distinctions do not rely on just the detection of the substance but on a complex analysis of the specimen washings and of the ratio of unadulterated drug to drug metabolites identified in the specimens.[22]

---

and brown hair. Goldberger et al. and Cone et al. each did control-group studies of groups of twenty comparing "known users" with "known abstainers." Although they raise some questions on the effectiveness of the washing techniques, they report that GC/MS of the hair samples in all cases identified the experimental subjects, as distinct from the controls, without error. Kidwell, "Caveats in Testing for Drugs"; Goldberger et al., "Testing Human Hair for Drugs"; Cone et al., "Testing Human Hair for Drugs."

21. M. Harkey and G. Henderson, "Hair Analysis for Drugs of Abuse: A Critical Review of the Technology" (Report to the Department of Alcohol and Drug Programs, State of California, Contract #D-0053-6, 1988).

22. W. Baumgartner and V. Hill, "Hair Analysis for Drugs of Abuse: Decontamination Issues" (Paper delivered at the 2nd International Congress of Therapeutic Drug Monitoring and Toxicology, Barcelona, Spain, 9-12 Oct. 1990).

There are other issues raised by critics. Hair exhibits substantial variation in physical size, rates of growth, and coloration. How these properties ought to be evaluated relative to hair analysis is a matter of debate. Some research has reported that differential properties such as hair color and texture may have an impact on hair analysis outcomes.[23] There has, however, been only very limited analysis presented regarding the actual degree of these potential variations.

All these concerns are issues that justify further refinement of hair analysis and further research, but the extent to which they justify rejecting current use of hair analysis is another matter. For the most part, critics of RIAH have not provided definitive data that substantiates their criticisms but rather have offered suggestive findings. In fact, and somewhat ironically, in several reports where aspects of the hair technique are criticized, the data generally show that RIAH readily identifies drug users and drug abstainers.

Hair analysis supporters argue that critics have generally failed to recognize the clinical utility of the technique, especially when it is used with other kinds of data in a real-world setting. While detailed knowledge of the biological mechanisms of incorporation, for instance, is interesting and important, statistical data showing the efficacy of the procedure are sufficient to justify using the procedure. Lack of detailed knowledge of basic hair physiology is not fatal to hair analysis. A similar argument is

23. Kidwell, "Caveats in Testing for Drugs."

raised regarding the nature of, among other things, substance bonding. To date, consistent clinical data support the accuracy of hair analysis when testing specimens are known to be from drug users, either when drug use is indicated by urinalysis or when specimens are analyzed using GC/MS.[24] Likewise, very recent research conducted by both Magura et al. and Mieczkowski et al. has shown, to some degree, the clinical utility of the technique in field settings with both criminal arrestees and drug treatment populations.[25] This work replicates similar findings reported by Baer et al. with probationers.[26]

One of the most neglected distinctions in the debate over hair analysis is the degree to which it can function to make useful clinical distinctions in a tested population as opposed to being a tool for illucidating basic biochemical processes. The advocates of hair analysis have argued that statistical correlation that is reliable and consistent has long been accepted as a sufficient rationale for the use of diagnostic and treatment modalities in medicine, even when underlying mechanisms are poorly understood or even mysterious. This pragmatic view is reflected currently in the use,

24. Graham et al., "Determination of Gestational Cocaine Exposure"; R. Welch et al., "Radioimmunoassay of Hair."

25. Magura et al., "Validity of Hair Analysis"; T. Mieczkowski et al., "The Concordance of Drug Use Indicators: Urine, Hair, and Self-Report" (Monograph submitted to the National Institute of Justice, Contract #90-IJ-CX-0023, 1991).

26. J. Baer et al., "Hair Analysis for the Detection of Drug Use in Pretrial, Probation, and Parole Populations."

for example, of some treatments for the acquired immune deficiency syndrome (AIDS) that are evaluated on the basis of whether or not they prolong life or ease the course of the disease, even if the reasons why they have the particular effect are not clear. Virtually all epidemiological studies using hair as an identifier of drug use have been supportive of its clinical utility. Yet, in spite of these findings, the technology continues to be referred to as "novice" or "as having attracted little attention by the scientific community."

Critics point out that among published studies there is substantial variation in the methods of washing and preparing hair samples for assay. There is not yet a universal standard for washing hair specimens, conducting the assay, or establishing quantitative outcomes that can be used to estimate consumption levels. Systematic comparison of hair analysis values will require a standardized assay method and will be greatly facilitated by a standard system of reporting outcomes. There is also disagreement over the meaning of hair specimen wash outcomes—referred to as wash kinetics—and their implications, since wash kinetics play an important role in determining the degree of potential passive exposure to drugs. Analysis outcomes appear to be affected by the type of extraction performed or the preparation method used to create an analyzable specimen. There are many different techniques available and reported in the literature for specimen washing and preparation. Thus the comparability of current studies is often questionable.

The Baumgartner technique is a case in point. It is done with a proprietary reagent used in preparing the hair sample. The reagent is currently undergoing patent application and has not, therefore, been publicly identified. Baumgartner and Hill have described their washing techniques and have produced a large amount of data with wash kinetics that show that external, passive, or migration concentrations can be distinguished from active use.[27] It is unlikely, however, that these findings will be generally accepted until the proprietary aspects are disclosed and independently evaluated.

Another area that is frequently mentioned by critics of hair analysis is that there is no established set of quality-control standards yet in place for laboratories doing this procedure. While this is true, this assertion requires some clarification. Certification and standardization cannot occur before the basic research has reached a certain critical mass, especially in terms of the accumulation of a substantial number of cases to assess natural variabilities and assay parameters. It is unclear what an organization like Psychemedics ought to do in response to this kind of criticism. One alternative is to stop doing the assay. Another is to evolve its own quality-assurance procedures until standard references are produced. Baumgartner has argued quite strongly that appropriate quality-assurance controls are available and are used by his organization. These include the constant use of in-

27. Baumgartner and Hill, "Hair Analysis for Drugs of Abuse."

ternal standards as well as externally submitted blind controls.

There are a number of valid and well-taken critiques that apply to hair analysis. Clearly, the technology should continue to undergo refinement and improvement. It is difficult, however, to see how these current criticisms fatally wound the technology. Hair analysis has sufficient scientific authority to be a useful clinical method at present, provided it is used conservatively and those who interpret its results are aware of the limitations and restrictions of the process. These generic caveats are, in fact, appropriate for a wide range of clinical biochemical assays used in a wide variety of circumstances, including urinalysis for drugs of abuse.

NONSCIENTIFIC ISSUES IN THE HAIR ANALYSIS CONTROVERSY

Among nontechnical issues contributing to the hair analysis controversy is the commercialization of the hair analysis process initiated when Werner Baumgartner founded the Psychemedics Corporation. Commercialization is a self-interest position and is often seen as being at odds with the need to preserve scientific objectivity. In essence, there is an innuendo that hair analysis has been "rushed to the market," that scientific rigor is compromised as a result, and perhaps even that hair analysis for illicit drugs, like the "nutritional hair analysis" of the 1970s, is a dishonest exploitation of the current concern with drug use.[28]

One must note in this regard that all currently employed urine screens are the products of private, profit-making corporations. Furthermore, Baumgartner has long claimed that, in spite of repeated efforts, he did not receive significant research support for his work from public granting agencies and thus turned to the market in order to sustain his work. Furthermore, Baumgartner has been aggressive in defending his research and publicly disputatious with his critics. The public arena in which this argument has taken place is an unfamiliar one for many scientists, and they are uncomfortable with and often distraught over controversy of this kind.[29] In the limited litigation involving hair analysis, courts have so far upheld the scientific validity of the assay processes.[30]

Advocates of hair analysis argue that a double standard is applied in what constitutes acceptable levels of scientific support for hair analysis in comparison to urine-based drug screens. The complaint is that hair analysis is held to a more stringent standard of proof of its efficacy than urinalysis was during its development and is today, even though the former is in wide use. The most obvious of these biases are the problems associated with hair analysis pertaining to passive contamination and individual biochemical variations. While these are important issues, they are equally a problem for urine-based testing, and no wide argument

28. S. Barrett, "Commercial Hair Analysis: Science or Scam?" *Journal of the American Medical Association*, 254:1041-45 (1985).

29. Kuhn, *Structure of Scientific Revolutions*; Paul Feyerabend, *Against Method* (New York: Schocken Books, 1982).

30. *United States* v. *Medina*, 749 F. Supp. 59 (E.D. N.Y. 1990).

is advanced by scientists for the cessation of urinalysis as a useful tool in identifying drug use. In fact, many of the same objections currently raised against hair analysis were raised at the inception of immunoassay urinalysis in the early 1970s but have ceased to cause much concern as urinalysis has become popular and widely utilized.[31]

In any event, what is the standard needed in order to obtain closure or validation of the analytic process? That no controversy should exist before the technique is used? Controversy, per se, should not be viewed as a negative. Scientific closure is—and will always remain—open-ended for any empirical work. All science should be viewed critically. All scientific principles and technologies are legitimated in degrees and over time and can always be called to task for paradoxes, unique or confounding cases, and the like. Perfect closure, a technology without questions or conundrums of any sort, is an impossibility. Thus questions raised about a scientific procedure should be put forward in a spirit of goodwill and with a sense of responsibility. Much of the sociological controversy associated with hair analysis focuses on the ability and authority to define what constitutes acceptable research data, to define what the consensus of the scientific community is regarding particular technology, and who is enti-

tled—and empowered—to hold a meaningful opinion regarding scientific issues.

Consider, for example, that a criticism frequently raised is that hair analysis has not established minimum dose requirements for its assay. But such data do not exist for urinalysis either. Furthermore, a number of questions raised about hair analysis and possible interpretative complications based on race, gender, and age have not been resolved or in some cases even studied for urinalysis.[32] Passive contamination as a problem for urinalysis has never been definitively resolved. While cutoff levels are the device used in urinalysis to control for the effects of passive contamination, they are arbitrary, clinically and not theoretically derived, often variable in their application from institution to institution, and still controversial today.[33] Positions are taken that urine cutoffs ought to be lower, to reduce false negatives, or higher, to prevent false positives. Yet few scientists advocate abandoning urinalysis testing because there is lack of consensus on cutoff values.

These debates call into question the basic purposes of drug assays and how these purposes affect the issues at hand for those who do clinical testing. Hair analysis has been called to task not because anyone has shown that it is an insensitive test but rather because its sensitivity is unknown since standard references are

31. Robert DuPont, "Comment on SOFT Report on Hair Testing" (Paper, Institute for Health and Behavior, 1991). See also R. Hawks and C. Chiang, *Urine Testing for Drugs of Abuse*, NIDA Research Monograph 73 (Washington, DC: Department of Health and Human Services, 1986).

32. W. Baumgartner, "Hair Analysis for Drugs of Abuse: Obstacles to a Powerful, New Technology" (Paper, Psychemedics Corporation, 1991).

33. A. McBay to Robert Bost, president of the Society of Forensic Toxicologists, 1990.

not available. This is so even though RIA as a urine technology has been shown to be highly sensitive. In a clinical setting, the conception of sensitivity reflects the ability of a test or diagnostic procedure to distinguish and detect status in a real clinical population. This is quite a different set of criteria from those that may be applied in a nonclinical laboratory setting, which may seek only to detect specific reagents whose presence and values do not necessarily correspond to any *in vivo* conditions relevant to a clinician. A review of the published literature supports that hair analysis distinguishes drug-positive hair from drug-negative hair quite readily and is effective in identifying drug-using individuals as distinct from drug-abstaining individuals in real-world settings.[34]

THE SOFT CONSENSUS PAPER AND THE FDA COMPLIANCE POLICY GUIDE

Finally, I shall take up two specific RIAH controversies that illustrate these issues. They are the Society of Forensic Toxicologists (SOFT) consensus paper on hair analysis, developed under the sponsorship of the National Institute on Drug Abuse (NIDA), and the U.S. Food and Drug Administration (FDA) compliance policy guide issued in May of 1990 regarding RIA test kits as "possibly" being used in relation to hair analysis. Both of these serve to illustrate the sociological dynamics involved in legitimating scientific work.

34. DuPont, "Comment on SOFT Report on Hair Testing."

The SOFT paper

In June of 1990, a conference was held under the auspices of SOFT at the request of NIDA. The objective of this conference was to evaluate the utility of hair as a drug-testing medium for purposes of screening for illicit drug exposure, with an emphasis on workplace testing. The session included presentations by nine scientists involved or interested in hair testing and by a federal judge, the Honorable Jack Weinstein, who had ruled in favor of the use of RIAH in court as evidence.[35]

A SOFT committee took the position that the use of hair analysis for employee and preemployment screening is premature and cannot be sustained by current information on hair analysis for drugs of abuse. The committee then went on to list a number of specific problems. The major objections were as follows:

1. There are no generally accepted analytic procedures for hair analysis.
2. There are no data on the accuracy, sensitivity, precision, specificity, or cutoff values for either screening or confirmatory procedures using hair.
3. There is no acceptable reference material to standardize analytic methods for quality assurance programs involving hair assays.

35. *United States* v. *Medina.* RIAH has been sustained by the courts, so far, each time it has been introduced as an evidentiary element. It is currently used for preemployment and employee drug screening and also has been used by several probation, parole, or similar agencies to monitor compliance with court or correctional stipulations.

The committee also raised other objections, which were directed at procedural matters, such as recommending the requirement to do confirmatory testing on any positive hair assay outcome—a policy that Psychemedics and virtually all urine-based testing laboratories follow for all specimens screened as positive. The SOFT paper also made what can best be described as nontechnical observations regarding the technology. These observations were that comparisons based on self-reported data are "anecdotal" and by implication unreliable and that requisite hair-testing technology—such as tandem mass spectrometry—is expensive and requires trained and skilled technicians to operate. The committee also raised the issue of the lack of knowledge on fundamental hair physiology and how that lack might affect the interpretation of test outcomes, although it did not suggest that any research yet exists that confirms these as problematic for hair assays. Finally, the committee suggested that until such fundamental knowledge is in hand, hair testing cannot be accurately interpreted.

The committee, however, in spite of these objections, supported the use of hair analysis for forensic testing "when supported by other evidence of drug use (e.g., urinalysis)" and "when performed under generally accepted guidelines for forensic drug testing." Two final caveats are attached to the report. One is a caution to not take any single item of the report out of context, and a second is that the document was prepared "by a committee from among those panelists participating in the conference discussion.

It does not represent an official position statement endorsed by the Society of Forensic Toxicologists at this time." The specific members of the committee are not identified.[36]

In response to the report, letters were directed to Dr. Robert Bost, president of SOFT. Among the authors were Dr. Werner Baumgartner; Dr. Robert DuPont, former director of the National Institute on Drug Abuse and Psychemedics science adviser; and Dr. Arthur McBay, a SOFT member and a scientific adviser to the Psychemedics Corporation. A number of objections were made to the SOFT report.[37] A summary of them follows:

1. The support of hair analysis for forensic purposes but not employment purposes is puzzling, since forensic use—involving potential loss of liberty and so forth—normally incurs more serious consequences than does preemployment or employment evaluation use. Furthermore, it is hard to understand why RIAH is acceptable in one setting and not another. Related to this is the SOFT recommendation for additional tissue or fluid support—for example, blood,

36. I have received from SOFT an excerpt from their newsletter *TOXTALK*, dated Dec. 1990, which discusses SOFT's involvement in the consensus report. In this excerpt, the panelists who prepared the SOFT report are identified. It also includes a motion made during a SOFT business meeting, but I cannot determine from the motion its exact meaning or intent in reference to the SOFT report.

37. Although the report did not mention Psychemedics by name, Psychemedics is the only laboratory in the country performing the large-scale screening of hair specimens for illicit drugs.

urine—for hair test procedures. The time frames for these media are not comparable to that for hair, so that direct comparisons of these test procedures could not validate or invalidate hair testing, and it is unspecified how the use of these additional media would clarify the outcome of hair analysis.

2. No laboratory site inspection or review of records of the Psychemedics Corporation or any other hair analysis facility took place prior to issuing the consensus report. Nor did the committee discuss, apparently, any delay in writing the report until such a visit could be made.

3. Historically, hair analysis has been used in forensic investigations without support from other tissues and has often been performed on single specimens. Indeed, research clearly demonstrates that GC/MS can identify some illicit drugs in a single strand of human hair.[38] The lack of multiple test media does not support an a priori rejection of the hair test results. This issue is not reconciled with the recommendation contained within the consensus report.

4. Preparation of "acceptable reference materials" is an unclear criticism in the report's context. Giving humans controlled doses of toxic substances, such as cocaine or amphetamine, in order to prepare reference materials is ethically unacceptable. Therefore, alternative methods—use of animal models, reliance on self-reported drug use or abstinence, artificially spiking samples to mimic consumption—are defensible and are used in quality-control and experimental designs. What would constitute acceptable suitable references is not specified in the SOFT report. Reference materials for urine are prepared by simply adding known quantities of drugs to samples of urine. Reference materials for hair cannot be prepared in this manner, since the required deposition of the drug must be in the interior of the hair. Furthermore, current work is ongoing to develop surrogate reference-production techniques. The National Institute of Justice has contracted with the National Institute for Standards and Testing to create standardized references for hair analysis laboratories.

5. The objections raised regarding the unknown sensitivity and precision of hair analysis are equally applicable to urine testing, yet urine testing is widely accepted while hair analysis is not. McBay for example, states that "the accuracy, precision, sensitivity, specificity, or appropriate cutoffs that define potentially false or negative results for either screening or confirmatory methods that are used for urine testing are questionable."[39] In general, the consensus report does not, in this regard, distinguish between problems that are universally true of all drug screen assays and those that may be specific to hair. As recently noted by the National Institute of Justice in discussing urinalysis, "Little research is available to guide the criminal justice community on how much of a given drug should be in the urine sample before the specimen can be declared positive."[40]

38. Suzuki, Hattori, and Asano, "Detection of Amphetamine and Meth-Amphetamine."

39. McBay to Bost.

40. C. Visher and K. McFadden, "A Comparison of Urinalysis Technologies for Drug

*The FDA compliance
    policy guide*

On 31 May 1990, the federal Food and Drug Administration issued a compliance policy guide entitled *RIA Analysis of Hair to Detect the Presence of Drugs of Abuse.* The FDA's stated motive for producing this guide, in which it expresses an opinion on the use of devices or materials appropriately regulated by the agency, cited the "growing interest in testing for drugs of abuse." Reagents and devices used for such testing are under regulation by the agency. The guide states that the "FDA is concerned that businesses may begin distributing kits for which efficacy has not been established for the purposes of testing hair for the presence of drugs of abuse." It further states that "over the past several years a number of experts, including FDA scientists, have reviewed published literature on RIA hair analysis for drugs of abuse and have concluded that the test is unproven." The guide then concludes by stating that "it is the FDA's view that RIA hair analysis for the presence of drugs of abuse is an unproven procedure unsupported by the scientific literature or well-controlled studies or clinical trials. The consensus of scientific opinion is that hair analysis by RIA for the presence of drugs of abuse is unreliable and is not generally recognized by qualified experts as effective." The guide mentions that it does not refer to GC/MS testing of hair specimens but only to RIA technology.

A review of the guide is revealing, especially in light of its claims that there is no scientific evidence to support RIAH and that the "consensus of scientific opinion" is that RIAH is ineffective. The guide includes a bibliography citing the scientific support for the FDA's position. The bibliography comprises eight publications. Of these eight, three have absolutely no relation to the use of RIA in hair testing nor do they have any relation to drugs of abuse in hair or other test media. They are instead research reports on trace metal analysis in hair, or keratin chemistry. Of the five remaining references, one is a book chapter by Harkey and Henderson that reports no research data but rather is a synopsis of existing research through 1988 and is essentially a brief version of an extensive report prepared by Henderson-Harkey, Inc., for the state of California evaluating RIAH.[41] The chapter, as well as the report, gives tentative validity to hair analysis, with much qualification about the need to do further research. It would be difficult to argue that the Harkey and Henderson chapter is consonant with the FDA statement that the procedure is "unreliable and ineffective." The four remaining references included in the guide's bibliography all support the effectiveness of RIAH.

It is very hard to understand how the offering of these references could in any way be seen as supportive of the conclusions that the guide has reached. Furthermore, although there are now more than seventy published

41. Harkey and Henderson, "Hair Analysis for Drugs of Abuse: A Critical Review of the Technology."

reports on RIAH and the efficacy of hair analysis, seven of the eight references used in the FDA guide's bibliography are more than eight years old. The only reference more recent than 1983 is the Harkey and Henderson chapter. Since the compliance policy guide was issued prior to the SOFT conference by several months, the FDA cannot derive its claim of the "consensus of scientific opinion" from the SOFT document. It is difficult to understand why the FDA, given this feeble documentation, made an effort to express an opinion so poorly supported.

The Psychemedics Corporation challenged the compliance guide and, in efforts to clarify and modify the content, initiated a dialogue with the FDA. The FDA took the position that it was not directing this guide at Psychemedics but only at the possibility that "businesses may begin distributing kits for which efficacy has not been established for the purposes of testing hair for the presence of drugs of abuse." The agency went on to state that the guide was "not directed at any clinical reference laboratory whose sole responsibility is to provide a service through the use of a previously manufactured device."[42] The ensuing dialogue between the FDA and Psychemedics then centered around the issue of exactly what aspects of RIAH the FDA considered unproven, whether it was the development or provision of RIAH

"kits" or whether it was the basic RIAH technology.

As of the writing of the present article, the issue is not yet resolved. The FDA has, to date, refused to modify its wording of the compliance guide. It has, however, received requests from legislators in the Congress to reconsider and report the outcome of those reconsiderations. Although Psychemedics is, to some degree, satisfied that the FDA has clarified its position regarding laboratories performing hair analysis, it continues to be concerned that the wording of the document and the breadth of its claims are unbalanced and damaging to the interests of RIAH technology in general and the corporation in particular.

It is hard to understand why the FDA produced this guide. Why did it use such a series of dated and inappropriate sources of support, and why did it express such a broad range of opinions on the technology if its sole concern was with the unregulated marketing of test kits? Since Psychemedics has never attempted to market an RIAH test kit—or even contemplated such a move—no overt or even planned entry of these devices into the marketplace could serve as the motivation for the FDA. The FDA action is very perplexing in view of the scientific evidence supporting the fundamental utility of RIA for detecting drugs in both urine and hair. This evidence is very well established.

42. U.S., Department of Health and Human Services, Food and Drug Administration, *RIA Analysis of Hair to Detect the Presence of Drugs of Abuse*, FDA Compliance Policy Guide no. 7124.06, 1990.

SUMMARY

It is important to recognize, when considering the FDA issue, that historically the federal government does not have a strong record of being in a leadership role in recognizing and regulating drug-testing technology. Former NIDA director and Psychemedics adviser Dr. Robert DuPont has stated:

Urine testing was widely used in practice for many years before NIDA certified the first laboratory or had any governmental standards for urine testing. Practice far preceded regulatory activities for urine testing in the workplace. Hair testing today has an enormous advantage over urine testing a decade ago because hair testing can use the same basic standards, and the modern drug-testing system, that is now commonplace for urine testing.... The same evolution is now taking place for hair testing that took place a decade ago for urine testing. It is proceeding based on sound research into hair testing and on the experience with urine testing. The everyday practice of hair testing in the workplace is now far ahead of the skeptics.[43]

Hair testing is a useful tool in studying drug epidemiology. To some degree, it has been negatively affected by various problems and controversies having little to do with the scientific merit of the technique. What needs to be done now is to move the technology forward with a comprehensive research program that will focus on two major themes. The first is basic research into fundamental physiological processes of hair formation and how the substances of interest are incorporated and retained in hair. This track represents a continuation of an already existing body of basic scientific work. This

43. DuPont, "Comment on SOFT Report on Hair Testing."

work should be continued because it will provide the requisite information for the interpretation of hair assays, regardless of the particular assay technique employed. Such research can also clarify the type of relationship that exists between dosage and assay levels in the hair.

A second research area, which needs support and has largely been neglected, is the development of a large epidemiological data base. Large-scale testing of select populations under anonymous and confidential circumstances needs to be done. These populations should include general population groups for the purposes of establishing statistical baselines, groups in drug treatment, and special groups such as drug-involved criminal offenders, populations released under court stipulations, and, certainly, occupational groups that have a bona fide need for scrupulous drug control, such as airline pilots. It is in this area of research that there is the least support currently. Without the establishment of a large epidemiological reference, proper framing of hair analysis outcomes is not possible. Even interpretation of the laboratory findings of basic research depends on this type of data as interpretive controls. Additionally, there is no reason why, as these large-scale epidemiological base populations are studied, they cannot also serve as pragmatic demonstrations of the implementation of a hair-testing protocol for practical application. Indeed, some such data that have been gathered in precisely this fashion already exist; however, their quantity is currently small. Also, a number of scientific issues could be evaluated in field settings that provide a natural-experiment context. For example, clients entering methadone treatment could be hair monitored to evaluate the appearance of methadone in the hair under controlled dosage conditions. Similar work could be done with clients entering treatment who are abstaining from drug use. The rate and degree of illicit-substance disappearance from the hair would be useful research data, and such a project could be readily carried out in current drug treatment settings. The ability to determine with high reliability relatively long-term retrospective drug use has many benefits for epidemiology and can prove useful in a variety of investigative settings, including the medical community, the drug treatment community, and the criminal justice system.

In effect, many of the questions surrounding hair analysis could be addressed and answered, and the useful properties of the process clearly determined. It is time to direct our research energies toward solving the remaining puzzles and answering the interesting questions that the existing work has posed. Hair analysis has much to offer.

ANNALS, *AAPSS,* **521,** May 1992

The Limits and Consequences of U.S. Foreign Drug Control Efforts

By PETER REUTER

ABSTRACT: Efforts to reduce cocaine production and exports from the Andean region continue to be an important component of U.S. drug control efforts. This article presents a simple economic analysis of the effects of major source-country control programs: eradication, crop substitution, and refinery destruction. When account is taken of the structure of prices in the cocaine industry and the ability of farmers and refiners to make behavioral adaptations, none of these programs has much prospect for affecting the flow of cocaine to the United States. Despite the continued failure of the programs and the analytic arguments against them, they continue to flourish budgetarily; they are protected by the rhetorical claims of the past, the need to appear to have a complete portfolio of programs, and the sheer momentum of drug control expenditures.

Peter Reuter is senior economist in the Washington office of RAND and codirector of RAND's Drug Policy Research Center. He earned his Ph.D. in economics at Yale University. His initial research dealt with the organization of criminal activities, resulting in the publication of Disorganized Crime: The Economics of the Visible Hand *(1983). His recent RAND publications include* Sealing the Borders, *a study of the effects of increased interdiction, and* Money from Crime: A Study of the Economics of Drug Dealing in Washington, D.C. *His current research focuses on European drug policies.*

NOTE: Support for the preparation of this article was provided by the Ford and Weingart foundations through grants to RAND's Drug Policy Research Center.

FOR twenty years, programs aimed at reducing the production and export of illicit drugs in foreign countries have played a major role in the rhetoric of drug control policy in the United States, though they have never accounted for much more than 5 percent of total federal drug control expenditures. Since 1970, drug control has often been the dominant issue in U.S. relationships with the Andean region and, at times, with Mexico, Pakistan, and Turkey.

The effort to control drug production overseas has generally been viewed as ineffective and perhaps even counterproductive, both for the producing nations and for U.S. diplomacy. Certainly, drug production in the traditional source countries has grown apace, notwithstanding increased funding for drug control provided by the United States and Western Europe to those nations. Mexico, the most cooperative of the source countries, continues to produce record amounts of heroin and marijuana, while Asian opium production grows by leaps and bounds.[1] The production and export of cocaine from the Andean region, the primary focus of concern throughout the 1980s, seems to continue almost unabated into the early 1990s. The decline following the August 1989 Colombian government crackdown against the Medellin cartel, precipitated by the cartel's assassination of the leading presidential candidate, turned out to provide only a brief hiatus. In part, this reflects the fact that the crack-down was intended to diminish the threat of the cartel to government authority rather than to reduce cocaine production.

U.S. pressures for source-country governments to act aggressively against the cocaine industry can be counterproductive if they raise hostility to the central government. That has been a particular concern in Peru, where the Sendero Luminoso guerrillas have been able to establish themselves as an alternative authority in the major coca-growing area.

Pessimism about source-country control programs, as they are generally known, is fairly widespread.[2] Indeed, outside of official documents it is difficult to find the slightest sign of optimism. But much of the pessimism reflects the failure of the United States to persuade the governments of the major cocaine and opium producers to attempt serious implementation of production controls. For both political and economic reasons, though mostly the former, these governments have been reluctant to take action against an industry that has become regionally, and sometimes nationally, important. The belief—usually implicit—of program advocates is that, if the producer governments could be persuaded to properly implement con-

---

1. National Narcotics Intelligence Consumers Committee, *Narcotics Intelligence Estimate*, (Washington, DC: Department of Justice, Drug Enforcement Administration, 1990).

2. Among recent prominent statements of this pessimism are Bruce Bagley, "Colombia and the War on Drugs," *Foreign Affairs* (Fall 1988); Rensselaer Lee, "Why the U.S. Cannot Stop South American Cocaine," *ORBIS* (Fall 1988). For a more complex view, see *Seizing Opportunities: Report of the Inter-American Commission on Drug Policy* (San Diego: University of California, Institute of the Americas and the Center for Iberian and Latin American Studies, 1991).

trol efforts, substantial reductions in the production of illegal drugs would result.

The argument of this article goes beyond that, at least for Andean cocaine production.[3] It suggests that the failure of source-country control may lie not so much in the difficulties of program implementation as in the basic structure of the drug industry. It seems unlikely that eradication, crop substitution, or any related effort aimed directly at coca growing and cocaine refining in Peru, Bolivia, and Colombia will make a significant difference to total Andean cocaine production, though it may affect the distribution of cocaine production among these countries.

The next section presents a framework for analysis of source-country control efforts. This is followed by a description and assessment of the kinds of programs that have been used to control drug production and exports in the Andean region. The final section discusses, in a highly speculative manner, the issue of why, in the face of the continuing lack of success and the increasing awareness of the systemic nature of that failure, source-country control programs continue to play a major role in the rhetoric of drug policy.

ANALYTIC FRAMEWORK: RISKS AND PRICES

The analysis here uses an approach that can be labeled "risks and

prices."[4] Its basic assumption is that supply-side programs focusing on parts of the distribution system distant from the consumer can only affect the price paid by the consumer. Such programs cannot restrict the physical availability of cocaine in the United States. There are simply too many farmers, refiners, exporters, and smugglers for enforcement to directly limit the amount available for U.S. consumption to, say, 100 tons per annum. The question, then, is how the international programs affect the risks and other costs of drug suppliers and how that, in turn, will affect retail prices in the United States.

Each kind of supply-side program —except for enforcement against retail markets[5]—directly affects a particular sector of the cocaine production and distribution system. For example, crop eradication raises the risks and costs faced by farmers; that should be reflected in the prices that refiners have to pay for leaf in order

3. The conclusions of this article are close to those of an earlier analysis that dealt primarily with opium control. See Peter Reuter, "Eternal Hope: America's Quest for Narcotics Control," *Public Interest* (Spring 1985).

4. A detailed account of this approach is given in Peter Reuter and Mark Kleiman, "Risks and Prices: An Economic Analysis of Drug Enforcement," in *Crime and Justice: An Annual Review of Research*, vol. 7, ed. Michael Tonry and Norval Morris (Chicago: University of Chicago Press, 1986). For refinements, see Jonathan Cave and Peter Reuter, *The Interdictor's Lot: A Dynamic Model of the Market for Drug Smuggling Services* (Santa Monica, CA: RAND, 1988); Mark Kleiman and Kerry Smith, "State and Local Drug Enforcement," in *Drugs and Crime*, ed. Michael Tonry and James Wilson (Chicago: University of Chicago Press, 1990).

5. The distinctive feature of enforcement against the retail transaction is that it imposes costs directly on the customer, not reflected in the price that is paid to the dealer. See Mark Moore, "Achieving Discrimination in the Effective Price of Heroin," *American Economic Review*, vol. 63 (May 1973).

to induce farmers to stay in the business. Refinery destruction, by raising the risks and costs of refiners, should increase the difference between the price refiners pay for leaf and the price they receive from exporters when they sell the refined product. Similarly, interdiction raises the risks and costs of smugglers and should increase the difference between import and export prices. Programs may have indirect effects on other sectors,[6] but the primary effect is sector specific.

The important consequence is the induced change not in returns received by participants at different points in the distribution and production system but in the final price paid by consumers. As the price of smuggling services rises, it is reasonable to assume that there will be an increase in the retail price of the drug. Though that may have a slight effect in the short run on consumption by addicted users, it may have a more substantial long-term effect by reducing the rate at which new users become heavy users, just as the effect of increases in cigarette taxes shows up primarily in reduced teenage smoking rates.[7]

6. For example, interdiction may affect the price of leaf. Interdiction raises both retail prices, reducing final demand, and the amount of leaf needed for a given final demand, because it raises the amount of cocaine shipped per kilogram consumed. The second effect is likely to outweigh the first under most assumptions about the relevant parameters. See Peter Reuter, Gordon Crawford, and Jonathan Cave, *Sealing the Borders: The Effect of Increased Military Involvement in Drug Interdiction* (Santa Monica, CA: RAND, 1988).

7. See Eugene Lewit and Douglas Coate, "The Potential for Using Excise Taxes to Reduce Smoking," *Journal of Health Economics*, vol. 1 (1982).

We assume that price increases at one stage of the production or distribution are passed on essentially additively; for example, an increase of $1000 in the landed price of cocaine will raise the final price by $1000 plus a modest amount representing increased inventory and risk-associated costs for those downstream. In effect, the assumption is of competition in each phase of distribution, with the markup determined not as a percentage of the purchase price but by the risks and other costs of operating at that level of the market. Caulkins presents an alternative model in which the price increases are multiplicative; for example, a 10 percent increase in the landed price of cocaine will generate roughly a 10 percent rise in the retail price.[8] Though Caulkins produces suggestive evidence of proportionality in historical prices within the United States, the model's assumptions about distributor behavior are counterintuitive and the evidence is not persuasive with respect to leaf and export prices.

Prices

An analysis of the price of cocaine at different points of the production and distribution system suggests the inherent limits of international programs, particularly those that focus on the farm sector. Table 1 presents the price chain for 1988, the most recent year for which I have prepared this analysis. The figures are very

8. Jonathan Caulkins, "The Distribution and Consumption of Illicit Drugs: Mathematical Models and Their Policy Implications" (Ph.D. diss., Massachusetts Institute of Technology, 1990).

TABLE 1

COCAINE PRICES THROUGH THE DISTRIBUTION CHAIN, 1988
(Per pure kilogram equivalent)

At the farm	$ 750
Export (Colombia)	$ 2,000
Import (Miami)	$ 15,000
Wholesale (1 kilogram in Detroit)	$ 23,000
Ounce (Detroit)	$ 47,000
Retail (1-gram units)	$135,000

SOURCE: U.S. Department of Justice, Drug Enforcement Administration.

rough; for example, the price of leaf required to produce a kilogram of cocaine may be anywhere between $500 and $1500.[9] Nonetheless, three points are very clear and not likely to be affected by any measurement problems. Certainly, they have been true for other years in which these price chains have been estimated.

First, leaf production accounts for an absolutely trivial share of the final price of cocaine to U.S. consumers, probably much less than 1 percent of that price. Second, even by the time the cocaine reaches the point of export, the price is still less than 5 percent, indeed perhaps only 2 percent, of the retail price. Third, smuggling costs—including the profits of smugglers—account for less than 10 percent of the retail price. Most of the cost of getting drugs to users is accounted for by payments to dealers near the end of the distribution system, probably because they bear most of the risks, both from the criminal justice system and from competitors.[10] Only if international pro-

grams can dramatically increase the risks and costs of these upstream components of the cocaine industry will they be able to make a difference in the United States. The following sections suggest why such a difference is unlikely to be attained.

SOURCE-COUNTRY PROGRAMS

It is useful to start by examining why cocaine consumed in the United States is both grown and refined in the Andes rather than in the United States. Ecological factors may be taken as of minor importance, given that, contrary to popular myth, coca can be grown in a variety of climatic and agricultural conditions; the primary source of coca for the legal markets of the late nineteenth century were commercial plantations in Java,[11] and the U.S. government grew coca in Florida, for medicinal purposes, during World War II.[12]

9. The range represents in part the enormous variation in leaf prices. In the Cochabamba region of Bolivia, since 1986, the range within a year has been at least 1 to 5.

10. The explanation for this observation probably lies in the fact that low-level dealers

have to spread their risks over a small quantity of cocaine relative to that over which smugglers and high-level dealers spread their risk. Hence the markup per gram, in absolute dollars, will be highest at the low end of the trade.

11. Richard Ashley, *Cocaine: Its History, Uses and Effects* (New York: Warner Books, 1975).

12. Ronald Siegel, personal communication, 1990.

Two elements probably explain the location of production. First, the factors involved in production and refining are relatively cheap in the Andes. For example, Bolivian farmers charge very little for their labor, compared to charges by their American counterparts; Greenfield cites a daily wage of about $3.50 in the Chapare in 1988, probably less than the hourly wage of most U.S. farm labor. Their alternative earnings opportunities are very weak. Greenfield also notes that coca growing is labor intensive; labor costs account for about 75 percent of first-year costs.[13]

Second, the risks imposed by source-country governments are very modest. Farmers face little risk of having their crops destroyed; eradication, excluding so-called set-aside purchases by the Bolivian government, has never reached even as high as 5 percent of coca cultivation in any of the Andean countries. Refiners and distributors face even less risk of going to prison, though in-country seizures of refined drugs have gone up substantially. Despite concerns that convicted drug dealers face too slight a prospect of prison time in the United States, dealer risks of incarceration are almost certainly much higher here than are grower, refiner, or distributor risks in the Andes. A combination of corruption, intimidation, and indifference explains the lack of stringency in enforcement against the bulk of those involved in drug production. Coca fields in the United

States would face substantial risks from crop-eradication efforts.

Programs aimed at reducing Andean exports of cocaine to the United States can be divided according to which participant they target: farmer, refiner, or trafficker. Each has distinctive limitations; space limitations permit analysis here only of the first two.

The farm sector

The programs aimed at coca farmers included the coercive—eradication—and the persuasive, in the form of crop substitution and land retirement. I eschew description of program details[14] and focus on the evidence as to their effectiveness.

Eradication. Throughout the 1980s the primary goal of the Bureau of International Narcotics Matters of the U.S. State Department was to induce the source countries to accept the necessity of eradication programs. Despite these efforts, none of the Andean countries has permitted the spraying of coca fields, and the U.S. government in 1991 seems to have lowered its emphasis on this program.

Could farmer costs be greatly increased through eradication? The experiences of the few intense eradication programs do not justify much optimism. Mexican opium growers were subject to an effective aerial eradication effort in the mid-1970s. At the time, they were growing their

13. Victoria Greenfield, "Bolivian Coca: A Perennial Leaf Crop Subject to Supply Reduction" (Ph.D. diss., University of California, Berkeley, 1991).

14. Little detailed research is available on these programs. See Rensselaer Lee, *White Labyrinth: Cocaine and Political Power* (New Brunswick, NJ: Transaction, 1989).

poppies in large, open, and accessible fields, in a relatively compact three-province area.[15] Aided by a lengthy and severe drought, the program was initially successful and reduced the Mexican production of opium, all of which was destined for the U.S. heroin market. Since the distribution channels from other production sources could not readily expand, this had a significant impact on American heroin consumption. Note that Mexico accounted for no more than 5 percent of world opium production.

Within five years, though, the Mexican industry had reestablished itself, with smaller fields, located in more remote areas that were better protected from aerial spraying. Opium growing had also now spread well beyond the original three northern provinces. Indeed, by the late 1980s substantial production was occurring over the southern Mexican border, in Guatemala. Though Mexican opium farmers had higher production costs than their Asian counterparts—with 1988 farmgate prices of $4000 per kilo, compared to $1000 in Burma—this does not seem to have led to any significant increase in the price of U.S. heroin. The production-cost difference was more than counterbalanced by lower international transportation costs.

More successful has been the eradication program aimed at American marijuana producers. These growers have adapted to the increasing intensity of the domestic eradication ef-

fort, moving their plants indoors, thus lowering their exposure, and using better growing techniques to increase per acre yields. But farmgate prices, even adjusted for higher delta-9-tetrahydrocannabinol (THC) content and inflation, have risen, perhaps substantially.[16] The growers may have been pushed to the margin of technological feasibility.

These experiences suggest the likely effects of a sustained and intense eradication campaign against the coca industry. Very exposed areas such as the Upper Huallaga Valley in Peru or the Chapare region of Bolivia, where coca is grown in large open fields, may essentially be eliminated from coca growing. More will be grown in areas, such as the Amazonian jungle, in which eradication is much more expensive and difficult. No doubt the leaf price will rise as farmers have to use less productive land, choose varieties of leaf with lower content of the desired alkaloid, spend more time getting the leaf to refiners, and so forth. It seems highly unlikely, however, that it will rise enough to increase U.S. cocaine prices noticeably. A tripling of the leaf price, so that $2250 was needed to purchase the leaf for a kilogram of cocaine, would still increase cocaine prices in the United States by less than 2 percent.

It is of interest to consider whether coca eradication could produce the

---

15. For details about this early period, see Richard Craig, "Operation Condor: Mexico's Anti-Drug Campaign Enters a New Era," *Journal of Interamerican Studies and World Affairs* (Aug. 1980).

16. Published reports of the Drug Enforcement Administration point to only modest increases in potency-adjusted prices in recent years. Anecdotal evidence suggests that the official prices now substantially understate actual prices; there are also reports of bouts of scarcity in various cities.

medium-term disruption in U.S. markets achieved by the Mexican program. Two differences seem important. First, a good deal of coca is grown for markets other than the United States; big cuts in production would lead to less use of coca products in the source countries rather than in the United States, since demand there is more sensitive to leaf-price changes. If reports from Brazil and Colombia about local consumption of refined products there are correct, then that may be a substantial quantity.[17] The rising share of Latin cocaine product apparently destined for European markets also presents a potential buffer for U.S. consumers.[18] In contrast, there was never evidence of significant Mexican heroin or opium consumption. Second, production is more dispersed, making it more difficult to eliminate most of it in a short period of time. A preemptive strike against the exposed areas is unlikely to cause disruption comparable to that achieved in Mexico in the mid-1970s. As just suggested, the development of jungle production in Brazil, where the plants are under a triple jungle canopy, adds to the difficulty now faced by the eradicators.

Crop substitution. Faced by the daunting political realities of programs that deprive large numbers of peasants of their livelihood, the Andean governments have chosen in recent years to stress noncoercive programs to persuade farmers to shift from coca to legitimate crops. These programs, called crop substitution, also have the attraction of generating additional funds from donor countries; Bolivia has been particularly effective in attracting these funds.[19]

Evidence on the effectiveness of crop-substitution programs is slender but discouraging. These programs have been tried for almost twenty years, mostly under the auspices of the United Nations Fund for Drug Abuse Control (UNFDAC). Most of the programs have been hampered by adverse operational conditions; for example, the relatively promising UNFDAC efforts aimed at Afghanistani opium production in the late 1970s came to an end when the central government lost control over the growing areas following the Soviet-led coup in Kabul. Only in Thailand have the programs claimed much success, and the rapid increase in Burmese production, serving the Thai heroin market at lower cost, probably explains the decline in indigenous opium production.

Analysis also suggests that crop-substitution programs offer no more long-term promise than does eradication as a method for reducing the flow of cocaine to the United States. The

17. This assumes that Brazilian and Colombian demand is more elastic than U.S. demand with respect to leaf price. The demand curves may be the same, but the retail price is more sensitive to leaf price in countries where dealer risks are low.

18. European border seizures of cocaine exceeded 12 tons in 1990, comparable to the 1983 levels in the United States. Yet data on European cocaine consumption point to a market that is still quite small.

19. See, for example, *National Strategy for Alternative Development, 1990,* an English-language document produced by the Presidency of the Republic of Bolivia. It argues for large infusions of capital from overseas.

programs assume that, through provision of improved infrastructure, subsidized fertilization or irrigation, and perhaps even price supports, legitimate crops can be made attractive to the peasant farmers who are currently growing coca leaf.[20] That in turn assumes that the price of coca leaf will stay fixed. But the elasticity of demand for cocaine in the United States with respect to the price of leaf in Bolivia is essentially zero, that is, a rise in leaf price will have almost no effect on U.S. consumption.[21] Cocaine refiners will be willing to pay very much more for coca leaf if they need to, and they will be able to fully pass on that increase to U.S. consumers with only negligible reduction in consumption. Peasant farmers will be better off with substitution programs that improve their productivity, but the flow of cocaine will be only very slightly diminished.[22]

Land buy-out. The Bolivian government has implemented a hybrid program, offering to pay coca farmers for taking land out of coca production. The price per hectare was set at $2000, and in 1990 for the first time a significant number of hectares were indeed taken out of production.

There are two weaknesses to this program. First, the effect of the program is to set a floor on the earnings of coca farmers. If the return from coca falls low enough, then $2000 becomes an attractive price for a hectare. In effect, the risks of putting land into coca cultivation are reduced, with the promise of a $2000 minimum payback. The second problem arises from the fact that the coca plant has a long productive lifetime but has lower yields after the tenth, perhaps even the seventh year.[23] At some point, the coca plant's yield falls to a level that makes the $2000 payment attractive. Spedding states that "most of the fields offered for eradication are already choked by weeds or too old to be of any value."[24]

In principle, both problems are soluble. The program could be restricted to land in coca cultivation before a certain date, thus not affecting incentives for new cultivation. The second problem could be eliminated by a similar limitation on the age of the plants eligible for purchase. These solutions, however, require that the government can create a register of coca lands and keep track of plant age. Without the cooperation of the peasantry, which is well organized in Bolivia to resist undesired government intrusions, neither is feasible.

20. These programs can have perverse effects. Sanabria claims that the introduction of a road into the Cochabamba region, intended to facilitate the marketing of legal produce, instead helped provide cocaine traffickers with a landing strip for their small planes. H. Sanabria, "Social and Economic Change in a Bolivian Highland Valley Peasant Community: The Impact of Migration and Coca" (Ph.D. diss., University of Wisconsin, Madison, 1989), cited in Greenfield, *Bolivian Coca*.

21. Even if U.S. demand for cocaine is elastic with respect to retail price, that price is very insensitive to changes in leaf price.

22. Note, though, that such programs may affect where coca is grown in the Andean region. A successful crop-substitution program in Bolivia would raise the price of coca in Bolivia and motivate refiners in Colombia to purchase more leaf in Peru.

23. Greenfield, *Bolivian Coca*.

24. A. L. Spedding, "Coca Eradication, A Remedy for Independence?—With a Postscript," *Anthropology Today*, 5(5) (Oct. 1989).

Refinery destruction

Since the mid-1980s, as the limitations of crop eradication have become more obvious, the U.S. government has promoted programs aimed at the destruction of cocaine refineries. Thus the U.S. Army, at the invitation of the Bolivian government, sent in troops and equipment in the summer of 1986 to assist Bolivian military and police units in eliminating local refineries in what was called Operation Blast Furnace. The U.S. government also regularly reports the number of refineries destroyed in source and transshipment countries.[25]

The rationale for these programs is that they will lower the demand for illicit leaf, by raising refiners' costs and eliminating refining capacity, and thus lower leaf price. With a lower leaf price, peasants will have less incentive to grow coca. At the same time, these programs have the considerable attraction of not imposing direct costs on peasant farmers. Thus they generate less political unrest.

Alas, there is again less to this than meets the eye. Cocaine refineries are not like oil-refining plants; they need involve no significant capital plant, frequently being constituted instead of very simple equipment, located in a primitive shack. This was the kind of facility turned up by Blast Furnace. They are easily and cheaply replaced. Refinery destruction is probably little more than the elimination of a specific location for a short period of time.

The official enthusiasm for refinery destruction bears some similarity to the American military attitude toward the destruction of Vietcong "arms factories" in the early 1960s; these factories were in fact very ad hoc and temporary structures, using indigenous and scrap materials to fabricate primitive light weaponry. Neil Sheehan, in his recent book on the Vietnam war, notes that U.S. field officers had "the impression that the words 'Viet Cong hamlet' and 'VC arms factory' conjured up in [the general's] mind World War II images of a German barracks and a munitions plant."[26] Some major cocaine refineries have been found, with true barracks and landing fields, but forcing refiners to be more covert offers no prospect for raising refining costs to a noticeably higher share of the retail price, given that small refiners do successfully compete in the industry currently.

Operation Blast Furnace is a case in point. The immediate effect of the operation was indeed a decline in leaf price; according to press reports, leaf price fell by 70 percent. However, consistent with rapid restoration of refining capacity, leaf price had risen to almost 90 percent of its earlier level six months after the completion of Blast Furnace.

Refiner margins are very small, perhaps no more than $1000 per kilogram. Assume that a refinery-destruction program was so successful that refiners had to process two kilos of leaf for every one that made

25. See the annual *International Narcotics Control Strategy Report*.

26. Neil Sheehan, *A Bright Shining Lie: John Paul Vann and America in Vietnam* (New York: Random House, 1989).

it to the point of export. Even with generous assumptions about risk aversion, that might raise the refining margin from $1000 to $4000. The same logic that points to the low probability of being able to achieve major increases in retail prices through raising leaf-production costs applies here as well.

CONCLUSION

Source-country programs, whether they be crop eradication, crop substitution, or refinery destruction, hold negligible prospects for reducing American cocaine consumption in the long run. This conclusion does not rest on the well-known frailties of the source-country governments, particularly that of Peru. Even if the Peruvian government were less corrupt, more stable, and more efficient, an intense eradication program is likely, at best, to cause a short-term interruption in the flow of cocaine to the United States. Forcing farmers to plant in smaller and less accessible fields would make a negligible difference to the U.S. consumer. Similarly, even if the source-country governments were able to provide the stable local conditions needed for delivery of the services necessary to make alternative crops viable in the major growing regions, it would not reduce the availability of coca leaf to refiners. Crop-substitution programs involve, in effect, a bidding war between the government on one hand and cocaine refiners on the other; even if refiners have to raise the price they pay for leaf by 200 percent to persuade a sufficient number of farmers to continue to raise coca, total U.S. demand

will be negligibly affected. The same analysis applies to programs that reduce barriers for a source country's legitimate products in the United States;[27] these are likely to do no more than redistribute coca production among the source countries.

Why do these programs continue to generate political support? The programs have demonstrably failed in the past. The arguments presented here have acquired broad currency in the debates of recent years.[28] The government of Peru, the primary coca-leaf-producing country, is barely functioning at all. The transfers of U.S. monies to aid farmers who are currently producing drugs that have devastated American cities do not have much popular appeal, particularly when farm programs in the United States are being cut. Yet President Bush's budget for fiscal year 1992 proposes significant increases in the funding of international control programs; from $307 million in fiscal year 1990, they are slated to rise to $612 million in fiscal year 1992.[29]

I suggest that there are three reasons for this continued popularity. First, there is a need to appear to be

27. The Colombian government complained bitterly in 1989 when the United States refused to help improve access for Colombian textile exports at the same time that large quantities of aid were being provided by the United States to assist in fighting the Medellin cartel.

28. See, for example, U.S., Congress, House, Government Operations Committee, *Stopping the Flood of Cocaine with Operation Snowcap: Is it Working?* 101st Cong, 2d sess., 14 Aug. 1990.

29. U.S., Office of National Drug Control Policy, *National Drug Control Strategy*, 1991, p. 140.

doing something about every aspect of the drug problem. Even if all the evidence and analysis points to the inefficacy of these programs, Congress and President Bush cannot readily abandon the rhetoric of two decades, unless alternative methods for source-country control can be found. But that explains only why the programs continue, not why they grow. Here I think we need to look at the dynamics of program budgets: a rising budgetary tide lifts all boats. The expansion of drug control expenditures at the federal level has raised spending on all these programs, the successful and the unsuccessful alike.

Second, foreign initiatives have a peculiar attraction for presidents. They provide opportunities for highly visible meetings in which the president is not merely a politician, allocating money to bureaucrats, but the leader of the nation taking responsible action in the world as a whole. Even now, the amounts being spent in the Andes constitute only a modest share of the federal drug control budget. For a few hundred million dollars, the president achieves a prominence that few domestic programs of similar size can provide.

Third, the possibility of success cannot absolutely be ruled out. The success of the Mexican opium spraying program, even though 15 years old, still lives as a vivid example of what can happen under the right conditions. Little enough analytic attention has been given to these issues that any proponent of source-country control efforts can bring up that success as evidence for the merit of continued overseas efforts. Opponents cannot readily find analyses that point to the special conditions distinguishing that case from the ones currently being considered.

Moreover, these programs do have real effects, even if not usually on U.S. drug consumption. They can have substantial impact on the source countries themselves. Crop-eradication programs may increase the power of guerrilla movements by increasing peasant hostility toward the central government; that is of particular importance in Peru. Crop-substitution programs, on the other hand, may help the central government increase its authority. Given that these programs seem likely to be an enduring part of U.S. foreign policy, and unlikely to help the United States, primary attention should be focused on choosing programs that do the least harm overseas.

ANNALS, *AAPSS*, **521**, May 1992

Heroin Policy for the Next Decade

By MARK A. R. KLEIMAN and JONATHAN P. CAULKINS

ABSTRACT: The supply of heroin in the United States appears to have grown substantially in recent years, although it is not clear what impact this has had on consumption. Conventional indicators have shown only modest increases, but for a variety of reasons one would not expect increases even if we are in the early years of a new heroin use epidemic. It is even less clear what, if anything, should be done. Drug control resources are finite. Making heroin a new policy focus may impose substantial opportunity costs as resources are diverted from other worthy programs. On the other hand, the history of cocaine in the late 1970s and early 1980s demonstrates that "wait and see" can be an extremely expensive option. A prudent course may be to implement relatively low-cost interventions that one would not regret undertaking even if a new epidemic never materialized and to enhance monitoring. If these enhanced monitoring programs gave strong signs of increasing use, particularly by new users, bolder interventions might be warranted.

Mark A. R. Kleiman is associate professor of public policy at the John F. Kennedy School of Government, Harvard University. His most recent book is Against Excess: Drug Policy for Results.

Jonathan P. Caulkins received his Ph.D. in operations research from the Massachusetts Institute of Technology and is assistant professor of operations research and public policy at Carnegie Mellon University's School of Urban and Public Affairs. His research focuses on mathematical models of illicit drug markets and drug policy.

BY several measures, the supply of heroin to the U.S. market has been increasing over the past several years, after more than a decade of relative stability.[1] The frequency of large-scale seizures has risen substantially, and the sizes of individual seizures continue to set records. Wholesale (kilogram-level) prices are substantially below those of the early 1980s. Retail-level purity has soared; levels higher than 40 percent are now routine in many large urban markets. The average retail price per pure milligram for 1990 in the largest market, New York City, was estimated to be barely over $1, a figure comparable, in inflation-adjusted terms, to the price that prevailed at the beginning of the last great heroin epidemic, in the mid-1960s.

The causes and consequences of this increase in supply are both unclear. This article begins by describing how and why shifts in supply can affect consumption and drug-related harm. It goes on to examine existing evidence; the data do not show clear signs of a new epidemic, but it is argued that this lack of news is not cause for complacency. The remainder of the article discusses what if anything should be done in light of this inconclusive evidence. Drug control resources are finite, and there are other aspects of the drug problem to compete for them. One would want to have a clear idea of the risks as well as the benefits of making heroin

1. *The Supply of Illicit Drugs to the United States* (Washington, DC: National Narcotics Intelligence Consumers Committee, 1990).

a new policy focus before reallocating resources. On the other hand, the history of cocaine in the late 1970s and early 1980s demonstrates that "wait and see" can be an extremely expensive option.

BACKGROUND

The heroin situation has some analogies with the global warming problem. In each case, some of the actions proposed to avert a possible disaster carry high costs. In each case, there are legitimate questions both about the dimensions, or even the occurrence, of that disaster in the absence of preventive action and about the capacity of the proposed actions to avert it assuming that the threat is genuine. The population of the next century may bitterly regret our current inaction on global warming as we, a decade hence, may regret our current inaction on the heroin supply; in each case, we might also find ourselves having taken costly and unnecessary preventive measures against a hypothetical and ultimately insubstantial threat.

A central difference between the two problems lies in our capacity to learn more within the span of time relevant to action. Most of our ignorance about global warming is rooted in our limited capacity to measure and model the processes of weather and climate; remedying this deficiency will require fundamental breakthroughs in scientific understanding and methodology. By contrast, much of our ignorance about the heroin situation originates in nothing more fundamental than the failure to mount data collection and analysis efforts well within the boundaries of proven social science methodology. Increasing the street epidemiology effort and preparing public-use tapes of the major drug data collection programs require only money and attention. An appropriate reaction to the heroin situation will therefore involve both the development of responses to an uncertain situation—which is to say, responses that will perform well against a wide range of possible values of unknown variables—and action to reduce the uncertainty itself.

Even in advance of the collection and analysis of masses of new data and large-scale reanalysis of existing data, it is possible to improve on our current state of knowledge about the heroin problem using only simple conceptual tools. Such tools are applied here to the conundrum that the evidence of substantial increases in heroin imports and reductions in purity-adjusted prices seems to be contradicted by the lack of increases in standard measures of heroin-related damage. We conclude that such increases should not necessarily be expected in the early stages of a new epidemic and hence that their failure to appear does not justify complacency. We recommend implementing several relatively inexpensive interventions that would likely prove beneficial even if a new epidemic never materialized, and we recommend enhancing monitoring. If the enhanced monitoring revealed substantial increases in use, particularly among novices, further actions could be taken.

The effect of supply conditions on consumption

All other things being equal, an increase in the average purity of heroin sold at retail and a decrease in the purity-adjusted price should be expected to raise heroin consumption. This follows from the basic theory of consumer choice: at lower prices, heroin will be more competitive both with competing mind-altering substances and with non-drug uses of money. This effect does not assume that all potential heroin users do explicit cost-benefit analyses of heroin and its alternatives, only that price is a consideration for some users, as it surely is for those who spend very large proportions of their personal budgets on heroin.

Moreover, the abstract theory of consumer choice is supported by concrete physiological, psychological, and sociological mechanisms acting at the individual and small-group levels. Most first-time users are given heroin rather than purchasing it,[2] and the cost of introducing a friend to the drug falls with the price of the drug. Higher doses, at least if they are anticipated, are likely to be more reinforcing, and virtually certain to be more dependency-producing, than lower ones. Not only does this mean that more "chippers"—occasional users—are likely to become chronic heavy users; it also implies increased difficulty in quitting for those who have already lost control of their her-

2. See John Kaplan, *The Hardest Drug: Heroin and Public Policy* (Chicago: University of Chicago Press, 1983), pp. 29-32.

oin habits. Most important of all, while injection is virtually the only practicable mode of administration for expensive, low-purity heroin, novices can use higher-purity heroin intranasally or by smoking. Thus the fall in prices makes the heroin experience available to those who, for reasons of discomfort, stigma, or the fear of infectious disease, will not inject drugs.[3]

The high price of heroin heretofore may have exerted a restraining effect on the tendency of some heavy cocaine users to combine the two drugs, either to obtain a polydrug effect or simply to ease the crash following a cocaine binge. It also made it less likely that heavy cocaine users, particularly crack smokers, would switch to heroin. As heroin prices fall, the migration path from cocaine use to heroin use will tend to become easier.

On the other hand, several mechanisms restrain the consumption of heroin, whatever happens to its price. The miserable condition of most of the highly visible heroin addicts has attached a substantial stigma to heroin use as perceived by virtually every social group and subculture. The association of heroin with acquired immune deficiency syndrome (AIDS) has driven the lesson home even more firmly. If there

were a sudden upsurge in heroin initiation, the presence of many (temporarily) happy consumers for the drug would tend to change the drug's street reputation, but in the meanwhile the reputation itself helps to block the very phenomenon that would change it.

In the absence of supply changes, the trend in heroin use would likely be down. The existing user base is being steadily eaten away by cessation of use and by mortality, already high and now aggravated by aging and AIDS.[4] The massive revulsion from illicit drug use resulting from the cocaine experience of the past decade is probably making itself felt even in the social milieus from which heroin users have traditionally been drawn. Growing supply may be relatively unimportant in the face of shrinking demand.

Moreover, price and purity represent only one aspect of the heroin supply situation. Retail availability, determined by the number, social and geographic distribution, and aggressiveness of retail dealers, shapes consumption patterns by determining the cost, in time and inconvenience, of searching for the drug.[5] In the case of crack, the spread of the epidemic from city to city was limited less by wholesale supplies, which were always ample, than by the existence of retail distribution channels.

3. For a discussion of the roles that intravenous drug use and prostitution play to support drug habits in spreading the human immunodeficiency virus (HIV), the virus of AIDS, see Don C. Des Jarlais and Samuel R. Friedman, "AIDS and Legal Access to Sterile Drug Injection Equipment," this issue of *The Annals* of the American Academy of Political and Social Science.

4. Jonathan P. Caulkins and Edward H. Kaplan, "AIDS' Impact on the Number of Intravenous Drug Users," *Interfaces*, 21(3):50-63 (1991).

5. Mark H. Moore, "Policies to Achieve Discrimination in the Effective Price of Heroin," *American Economic Review*, 63:270-79 (1973).

The number of retail heroin dealers today is surely a small fraction of the number of retail cocaine and crack dealers, and the falling price of heroin itself—the raw material of retail dealing—does little directly to change that lack of distribution capacity.

In the long run, if lower prices and higher purities begin to attract a larger number of users, they will tend to increase the financial rewards of retail heroin dealing. (The market for crack cocaine illustrates this phenomenon: high volumes generate large retail incomes, even at low unit prices.[6]) In the short run, however, lower prices may reduce retail earnings while also reducing the need of current heroin users for income to support their habits. On the other hand, as the number of new users rises, they will provide both a market and a labor supply for the retail distribution system. And as the market grows, the ratio of enforcement to market size decreases, so enforcement-imposed costs shrink, making the market all the more appealing.[7] As is true with the drug's word-of-mouth reputation, its limited retail distribution network acts as a brake on the development of an initial cadre of new users, but once that cadre forms, its growth will tend to be self-stimulating. Hence, for a variety of reasons, the heroin market is inherently less stable than markets for most licit

goods. Once it begins to grow, that growth may fuel further growth.

Effects of
supply conditions
on drug-related harm

Lower wholesale prices and the resulting higher retail purities have a mix of effects, some harmful, some beneficial. On one hand, high price represents a barrier to initiation and a source of continuing pressure on current users to limit their consumption or to quit entirely. On the other hand, high price contributes to the poverty of users and thus to their ill health and, very possibly, their criminal activity. High price and low purity also place a premium on injection as the most economical way to use heroin and may contribute to needle sharing. In effect, high prices reduce the number of milligrams of heroin used but increase the average damage done by each milligram.[8] Lower prices reverse these effects.

One traditional concern about increasing purity is that it will result in an increased frequency of death and injury due to unintentional overdose. But the rate of unintentional overdose may well be related to the uncertainty in purity as much as to its absolute level, and higher purity will tend to decrease, rather than increase, that uncertainty. A heroin user accustomed to 5 percent pure heroin who gets 50 percent pure instead can wind up giving himself 10 times as much pure heroin as he ex-

6. Peter Reuter, Robert MacCoun, and Patricia Murphy, *Money from Crime: A Study of the Economics of Drug Dealing in Washington, D.C.* (Santa Monica, CA: RAND, 1990).

7. Jonathan P. Caulkins, "Distribution and Consumption of Illicit Drugs: Some Mathematical Models and Their Policy Implications" (Ph.D. diss., Massachusetts Institute of Technology, 1990).

8. Mark H. Moore, "Limiting Supplies of Drugs to Illicit Markets," *Journal of Drug Issues*, Spring 1979, pp. 291-308.

pects, with devastating effects. A user accustomed to 50 percent pure heroin faces no such risk; at worst, the drug supply might be twice as potent as expected. Moreover, higher purity means that a user of any given volume of heroin has to absorb a smaller amount of diluents and adulterants.

On the other hand, it seems likely that lower prices will increase the average daily consumption among chronic heavy heroin users. Increased consumption, to the extent that it occurs, will tend to counteract the benefits of the reduced cost of living represented by a decline in heroin price. In the extreme, if the purity-adjusted price fell by 50 percent, but tolerance and hence consumption doubled, drug users' personal financial situation would not change at all.

Furthermore, increased consumption may narrow the range between the desired dose and a fatal overdose because tolerance of the drug's psychological effects builds up more quickly than tolerance of its effects on motor function. Additionally, heroin users accustomed to very high doses are likely to experience more unpleasant withdrawal syndromes than are low-dose users; this will tend to reduce the frequency of unsupervised withdrawal and pose a problem for treatment providers.

The beneficial effects of reduced prices in terms of increased welfare and decreased criminality of current users take effect more or less immediately. The harmful effects of increased consumption take place more slowly, since individual heroin habits and social practices around heroin use are strongly inertial. Thus, like a dose of heroin to an addict in withdrawal, falling prices are likely to generate short-term relief at the cost of long-term problems.

*Evidence on current
    trends in use and harm*

To date, there is remarkably little hard evidence that a new heroin epidemic has begun. But this may say as much about the data collection systems in place as it does about the existence—or not—of significant trends.

The seizure data themselves provide strong evidence that the physical volume of heroin being consumed has increased. In the very short run, increased shipments need not reflect increased consumption; slack demand can create involuntary inventory buildup of illicit as well as licit goods. But just as unsold automobiles on car dealers' lots eventually lead to reduced production, unsold heroin in retail dealers' stashes will reduce demand at wholesale, and importers will quickly learn that even a technically successful smuggling venture fails to earn an economic reward. Thus the fact that seizures have risen, not for one or two quarters or even for a year, but for several years in succession strongly suggests that more heroin is going into users' bodies now than was the case five years ago.[9]

This rise, in turn, must reflect some combination of more users and more consumption per user. Increasing tol-

9. For seizure statistics, see Kathleen Maguire and Timothy J. Flanagan, eds., *Sourcebook of Criminal Justice Statistics* (Washington, DC: Government Printing Office, 1991), pp. 462-64.

erance and possible shifts to less efficient modes of administration— away from intravenous injection to smoking or insufflation—imply that the number of hours or days each user spends under the influence of heroin will grow more slowly than the physical dosage per user. The physical consumption of heroin would double, for example, if the user population and doses per user per day both remained fixed while the heroin content of each dose doubled as a result of a purity increase from 10 to 20 percent.

The question, then, is how much of the additional consumption supply of heroin is attributable to an increase in the number of users—by increasing rates of initiation and relapse from abstinence or by decreasing quit-attempt rates—and how much is attributable simply to an increase in consumption rates by existing users. The former set of effects is far more worrisome than the latter.

Survey evidence is of little value here. Heroin use is too rare and too socially marginal an activity to be reliably measured by administering questionnaires to national probability samples. Street ethnography, particularly the systematic variety as practiced by the Street Studies Unit in New York City, has better prospects for noticing—though not for measuring—changes, but street ethnographers of necessity start from known populations of users and may easily miss pockets of new users developing at a social distance from existing users. In addition, the capability of New York's street studies is unique; there is no comparable capacity to detect the early stages of a microepidemic in Boston or Kansas City. The Community Epidemiology Work Groups are only a partial substitute.

The other systematic data collection efforts tend to count drug users in trouble and thus to miss drug users just starting out. The Drug Abuse Warning Network (DAWN) counts users injured or killed, the Drug Use Forecasting (DUF) system counts arrested users, and the drug treatment system counts users who have lost control of their habits. Any of these systems would notice a truly massive upsurge; if the number of heroin users had doubled, almost certainly the numbers of injuries, deaths, arrests, and—somewhat later—treatment entries would reflect that fact. But if the number of initiations had merely gone from a few tens of thousands—roughly replacement level for a chronic user population in the hundreds of thousands—to twice that level, the addition of a few more tens of thousands of new, and consequently low-problem-incidence, users to the existing population might not show up for several years. Furthermore, despite their names, these data collection efforts are lagging, not leading, indicators of initiation rates, because most users do not experience such severe problems immediately upon initiation.

Moreover, the short-term benefits of lower heroin prices may mask some of the effects of rising initiation, for example, arrestee heroin use as measured by DUF. If lower prices have (temporarily) reduced the rate of income-producing crime by existing users, that will at least partially compensate for the addition of some new users. That is, some users will already be criminally involved; the lag before they appear in DUF is only as long as it takes for them to be arrested again. Some criminally involved current users, however, have extraordinarily high offense rates. A modest percentage reduction in the offense rates of even a relatively small number of these individuals could mask the appearance of a relatively large number of new drug users who commit crimes at a less frenzied pace, including some who finance drug use predominantly or entirely from licit income.

As discussed previously, it is not clear what effect steadily lower prices and higher purities have on accident rates or treatment-entry rates. In any case, the combined effects of the continued aging of the existing user cohort and the HIV/AIDS epidemic may overwhelm any effect of the addition of new users to the pipeline.

The two clearest signs of a growing number of new users would be the entry into treatment of large numbers of younger users, with more recent dates of first use, and of users self-administering in modes other than injection. Both of these effects are indeed showing up in New York City, with one-third of current heroin treatment entrants reporting intranasal administration as their primary mode.[10] But these data, while interesting, are far from dramatic even in New York. As yet, there are no comparable data on treatment entrants from elsewhere in the country, although national data on emergency room visits hint at such a trend.

WHAT IS TO BE DONE?

Deciding whether a new heroin epidemic is on the way and plotting its course is of importance only insofar as there are programs that ought to be pursued or not, depending on whether or not heroin use is rising and by how much. Assuming, for the purposes of argument, that increased availability is leading, or will lead, to a growing user population, what instruments are available for dealing with that situation?

Preventing or reversing increased supply

If falling heroin prices pose a problem, one solution is to take action to increase prices. This is primarily the domain of law enforcement. In general, programs that impose costs on the heroin industry, via seizure or destruction of drugs, seizure and forfeiture of other assets, or imprisonment of heroin entrepreneurs and their employees, tend to force prices up.[11] Redirecting law enforcement resources from investigations aimed at other drugs will thus help counteract the trend toward lower heroin prices —while leading to lower prices, other things being equal, for the drugs from which enforcement attention is diverted. Since the effective enforce-

10. Arthur Y. Webb, Paul C. Puccio, and Ronald S. Simeone, *Current Drug Use Trends in New York City* (New York: New York State Division of Substance Abuse Services, 1991), pp. 5-8.

11. Peter Reuter and Mark Kleiman, "Risks and Prices: An Economic Analysis of Drug Enforcement," in *Crime and Justice: An Annual Review of Research*, ed. Norval Morris and Michael Tonry (Chicago: University of Chicago Press, 1986).

ment pressure on a drug market—the cost imposed per physical unit of drug sold—is roughly proportional to the ratio of enforcement effort to market size, there are advantages to redirecting enforcement effort from large and stable or declining markets toward small and growing ones.[12] If the heroin market is growing in terms of physical volume, the amount of effort required to retard that growth now is considerably smaller than the amount that will be required to retard it two years from now.

In addition to the horizontal competition for resources among drug categories, there is also a vertical competition for resources among source control, high-seas and border interdiction, high-level domestic law enforcement, and retail-level law enforcement. Source control and interdiction have very large yields of drugs destroyed or seized per dollar spent,[13] but there are good reasons to doubt that their effects on prices are comparably great.[14] Pursuing high-level domestic enforcement, such as that conducted by the Drug Enforcement Administration, may offer the most

promise for increasing prices. A relatively small number of agents work on cases against high-level domestic distributors, yet prices increase dramatically at that point in the distribution chain.[15]

Dollar prices are not all that affects consumption, however. Retail enforcement can restrict availability at the point of purchase and drive up search-time costs. There may be more to be gained from aggressive retail-level enforcement, with the aim of preventing the development of new open heroin markets and thus continuing to make heroin difficult to purchase, than there is from raising prices. This may be particularly true inasmuch as users finance increased dollar cost through increased criminal activity; search-time costs cannot be paid in money and so are less likely to lead to increased property crime.[16] But this depends on the behavior of local law enforcement agencies and is thus difficult to arrange as a matter of national policy.

*Preventing increases in
    use given greater supply*

If heroin becomes increasingly available, the value of prevention efforts aimed specifically at heroin will tend to increase. Unfortunately, the populations most likely to start using heroin are among those least likely to

12. Mark A. R. Kleiman, "Modeling Drug Markets: An Overview," in *Modeling Drug Markets* (Cambridge, MA: Harvard University, John F. Kennedy School of Government, Program in Criminal Justice Policy and Management, 1991); idem, "Compliance and Enforcement in a Binary-Choice Framework," in ibid.; Caulkins, "Distribution and Consumption of Illicit Drugs."

13. Wharton Econometrics Forecasting Associates, *Anti-Drug Law Enforcement Efforts and Their Impact* (Washington, DC: Department of the Treasury, 1987).

14. Peter Reuter, Gordon Crawford, and Jonathan Cave, *Sealing the Borders: The Effects of Increased Military Participation in Drug Interdiction* (Santa Monica, CA: RAND, 1988).

15. Jonathan Cave and Peter Reuter, *The Interdictor's Lot: A Dynamic Model of the Market for Drug Smuggling Services* (Santa Monica, CA: RAND, 1988).

16. Mark A. R. Kleiman and Kerry Smith, "State and Local Drug Enforcement: In Search of a Strategy," in *Drugs and Crime*, ed. James Q. Wilson and Michael Tonry (Chicago: University of Chicago, 1990).

be receptive to officially generated messages. Nevertheless, in addition to reinforcing heroin's already bad reputation, there would be some value in warning potential new users that the risk of addiction is generic to the drug, not specific to intravenous injection. The danger here would be that prevention efforts could have the effect of spreading the message that heroin can be snorted or smoked as well as injected.

One low-cost preliminary step would be to launch a pilot study of a sample of young adults from high-HIV-seroprevalence census tracts in New York City to determine their attitudes and beliefs about heroin. The results of the study would be an aid to the design of appropriate messages for prevention efforts.

In addition to choosing messages, a prevention campaign needs to consider target audiences and communications vehicles. Even if the heroin-using population grows substantially, it is likely to remain heavily concentrated geographically and sociologically; if there is a new population of heroin users, it will probably look like the existing population but twenty years younger—and perhaps more evenly divided by gender. This concentration makes the use of mass media not only inefficient but substantively unwise; there is no point in stirring up curiosity about heroin in those who would otherwise never think of it without a shudder.

Again, if heroin follows its previous patterns, the value of school-based programs will be limited by the fact that heroin initiation tends to take place in young adulthood rather than adolescence and that those most

likely to become its users are most likely to be frequent absentees and early dropouts. One common characteristic of many of the 1967-73 cohort of heroin users was their early involvement with the criminal justice system, an involvement that tended to predate their heroin use. This suggests that big-city arrestee populations, including juveniles, may be good targets for anti-heroin messages. Even given the obvious problems, jails and police lockups are probably underutilized as sites for drug education. In addition, there might be value in giving drug prevention training and materials to parole and probation officers and to criminal defense lawyers, including public defender staffs and other publicly paid counsel.

Confronting increased heroin use

Neither supply control nor prevention efforts are likely to be sufficient to forestall all of the increase in heroin consumption that greater availability could cause. This raises the question of how to protect, insofar as possible, a new cohort of heroin users from the risks of heroin use and to protect their neighbors and families from the behavioral consequences of the use of an expensive and dependency-inducing drug. Achieving this protection means designing a new set of secondary and tertiary prevention efforts to match the characteristics of the new heroin-using population and adjusting the treatment system to meet a new set of demands.

The most novel tertiary-prevention issue is how to persuade those who begin to use heroin intranasally or by smoking not to switch to injection as their growing drug habits begin to put pressure on their budgets. (In this connection, a great deal could be learned by conducting interviews with a sample of recent-onset intravenous heroin users entering treatment to determine how many of them started as intranasal users.) Even more than primary-prevention efforts, these messages would have to be narrowly targeted to appropriate audiences to avoid an unwanted advertising effect.

The other post-primary prevention, treatment, and treatment-outreach issues are all familiar ones. Just as a treatment system too centered on the problems of forty-year-old male heroin injectors had to be reshaped to meet the cocaine epidemic, the rising generation of heroin users, if there is one, will require services appropriate to its needs. At first, neither the existing heroin programs—still focused on the older cohort—nor the existing programs for younger users—still focused on cocaine—will be fully ready to do the job.

Methadone programs will face a peculiar set of pressures if the typical daily street habit rises. On one hand, the dose of methadone required to induce treatment entrance and prevent withdrawal discomfort and consequent dropout is likely to be higher for clients entering with larger habits. On the other hand, using larger doses with new clients will make it more difficult to keep existing clients content at current dosages. European clinical experience, gained in a setting of low prices and high doses, may

become more relevant for the United States than it has been heretofore.

Monitoring systems

The foregoing discussion suggests that there are substantial policy choices to which the question of how fast the number of heroin users is growing would be directly relevant. This raises the question of how to find out.

To some extent, existing data sources can be tapped for evidence. Stratification of DAWN heroin reports by age of patient, for example, would help to separate out incidents involving new, younger users from those that involve the existing heroin cohort and would thus create a more sensitive measure of initiation rates. Similarly, analysis of treatment-entry data, including time since first use for heroin users and secondary drugs for those whose primary drug is other than heroin, could be illuminating.

Some of the most powerful evidence is likely to come from targeted surveys and from street ethnography. The problem is to identify appropriate sample frames for surveys—here again, criminal justice populations leap to mind—and appropriate starting points for ethnographic investigation—new treatment entrants, if they can be located though the veil of confidentiality, might be a good place to start. The DUF system, which asks its interviewees about their year of first use, will tend to detect a rise in recent initiations before most other data collection efforts. The expansion of the sample size for the National Household Survey on Drug Abuse, and the deliberate oversampling of young adults in high-prevalence areas, will also be helpful in measuring changes in the prevalence of heroin use. Unfortunately, the survey does not ask about duration of use and therefore provides no direct evidence on incidence.

Finally, the independent variable in the causal equation—the price and purity of heroin sold on the street—could be measured with far more precision. Simply creating a national data base analogous to the Drug Enforcement Administration's System to Retrieve Information from Drug Evidence that included data from all local, state, and federal enforcement agencies would be a great first step. But any attempt to use enforcement data to study the retail drug markets will be limited by the fact that undercover drug purchases are not designed or executed with research purposes and standards in mind. There may be a need for systematic retail drug-purchase activity designed explicitly as a research tool, with careful attention to issues such as sampling frames, test-retest validity, and the like. Statistically valid local price and purity data for the cities with the dozen largest heroin markets could be obtained for relatively little money. To these could be added a panel survey of users to attempt to measure search time and other nonprice components of availability.

CONCLUSION

While it is implausible that the United States is about to experience a heroin epidemic comparable in scope to the current cocaine epidemic, it is almost equally implausible that the continued availability of heroin at historically low prices and high purities will have no effect at all on the number of new heroin users. Since undue delay can be expensive, and most of the existing sources of data are likely to lag substantially behind the problem itself, it may be wise to take some relatively low-cost actions now, while simultaneously increasing monitoring efforts.

These low-cost actions might include criminal-justice-system-based education programs designed to deter intravenous drug use and to inform potential users that heroin can be dependency-forming even if it is not injected. There may also be a need to expand and redesign treatment programs to accommodate younger heroin users. If the enhanced monitoring programs discussed in the preceding section give signs that another heroin epidemic is under way, then more expensive options such as redirecting enforcement resources toward heroin may be appropriate.

At this point it is difficult to predict what will happen. Supply conditions are not unlike those that preceded the last heroin epidemic, but other things have changed. Knowledge of heroin's danger is more widespread, and AIDS adds a new dimension to those dangers. It would be unwise to either do nothing or to act as if a new epidemic were certain.

ANNALS, *AAPSS,* **521,** May 1992

How to Maximize Utilization of Evaluation Research by Policymakers

By DOUGLAS S. LIPTON

ABSTRACT: To conduct evaluation research and prepare reports that are most likely to be utilized by policymakers, one must understand the policymakers' perception of research and researchers. Policymakers believe it is their job to carry out their constituents' demands regardless of the results of evaluation research—only one contending judgment among many desiderata. The quality of the research is extraneous to making decisions. The more complex the evaluation, the more jargon, the more equivocal the conclusions, the more caveats in the preamble, the more sensitive the issue, the more complex the writing, the more obscure the evaluator, the more apt that the report will be discarded by policymakers and legislators. Their attitude mandates reporting that focuses on findings critical to policy issues, presents jargon-free findings concisely and clearly, avoids making recommendations, and relegates discussions of methodology to the appendix.

After completing doctoral work at Vanderbilt University in 1963, Douglas S. Lipton served as deputy director of several New York State criminal justice agencies and as deputy director of the state's Division of Substance Abuse Services. He directed state drug abuse research for 18 years. Since 1988, he has been the director of the Research Institute at Narcotic and Drug Research, Inc., a not-for-profit research and training firm. He has published more than 100 articles and several books.

SOCIETY'S problems are unlikely to ever disappear. Our optimism, nevertheless, is guarded but hopeful, and we pursue solutions to them. We seek to bring the best of our skills to bear in aid of that cause. We do this by suggesting possible solutions and evaluating the outcome—evaluation products that speak to the critical issues of effectiveness and cost. Still, the best of such products are not ultimately judged by academic standards but rather by their utilization. In other words, in aid of public policymaking it is not enough that our professional skills are judged as optimal from the standpoint of other evaluation researchers, but those engaged in the process of implementing solutions—the policymakers—have to feel the same way or at least sufficiently confident that the evaluation outcome is clear, accurate, and reliable. The best-quality evaluation study whose report never leaves the shelf, that is, is never utilized, may as well never have been undertaken.

This article attempts to set forth three levers to increase the probability that evaluation research products will be used by policymakers and legislators. First, some distinctions are drawn that are useful in understanding why some research is not utilized and why some evaluators are not trusted. Then, legislators and policymakers' perceptions about evaluation, its uses, and its limitations are presented. Finally, practical reality-tested recommendations are offered for maximizing the likelihood that utilization will occur. Examples are given throughout from the contro-

versial field of drug abuse treatment evaluation research.

Over the last several decades, professional social scientists have taken interest in the question of how best to use professional data gathering and analysis to help solve society's problems. The investment in evaluation has meant that social scientists have had to convince policymakers that their product was worthy, while they have had to satisfy themselves, and their academic colleagues, that it was a useful and academically satisfying pursuit. As evaluation grew as an industry, the making of evaluations and pursuant analyses became more expensive—at the same time the reports grew no clearer and the results no less equivocal.

Referring to these skills of social inquiry, Professor Lindblom of Yale has said "that power in contemporary society is passing from those who hold conventional sources of authority, like arms, public office, or wealth, to those who *know*—those with the skills, the time, and the funds for analyzing the society's problems."[1] In a similar vein, J. K. Galbraith says, "Power is shifting to people with knowledge, experience and talent who are bound together in organizations."[2] Both scholars imply the power inherent in possessing special

1. Charles E. Lindblom, "Who Needs What Social Research for Policy Making," *Proceedings of the New York Education Policy Seminar* (Albany: State University of New York, Nelson A. Rockefeller Institute of Government, 1984), 1(1):3.
2. John K. Galbraith, *The New Industrial State*, 3d ed. (Boston: Houghton Mifflin, 1978), p. 61.

knowledge about what works in solving society's problems. Neither treats, however, the translation of the knowledge to policy, that is, the manner through which the knowledge is converted to become utilized for policy implementation.

Certainly, neither would celebrate the science-for-its-own-sake scientist who ignores society's problems and simply follows his or her own curiosity. It is axiomatic in today's scientific arena, particularly in that aspect of science dealing with human problems, that professional researchers be concerned in an unbiased—nonpartisan—way with the values or interests of the whole society. This does not mean that researchers must pursue research tasks in an uncommitted or dispassionate manner, however. The social science credo as expounded in graduate schools is that they should analyze problems with an eye on the public interest rather than on the special interests of some group in the society. We hold, as it were, that their responsibility is to avoid bias and to accord equal legitimacy to every value or interest. This is a very difficult stance to take for analysts or scientists who are not independent university-based scholars but who are employees of government agencies. Status in the field of evaluation research and policy analysis in part rests upon how free one is to pursue nonpartisan public-interest research questions. The more one is seen as allied with a particular special interest, the greater the loss of status in the eyes of other scientists and analysts and the greater the loss of credibility in the eyes of competing agencies, policymakers, and legislators.

Haveman and Margolis imply that the only way policy analysts and research evaluators can escape the value trap—that is, can capture every major aspect of the public interest in an unbiased way—is to use cost-benefit analysis: "Isolate the full set of impacts which [a proposed policy] generates." Then "attach a value to each input and output." Then "choose that policy for which the excess of benefits over cost is as great as possible."[3] While this message is rather extreme, it is clear nevertheless that good policy analysis and good program evaluation obligate one to take the larger view. It minimizes the potential and opportunity for one's own values to intrude.

A distinction must be drawn between analysts who work for or are closely attached to government agencies and who are limited in the manner of inquiry and the questions they may pursue—and who must perforce acknowledge that they take a particular perspective—and those persons who, while employed by government agencies as in-house researchers and consultant-researchers, still are free to conduct nonpartisan and unbiased research and analyses. The limitations on the latter are not in the manner of inquiry and questions researched but in the manner of dissemination and in the freedom to share the findings, in who gets to see the results.

3. Robert H. Haveman and Julius Margolis, eds., *Public Expenditure and Policy Analysis* (Chicago: Markham, 1970), pp. 7-8.

An underlying principle that follows from this is that professional research inquiry speaks only to the people who have to make the policy decisions, as pointed out by Hoole.[4] Who needs the results of professional inquiry; who needs the results of evaluations; who are the policymakers? The president of the United States, senators, congressmen and -women, state legislators, governmental agency heads, mayors, party leaders, corporate executives, and policy staff and advisers to these persons. Professional researchers most frequently—and comfortably—write for and present their findings to each other, rather than to the decision makers. It takes special pains to formulate issues and construct analyses—as well as to write prose—to meet policymakers even halfway. This means that the professional researcher or analyst has to understand the decision maker's problem as the decision maker sees it, not as the academic researcher defines it. Simply put by Laurence E. Lynn, speaking for the National Research Council, "From the point of view of [public officials], policy-relevant research is research that helps them carry out their roles and achieve goals they consider important."[5]

And then there is the issue of policy recommendations. There is controversy over whether a research evaluator or a policy analyst has more than a fact-finding role in making policy recommendations. In other words, should the researcher or analyst actually make policy recommendations? The answer to this question relies more on whether the policymaker has asked for recommendations and on the degree of personal distance between them, that is, on how much trust the policymaker has in the researcher. As Chelimsky puts it,

It was pointed out, over and over again, that the most important factor in assuring the use of evaluation findings was *not* the quality of the evaluation but the existence of a decision maker who wants and needs an evaluation and has committed himself to implementing its findings.[6]

Most often, policy analysis takes the form of the examination of a question of policy, often requiring problem reformulation, in any case requiring some canvassing of possible solutions, and normally culminating in a judgment as to what is most expeditious or cost beneficial. In some contrast, evaluation research queries the efficacy of a solution or method, tests outcomes using conventional statistical techniques, and presents conclusions regarding the solution's utility and the probable stability of that finding. Neither path takes us directly to recommendations per se, but much of today's guidance for policy scientists criticizes the fact-finding role as insufficient and suggests that the process should yield advice to the decision maker on what to do and which

4. Francis W. Hoole, *Evaluation Research and Development Activities* (Beverly Hills, CA: Sage, 1978), p. 167.

5. Laurence E. Lynn, Jr., ed., *Knowledge and Policy* (Washington, DC: National Academy of Sciences, 1978), p. 16.

6. Eleanor Chelimsky, ed., *A Symposium on the Use of Evaluation by Federal Agencies*, vol. 2 (McLean, VA: Mitre, 1977), p. 31.

vetted alternatives are worth his or her final consideration.[7]

Recently, Davis and Salasin; Ianni and Orr; Rossi; and Lawrence and Cook[8] have all noted the shift in emphasis away from rigorous methodology to making evaluation findings useful by policymakers, program administrators, and legislators. There has been a constant call to make evaluation products more utilizable, beginning with Weiss through Stasser et al. and Love.[9] Evaluation research-

ers[10] recognize this, as do U.S. senators[11] and congressmen.[12] Unfortunately, there has been poor communication between evaluators and the consumers of evaluation. Havelock refers to it as a "dialogue among the hearing and speaking impaired."[13] Congress has itself recognized this and partly out of frustration generated a set of prescriptions to guide evaluations that they request so as to enhance utilization.[14] The General Accounting Office and the Office of Management and Budget have also issued specific implications and related criteria for enhancing this communication process. Young and Comtois synthesized the General Accounting Office formulation into four points:

1. Evaluations must be utilization focused. Planning for utilization must be an integral part of evaluation planning from the beginning.

2. Criteria for assessing the use-relevance of program evaluations are relative rather than absolute. They

7. Phillip M. Gregg, ed., *Problems of Theory in Policy Analysis* (Lexington, MA: D. C. Heath, 1976), p. 86. Of 9 authors, 8 endorse analysts' and researchers' making recommendations, as does Lindblom, "Who Needs What Social Research," p. 8.

8. Howard R. Davis and Susan E. Salasin, "The Utilization of Evaluation," in *Handbook of Evaluation Research*, ed. E. L. Streuning and M. Gutentag (Beverly Hills, CA: Sage, 1975), vol. 1; Frederick A. J. Ianni and M. T. Orr, "Toward a Rapprochement of Quantitative and Qualitative Methodologies," in *Qualitative and Quantitative Methods in Evaluation Research*, ed. T. D. Cook and C. S. Reichardt (Beverly Hills, CA: Sage, 1979), pp. 87-98; Peter H. Rossi, "Past, Present and Future Prospects of Evaluation Research," in *Improving Evaluations*, ed. L. E. Datta and R. Perloff (Beverly Hills, CA: Sage, 1979), pp. 17-34; John E. S. Lawrence and Thomas J. Cook, "Designing Useful Evaluations," *Evaluation and Program Planning*, 5(4):327-36 (1982).

9. Carol H. Weiss, *Evaluation Research: Methods of Assessing Program Effectiveness* (Englewood Cliffs, NJ: Prentice-Hall, 1972); S. Stasser et al., "Why Some Evaluation Studies Are Useful and Others Not: Facilitators and Obstacles to the Use of Evaluation Research in Hospital Settings," *Evaluation Studies*, Jan.-Feb. 1983, pp. 69-91; A. J. Love, "The Developmental Evaluation Sequence (DES): An Effective Method for Increasing the Responsiveness and Utilization of International Evaluation Efforts" (Paper delivered at the annual meeting of the Evaluation Research Society, Baltimore, MD, Oct. 1982).

10. Daniel Koretz, "Developing Useful Evaluations: A Case History and Some Practical Guidelines," in *New Directions for Program Evaluation: Making Evaluation Research Useful to Congress*, ed. L. Saxe and D. Koretz (San Francisco: Jossey-Bass, 1982), pp. 25-50.

11. Harrison A. Williams, Jr., "Foreword," in *Evaluation in Legislation*, ed. F. M. Zweig (Beverly Hills, CA: Sage, 1979), pp. 7-9.

12. Pamela Doty, "The Role of the Evaluation Research Broker," in *New Directions for Program Evaluation*, ed. Saxe and Koretz, pp. 51-71.

13. Walter Havelock, untitled talk delivered to a panel of experts convened by the National Clearinghouse for Alcohol Information, Rockville, MD, 24 Feb. 1981.

14. Ronald L. Hicks, "Sunset Legislation," in *Evaluation in Legislation*, ed. Zweig, p. 25.

are themselves a proper topic for negotiation and agreement between evaluators and decision makers.

3. An important factor in utilization is an interactive process between decision makers and evaluators. Such a process can assure that decision makers are committed to use and that evaluators will produce useful findings. Yet it must be accomplished without infringing on the necessary independent stance of the evaluator.

4. Other factors such as question appropriateness, methodology, and dissemination are also important. But adequacy on those dimensions is made more likely by the interactive process.[15]

The persistence of impaired communication between evaluators and policymakers stems from differences in education and training, world-views, expectations and frames of reference, constituencies, success criteria, and language. The frustration suffered on both sides of the communication process does not seem to have abated since the late 1970s, when reams of guidelines were produced to facilitate the communication.[16] The guidelines are directed at evaluators, but this emphasis is misplaced. The key to achieving successful utilization of evaluation results lies in understanding the perceptions of policymakers and legislators. The following general statements, drawn

loosely from Brandl[17] and others, typify the policymakers' perceptions and frame of reference regarding evaluation, its uses, and its limitations.

POLICYMAKERS' PERCEPTIONS

1. Policymakers and legislators know that evaluations do not always yield truth. They sense there is some arbitrariness to all scientific work, especially evaluations.[18] Policymakers are aware of holes in methodology, and they know that much of the logic of evaluation research rests on unverifiable assumptions. They believe that evaluations mix objective analysis with political judgments that they are better equipped to make on their own. For example, the evaluation-research-produced contention that some methadone patients are not suited for abstinence and should remain on methadone maintenance for the balance of their lives is rejected by those policymakers and legislators who believe methadone treatment simply substitutes one evil narcotic for another.

2. Policymakers and legislators are aware that evaluations always answer questions somewhat different from the ones that they are asking.[19] Correctional administrators,

15. Carlotta J. Young and Joseph Comtois, "Increasing Congressional Utilization of Evaluation," in *Evaluation in Legislation*, ed. Zweig, p. 58.

16. Keith E. Marvin, "Evaluation for Congressional Committees," in *Evaluation in Legislation*, ed. Zweig, p. 49.

17. John E. Brandl, "Policy Evaluation and the Work of Legislatures," in *New Directions for Program Evaluation: Utilization of Evaluative Information*, ed. L. A. Brankamp and R. D. Brown (San Francisco: Jossey-Bass, 1980), pp. 37-43.

18. Leonard Rutman, "Barriers to the Utilization of Evaluation Research" (Paper delivered at the annual meeting of the Society for the Study of Social Problems, Chicago, IL, Sept. 1977).

19. John W. Scanlon et al., "Evaluability Assessment: Avoiding Type III and IV Er-

for example, are more interested in how well behaved and trouble free a group of program participants are likely to be than how well they recover from their addiction or how low their recidivism rate is after they leave the institution. In another example, it may be true that program evaluation shows that methadone-maintenance treatment reduces crime and improves social functioning, but how many addicts are really cured? Congressional committee members and the senior committee staff are generally under enormous time pressure when Congress is in session. Hence these people have little time or patience for issues not relevant to their focal concerns.[20]

3. Policymakers and legislators have neither the time nor the inclination to assess the quality of an evaluation.[21] If the basic finding is in agreement with their existing views, they will include the report in their armamentarium and wave it high in support of their argument. If the basic finding is antithetical to their views, they will reject it as biased, serving the opposition's cause, and/or shelve

it. The quality, methodology, and skill used are irrelevant. As pragmatic James Q. Wilson aptly puts it,

When [organizations] use social science at all, it will be on an ad hoc, improvised, quick-and-dirty basis. A key official, needing to take a position, respond to a crisis, or support a view that is under challenge, will ask an assistant to "get me some facts." . . . social science is used as ammunition, not as a method, and the official's opponents will also use similar ammunition. . . . there will be many shots fired, but few casualties except the truth.[22]

It is lamentable indeed that officials wish to grab whatever social science research results are convenient and favorable to their view. Cox[23] puts it this way: "Evaluation data will be grist for the informational mill and will be evaluated more against the overall informational context than against canons of scientific merit." Patton et al.'s conclusion from their survey of federal decision makers was that "there is little in our data to suggest that improving the methodological quality in and of itself will have much effect on increasing the utilization of evaluation research."[24] And, there are always those staff members who search for and find any

rors," in *Evaluation Management*, ed. G. R. Gilbert and P. J. Conklin (Charlottesville, VA: Twentieth U.S. Civil Service Commission, 1977), p. 264.

20. Hicks, "Sunset Legislation," p. 25.

21. R. Carlson, "Pouring Conceptual Foundations: A Utilization Role and Process for Evaluative Research," in *The Evaluator and Management*, ed. H. Schulberg and J. Jerrel (San Francisco: Jossey-Bass, 1979), pp. 55-67; J. A. Messina, "The Underutilization of Evaluation Research in the Field of Criminal Justice: Do Policy Makers Understand Social Scientific Methods?" (Paper delivered at the annual meeting of the Evaluation Research Society, Baltimore, MD, Oct. 1982).

22. James Q. Wilson, "Social Science and Public Policy," in *Knowledge and Policy*, ed. Lynn, p. 92.

23. Gary B. Cox, "Managerial Style: Implications for the Utilization of Program Evaluation Information," *Evaluation Quarterly*, 1(3):506 (1977).

24. Michael Q. Patton et al., "In Search of Impact: An Analysis of the Utilization of Federal Health Evaluation Research," in *Using Social Research in Public Policy Making*, ed. C. H. Weiss (Lexington, MA: Lexington Books, 1977), p. 151.

flaws in the numbers and then eagerly take issue with all the findings if they are contrary to their employer's views.

4. As evaluators become directly involved in program work or in policymaking, they trade their independence for influence. Policymakers and legislators know that truth is no longer the evaluators' sole objective at this stage and suspect them of advocacy. For example, those evaluators who become overly committed to the public interest as they see it often do themselves and their ideas a disservice in the marketplace of ideas. While declared extremism on the left or the right is useful for building an ardent base of support among one's fellow travelers, it tends to be an ineffective platform from which evaluators or analysts can gather the support of a majority. True partisanship in an evaluator therefore requires disguise of one's partisan views. The marketplace of evaluation research has not developed a truth-in-labeling law. Knowledge that this disguise must exist lies as one root of policymakers' distrust of those who characterize themselves as speaking fervently in the public interest.

The other root lies in the soil of fervent advocacy. Partly in response to criticisms that evaluators did not come to grips with the black box of drug abuse treatment, and that evaluators waited too long before sharing their knowledge of a given program's efficacy, formative evaluation emerged to allow evaluators to promptly feed back results to program personnel so that they might modify their program accordingly. In this kind of evaluation, the evaluator determines what the program administration and staff want their program to do, observes and analyzes the process of treatment, and assists the staff in modifying procedures during the course of the evaluation as necessary. This frequently involves working closely with program staff especially during early phases of program development. Such interaction often yields better data and an insightful understanding of the treatment method as well as a mutually respectful partnership between evaluators and program staff. The more that evaluators do this, however, the more apt they are to be viewed by policymakers as compromised, trading their independent objectivity for interest in the program's success.[25] Policymakers and legislators then suspect that the evaluators are nonobjective advocates, and their results will not be believed as valid and reliable.

5. Policymakers and legislators do not believe that truth determines what is right and proper. The political reality does. The social scientist's forte is knowledge. His or her special training and professional qualifications fit the task of formulating methods for pursuing answers to questions of efficacy and, in their view, do not fit the task of formulating and implementing policy. A policymaker can righteously assert that no monetary expert or economist has sufficient competence to give a policymaker good advice on weighing the interests of the unemployed against

25. Carol H. Weiss and Michael J. Bucavalas, "Truth Tests and Utility Tests: Decision-Makers' Frames of Reference for Social Science Research," *American Sociological Review*, 45:302-13 (Apr. 1980).

those of the employed. Similarly, policymakers know that a professionally trained evaluator cannot by reason of his or her training advise a policymaker on the degree to which the desires of pro-choice advocates should prevail over those of pro-life advocates. Of course, it is not really a question of competence, but of will and commitment, for which he or she has authority. For example, it may be true that more drug abuse treatment clients remain drug free longer after having been treated for one to two years in community residential treatment, but that does not imply that therapeutic communities should be mandated or paid for by the state. Further, it may also be true that risks for infection with human immunodeficiency virus (HIV) are significantly reduced by establishing needle exchanges for intravenous drug users, but it does not follow from a political standpoint that such facilities should be created and run by government or be endorsed by it. Similarly, moral and political considerations currently block the dispensing of condoms and the dissemination of safe-sex information for prevention of acquired immune deficiency syndrome (AIDS) in jails and prisons despite the evidence that such risk-reduction techniques are efficacious.

6. Policymakers and legislators believe their job is to carry out their constituents' wishes, regardless of what evaluations show. The call for evaluation results generally does not arise out of a dispassionate quest for knowledge but typically arises in a political arena of resolving conflict over competing values, responding to public fears, and distributing scarce resources among competing groups. Professional researchers are not viewed as having special competence to advise on the reconciliation of interests in conflict. Whether one group should prevail over or be asked to give way to another is not something on which they have knowledge, and the issue on which the policymaker needs advice when faced with the conflict is not finally an issue on which knowledge of efficacy is decisive or instrumental. As Lindblom avers, "One cannot know what is to be done in such a situation. What is required is an act of choice, commitment, or will."[26] If a methadone maintenance clinic is stirring up a neighborhood because of loitering and the neighborhood folks bring their legislator in as a contingent ally, no positive-outcome findings about the specific program, or about methadone in general, will be sufficient to overcome the larger political judgment. Nor can the findings of evaluation research reverse well-established popular convictions that are publicly supported by policymakers. For example, methadone maintenance treatment is perceived by many minority-group members to be a means of controlling young urban black men. For their representatives, research conclusions that methadone maintenance treatment is successful have no utility, and methadone is perforce seen as genocidal regardless of research findings.

7. Policymakers and legislators face myriad desiderata with any decision; evaluation results are only

26. Lindblom, "Who Needs What Social Research," p. 10.

one contending consideration.[27] Budgetary considerations, moral considerations, constituents' wishes, public opinion, conventional wisdom, image concerns, reappointment or reelection issues, as well as competing worthy agencies and organizations vie for the attention of policymakers and legislators. The more complex the evaluation, the more jargon in the language, the more hidden or equivocal the conclusion, the more caveats in the preamble, the thicker the report, the more obscure the evaluator, the more sensitive the issue, the more apt the policymaker is to discard, ignore, or attack the evaluation. If he or she attacks it, the evaluator at least has a fighting chance to defend it, but, unfortunately, the policymaker usually shelves the report—the worst possible outcome.

RECOMMENDATIONS FOR MAXIMIZING UTILIZATION

Implicit in the points raised is a set of recommendations for maximizing utilization by the policymaker. Having been both a policymaker and a research director in government agencies for almost thirty years, I am perhaps in a good place from which to speak to the issue of maximizing utilization for the policymaker.

To maximize policymakers' utilization, a dialogue must be established with the primary potential user—the policymaker or the legislator and/or key staff,[28] and this must be done early—that is, from the beginning. Ball and Anderson; Riecken and Boruch; and Young and Comtois all emphasize the importance of initiating involvement with the prospective consumer of the evaluation early.[29] Johnston stresses ongoing interaction "from the very first," then during the course of the evaluation at several points as "an investment in the ultimate utilization of the research."[30] The researcher must identify critical questions and the critical audiences the user has. From the critical questions a mission statement for the evaluation can be created with which the policymaker can agree. The policymaker then becomes a stakeholder in the evaluation. Also, the researcher and the policymaker should together develop a schedule so that no unrealistic time or product expectations are created.

27. Douglas S. Lipton and Philip Appel, "The State Perspective," in *Drug Abuse Treatment Evaluation: Strategies, Progress, and Prospects*, F. M. Tims and J. P. Ludford (Rockville, MD: National Institute on Drug Abuse, 1986), pp. 151-66.

28. Howard R. Davis and Susan E. Salasin, "The Utilization of Evaluation," in *Handbook of Evaluation Research*, ed. Streuning and Gutentag, vol. 1; Gary B. Cox, "Managerial Style: Implications for the Utilization of Program Evaluation Information," *Evaluation Quarterly*, 1(3):499-508 (1977).

29. Samuel Ball and Scarvia B. Anderson, "Dissemination, Communication and Utilization," *Education and Urban Society*, 9:451-70 (1977); Henry W. Riecken and Robert F. Boruch, *Social Experimentation: A Method for Planning and Evaluating Social Intervention* (New York: Academic Press, 1974); Carlotta J. Young and Joseph Comtois, "Increasing Congressional Utilization of Evaluation," in *Evaluation in Legislation*, ed. Zweig, pp. 57-79.

30. J. Johnston, "What We Know about the Researcher and Research Methods in Evaluation" (Paper delivered at the annual meeting of the American Educational Research Association, Toronto, ON, Canada, 27 Mar. 1978), p. 11.

Evaluations take time to produce, but short-term products are possible and useful. Both long- and short-term products should be forecast. With knowledge of the critical user's audiences in mind, the researcher can tailor the presentation of findings appropriately.

The continuing communication between evaluator and ultimate user is important if not vital. As Weiss points out, "Not only does [the users'] participation help in the definition of evaluation goals and the maintenance of study procedure, but it may change the image of evaluation from 'critical spying' to collaborative effort to understand and improve."[31] Such participation allowing review by the user yields "a sense of control, a sense of power over things."[32] Lack of contact seriously endangers the entire effort. As Hicks states in the context of evaluations for Congress,

Contact must be maintained. The evaluator must not allow separation or isolation for the staff person (and I stress the singular) who will be overseeing the evaluation study. The price of even inadvertent separation will likely be a product that is off the mark or overlooks some important factors. The evaluator's work may be found incomprehensible, irrelevant, impractical, or just not useful.[33]

Utilization will also be maximized if the evaluator develops a policy rationale for the research. The policy implications of evaluation reports are singularly paramount. Thus the research-paper format learned in graduate school is inappropriate for the policymaker—that style turns policymakers off. There should be a clear-cut policy rationale for the document, with the guiding questions that are program related, properly focused, and of interest to users set forth at the outset. Wholey et al.; Cox; Goldstein et al.; Patton et al.; Young and Comtois; Lawrence and Cook; and Love and many others have stressed how important this is.[34] The absence of a clear-cut policy rationale is viewed by policymakers as self-aggrandizing. That is, the report may be perceived as serving no other purpose than to enhance the evaluator's résumé and, if a consultant, his or her annual income.

Third, to achieve maximum utilization, evaluation research must move swiftly to produce; only a researcher is patient enough to wait two or three years for an answer to a question. Long-term evaluation

31. Carol H. Weiss, "Utilization of Evaluation: Toward Comparative Study," in *Readings in Evaluation Research*, ed. F. G. Caro (New York: Russell Sage Foundation, 1971), p. 141.

32. Clark C. Abt, "The State of the Art of Program Evaluation," in *Congressional Research Service, Legislative Oversight and Program Evaluation* (Washington, DC: Government Printing Office, 1976), p. 322.

33. Hicks, "Sunset Legislation," p. 26.

34. Joseph S. Wholey et al., *Federal Evaluation Policy* (Washington, DC: Urban Institute, 1970); Cox, "Managerial Style"; M. S. Goldstein, A. C. Marcus, and N. P. Rausch, "The Nonutilization of Evaluation Research," *Pacific Sociological Review*, 21:21-44 (1978); Michael Q. Patton et al., "In Search of Impact: An Analysis of the Utilization of Federal Health Evaluation Research," in *Using Social Research in Public Policy Making*, ed. Weiss, pp. 141-64; Young and Comtois, "Increasing Congressional Utilization of Evaluation"; Lawrence and Cook, "Designing Useful Evaluations"; Love, "Developmental Evaluation Sequence."

products are tolerable only when short-term products are available. This is even more true for policymakers and legislators whose terms are likely to be shorter than the length of the evaluation study. In addressing important questions, even interim findings and partial answers are useful, and they create momentum for more support. The acceptance of short-term products by the consumer implies that the evaluator must also accept incremental improvements in data quality, data systems, levels of cooperation, fiscal resources, and quality and quantity of staff. The search for perfection in evaluation is, as it is elsewhere, always fruitless. To delay short-term production on the basis of not having reached excellence in all these factors dooms the effort. Hence it is important to move with progressive refinement. This means that, initially, researchers must be willing to make crude or rough estimates in order to respond to information requests swiftly. Impossibly broad questions by the consumer can be divided into specific answerable ones. Partitioning the evaluation study according to the kinds of questions or issues that can be addressed early with available data and standard techniques and those requiring greater lengths of time and instrument development, and sharing these expectations with the consumer, is strategically sound.

Fourth, a format should be adopted for the evaluation product that will maximize utilization. Hicks says, "Above all be clear and concise. Technical conclusions must be put forward in such a way that most people can readily understand their meaning and significance."[35]

It is advisable to produce reports in four parts,[36] bearing in mind three guideposts: the answers to the critical questions should be put up front; accountability for critical resources should be provided—cost benefits and cost effectiveness; and clear action steps should be specified.

The executive summary and conclusions must come first. This part should not exceed two pages. Policymakers and legislators receive forty or more reports a day, and they have no time and little patience for nonrelevant material. President Nixon demanded one-page summaries. The executive summary should cite the main points clearly in everyday language; jargon should be avoided. If the policymaker encounters social science or technical jargon—or deltas, lambdas, and sigma hats—he or she will not go on. It is essential to maintain a focus on the critical policy questions behind the evaluation. "Nice-to-know" information or impractical alternatives or recommendations are not acceptable. The main points should respond to the user's critical questions and be tailored to the critical audiences, not the evaluators. It is also essential to avoid embedding a critical point in the middle or toward the end of the document.

35. Hicks, "Sunset Legislation," p. 25.
36. Douglas S. Lipton, "Lipton's Laws or Bringing Utilization to the Max" (Paper delivered at Narcotic and Drug Research, Inc., Project Reform National Training Workshop, Wilmington, DE, 19 Dec. 1989).

The body of the report should be presented like a table of contents with summarizing headlines. If tables are included, they should be clearly understood by laypersons; rarely should more than two variables be portrayed in a figure, and numbers from table to table, figure to figure, should never contradict each other. There is always someone who checks these numbers, and if they do not agree, the credibility of the entire document will be called into question. Provide policymakers and legislators with findings and conclusions, not with recommendations, unless the latter have been specifically requested. The making of recommendations and policies is the policymaker's and legislator's responsibility. Agency directors and senior administrators or advisers, on the other hand, may appreciate recommendations in addition to conclusions if there is a trust relationship established between them and the evaluator.

Conclusions should be written in short paragraphs, preferably in "bullet" form. Keep each bullet to a single thought without "buts" or caveats. This saves wading through ponderous rhetoric to find the conclusions, and the bullets can be used by decision makers immediately as announcements or sound bites for media purposes. Bullets should be written on the stand-alone principle, with short and pithy sentences that can be quoted in legislative or cabinet-level debates or in interviews with the public media. If recommendations have been requested and approved, they should also be formatted as bullets and incorporated into the executive summary. Quantitative facts that are reinforced and livened by qualitative data—anecdotes—should be used to convey central points.

Technical material including methodology, technical and complex tables, statistical procedures, technical caveats, and cost-benefit calculations should all be placed in an appendix. Such material is disconcerting and annoying to legislators and policymakers when it appears in the main body of the report. Of course, it is necessary and useful for technical staff and other evaluators, but it should be appended to the main body of the report to the policymakers. For a research audience, however, it may be incorporated in the body of the text.

The report must be sensitive to the critical audiences. For example, the results could be organized by political jurisdiction before they are presented by census tract. Policymakers and legislators cannot relate to problem estimates for areas that have no political reality. Statewide epidemiologic estimates or national estimates, for instance, have little applicability to individual localities or counties and give little opportunity for elected representatives to tie the results to their constituents' needs. The evaluators thus have an obligation to understand something of the political dynamics of the questions they investigate and to gather, analyze, and present data within meaningful configurations so that first action steps can be readily seen and targeted. Displaying data by census tract, unless the tracts are coterminous with political districts, defies this principle. This is also true for studies that report estimates for artificial area clusters or regions such as "upstate," the Southwest, and New England.

The report should stay focused on the critical policy-relevant questions. Evaluation results have to compete in a political decision-making arena with other weighty desiderata. Focusing on critical issues improves the chances that evaluation results will have an impact. The more undifferentiated nice-to-know material that is added to the body, the less likely the evaluation report will be utilized and have an impact.

The evaluator must be sensitive to fiscal realities. Advocating increased expenditures for measures or programs when tax levies are declining or when the economic climate is dictating layoffs or when hold-fast budgets are politically necessary can substantially reduce the evaluator's claim of objectivity and calls into question his or her realism, however strongly warranted the expenditures might be. Accountability should be foremost in the report, in light of certain competition from other programs and agencies and organizations for scarce dollars. Data should be presented on the cost-effectiveness of the program, and the conclusions should include a cost-benefit statement. Justifications for increasing—or even sustaining—fiscal support must be accompanied with projections of offsetting revenues or reduced expenditures. Sections in the body of the report demonstrating how increased expenditures could be managed by cost sharing, deferring expenditures,

or recasting budget lines must be accompanied in the appendix with specific details. Simple advocacy of such tactics is often only visionary.

Finally, the report should recommend action—first steps—not visions. It is also essential to be realistic in a political sense with regard to action. The evaluator must keep the end in sight, and the end is not the submission of the report. The test of the evaluator's report will be on the floor of the Congress or the state assembly, or in the Cabinet, or in the commissioner's chambers. The goal is meaningful public policy followed by action. There are many factors that need to be weighed in determining what actions to take and when to take them, especially in light of the vagaries of public support. The evaluation is likely to have greater constructive influence if clear first steps are tied to the conclusions. First steps are politically feasible, specific, practical, tied to the critical issues that initiated the evaluation activity in the first place, visible, and, above all, not utopian. Utopian solutions typically are not feasible because they are too costly; too discordant with society's practices, institutions, and fundamental values; without hope of political support; or impossible to inaugurate without wholesale social transformation. This does not mean that long-range solutions with utopian features should never be prescribed but rather that the initiation of any process of change needs a practical footing—first steps.

Book Department

INTERNATIONAL RELATIONS AND POLITICS

HERF, JEFFREY. *War by Other Means: Soviet Power, West German Resistance, and the Battle of the Euromissiles.* Pp. xiii, 357. New York: Free Press, 1991. $27.95.

Any study of recent events creates a challenge for both an author and a reviewer. Making sense of past news is difficult since none of us can keep pace with newspaper headlines, much less the realities of our times. Struggling to maintain both currency and order with some comprehension is not an easy task.

Jeffrey Herf's book reflects these challenges. His interest and his theme are both history and current events. He has several interrelated purposes, all revolving around Germany: political culture, basic diplomacy, international issues, and security needs. These concerns come together, for him, in the missile arguments of the 1980s. He posits the basic concept that the struggle over the Euromissiles was the final dispute of the Cold War. Herf believes that the revolutionary changes of 1989 stemmed, in part, from the resolve of some stalwart intellectuals and leaders who insisted on arguing the missile issues to a successful conclusion.

The result provides interesting reading—Herf writes well—in that the author makes his views clear and firm. In presenting his case, he encounters difficulty because the facts are opaque at best due to their proximity in time. He must struggle with the available materials while providing the reader some impressionistic insights. The problem is that he must credit the actors with an orderly, comprehensive, known role in a play founded on an uncertain script, namely, the reported details, the publicly accessible information, the immediate circumstances. The result provides a useful narrative but one based on Herf's collection of papers and personal analysis. Rather than letting the material dictate the narrative, his creativeness provides the continuity.

Herf has labored with diligence. Nonetheless, he must skimp on some important facts. One needs to know the military details, the American and Soviet positions, the total situation. Since he cannot achieve such goals with the available records, he divides his book into two parts. In one segment, concerning earlier history, he summarizes past events and opinions, while in the other portion he describes the German debates and activities over the missile question. It is awkward.

In sum, Herf provides a useful chronicle of the missile issue and one worthy of reading. I must add that his publisher let him down; the binding is imperfect and the footnote format is unhelpful. Nonetheless, the book can be recommended as a fine interim study of an interesting subject.

CHARLES BURDICK

San Jose State University
California

KNOKE, DAVID. *Organizing for Collective Action: The Political Economies of Associations*. Pp. xiv, 258. New York: Aldine de Gruyter, 1990. $39.95.

Commentators from Alexis de Tocqueville to George Bush have stressed the centrality of voluntary associations, collective action organizations (CAOs), for the maintenance of modern democratic societies in general and of American society in particular. In the work under review, sociologist David Knoke sets out to present "an initial step in a larger program of theory construction and empirical assessment necessary to improve our understanding of collective action organizations." Given current political events in the United States and in Eastern Europe, Knoke's work should be of great interest to both social scientists and policymakers. They should be warned, however, that this is difficult reading and requires some familiarity with statistical analysis, such as factor analysis and regression

analysis, and with theoretical and metatheoretical concerns.

Although Knoke is certainly interested in CAOs, he never loses sight of his program of theory construction. CAOs comprise two interdependent components—the individual member and the institution—and, therefore, provide an opportunity to examine questions concerning the reciprocal relationships between individuals and collectivities. For instance, in explaining how individuals become involved in CAOs, Knoke argues that one must simultaneously take into account rational cost-benefit calculations, desires to conform to group norms, and affective ties to the group. This multimotivational model, in turn, offers a framework for an understanding of how social integration in a complex industrial society can be achieved.

Knoke proposes that the components of a CAO's political economy be thought of in terms of external environment, internal economy, internal polity, and external polity. The bulk of the book is devoted to the testing of 27 theoretical propositions designed to explain relationships among organizational and individual variables. An example of a proposition is, "The more intense members' interests in organizational policy issues, the greater their communication interaction." The propositions are tested on data obtained from two interconnected surveys. The first involved telephone interviews with leaders of 459 national associations, and the second involved questionnaire responses from over 8700 members of 35 of these associations. The sample included unions, trade associations, professional societies, recreational organizations, and other associations.

In terms of organizational economy, the most interesting findings are that members are likely to give more money to a more bureaucratized association, that principles of fairness and altruistic norms regarding the well-being of members and nonmembers are "exceptionally powerful social forces shaping the collective action decisions of individuals," and that members support organizations financially when the organizations "match incentive offerings with the members' incentive demands." In terms of organizational polity, Knoke's most important observation is that "minority control in American associations seems to be severely constrained by pervasive cultural expectations that the membership will retain ultimate authority and influence over collective actions." This cultural explanation does not provide grounds for optimism concerning the development of pluralism in Eastern Europe, nor does it provide grounds for complacency concerning the inevitability of pluralism in the United States.

MARK OROMANER

Hudson County Community
  College
Jersey City
New Jersey

STUART, DOUGLAS and WILLIAM TOW. *The Limits of Alliance: NATO Out-of-Area Problems since 1949.* Pp. x, 383. Baltimore, MD: Johns Hopkins University Press, 1990. $42.50.

This book fills an important gap in the literature about alliances. It provides a comprehensive and critical analysis of a problem that has bedeviled the North Atlantic Treaty Organization (NATO) since its inception, the persistent difficulty that allies have of reconciling their mutual commitments to an alliance with their own national interests in areas outside the domain of the North Atlantic Treaty.

We are all familiar with the classical challenges to NATO unity, such as the Algerian question and the Suez crisis, but this study provides a systematic examination of a wide range of additional intra-alliance disputes, from the Korean conflict and ANZUS to the Falklands war and the various events in the Middle East and Persian Gulf. Regrettably, the book was written one year too early and was unable to incorporate the questions about NATO cooperation arising out of the gulf war. Nonetheless, Stuart and Tow do an excellent job of providing a framework and a historical context for assessing the events of 1991.

Focusing primarily on the tensions arising between the three alliance leaders, the United States, Great Britain, and France, the book provides a rich portrait of both the competing interests and the personalities involved, capturing, for example, the acerbic exchanges between Henry Kissinger and Michel Jobert in the mid-1970s over alliance cooperation in the Middle East. Stuart and Tow do not shy away from judgments, either. They explain Britain's special relationship with the United States, for instance, by describing Britain as "being treated by Washington like a venerable but somewhat doddering great-aunt rather than an essential ally." They place the blame for this at the feet of the British as much as the Americans.

The book presents a useful and clearly delineated classification of disputes and responses and considers the impact they have had on the alliance. It also touches on the centrifugal impact of the independent policies of other allies, such as Turkey, Greece, Spain, and Portugal. While not its major purpose, the book does make an effort to relate its analysis to more general theories of alliances.

Stuart and Tow conclude that although most allies expect alliance cooperation in their out-of-area-problems, they seldom get it; and that the lack of cooperation is no deterrent to unilateral action. So long as there was an underlying consensus on the Soviet threat to Western

Europe, the alliance could overcome these competing interests; in its absence, NATO is likely to collapse.

HAROLD MOLINEU

Ohio University
Athens

AFRICA, ASIA, AND LATIN AMERICA

BRASS, PAUL R. *The New Cambridge History of India*. Vol. 4, pt. 1, *The Politics of India since Independence*. Pp. xvi, 357. New York: Cambridge University Press, 1990. No price.

How can the shifting patterns of contemporary Indian politics be captured in a work expected to provide a benchmark for historians for many years? The previous *Cambridge History of India* ended with a volume issued in 1932. Paul Brass dates his preface 27 February 1989, presumably his cutoff date. Since then we have seen the rise of the Bharatiya Janata Party as the main contender for power, the death of Rajiv Gandhi, and the general election of 1991, together with many less disturbing developments. Brass tackles his problem by subsuming the chronological approach in a structural analysis of the forces shaping the contemporary scene. What seems to emerge is that the Nehru era, with its regard for democratic, federal norms, did not set the foundation for the Indira and Rajiv regimes that followed.

Ideology has collapsed underneath social and economic pressures, though it is still invoked all the time. Brass organizes his material under three main headings: political change; pluralism and national integration; and political economy. His work is marked by a strong unifying context, incorporating a wealth of significant illustrative detail. From his references and citations we discover just how thorough his background work has been. If this book is not an easy one to read, this is certainly not because the author writes in an obscure style; it is because he has aggregated all the features of the world's largest political system that has operated the apparatus of democracy. He depicts Indian politics as inherently unstable. He argues that the economy is "based on rural-urban disparities and gross inequalities in income." There has been a drive "for equality with the advanced industrial countries . . . measured in terms of the output of iron and steel, the size of the [gross domestic product], possession of modern weaponry" but not in terms of internal social and economic equality. Analyses "come primarily from the Marxist Left who retain an unshakeable faith in centrally-directed planning, huge public investments," and so forth. Paradoxically, this critique emphasizes the wealth of the better-off farmers—often termed "kulaks"—as the main cause of rural poverty. Brass alleges that the main beneficiaries of development policies are actually the politicians "and their corrupt allies and dependents in the bureaucracy."

Altogether, the Brass assessment of the contemporary Indian polity is grim. The center routinely suspends the powers of the state governments. Corruption has filtered up into the elite administrative service so that "nothing can be done without payment." Violence is an accepted feature of the police, and for many a police job "is a way to make illegal income."

Brass advocates a drastic reduction in the swollen ranks of the bureaucracy. Not, perhaps, very probable. He questions whether "India's recent political difficulties are a pre-fascist stage": the entire system is in crisis. Many Indian scholars will question this interpretation, but, when it is supported by so much carefully marshaled evidence, his indictment is not easy to dismiss.

HUGH TINKER

University of Lancaster
England

LIBBY, RONALD T. *Hawke's Law: The Politics of Mining and Aboriginal Land Rights in Australia.* Pp. xxvi, 175. Perth: University of Western Australia Press, 1989. $A25.00. As of March 1992, University Park: Pennsylvania State University Press, 1992. $16.95.

This is a sound and intellectually attractive book. While Ronald Libby deals with what in a sense is a case study, the study exposes significant features and forces in Australian political life, underscores many of the dilemmas that surround the issue of development versus social justice and life quality, and offers perspectives on relevant theoretical questions. The book is underpinned by sound scholarship and includes critical data gleaned from previously unaccessed sources.

The book is basically about the manner in which the mining industry in the state of Western Australia, long well connected with government and relatively complacent about its preferred position, was given a rude shock by the election of Australian Labor Party (ALP) governments in Western Australia and at the federal level. The ALP came to office broadly committed to legislating substantial land rights for Aboriginals, which would include Aboriginal authority to regulate mining and even to veto it. These ends were being pressed not only by various sectors of the Aboriginal community, but by activist white lobbies as well.

The result was the mounting by the mining industry of a spirited campaign to frustrate Labor's intentions. Its success was short of complete but significant nonetheless. Libby argues that such success was not gained through conventional lobbying of the formal political system. Rather, it foremost resulted from a powerful, publicly directed publicity strike. As Libby writes, the publicity campaign transformed an unpopular issue with a low public profile into an unpopular issue with a high public profile. Fear of surrendering the economic growth benefits conferred by overseas earnings through natural resources and, second, popular unease about massive concessions to Aboriginals were the nerves touched.

Alarmed public opinion in turn frightened Brian Burke's state government, leading it to forsake serious land reform. Bob Hawke's Labor government in Canberra was somewhat less pusillanimous but not politically untroubled. It was loath to force itself upon its sister party in Western Australia, and in the event, it was badly fractionalized by an intraparty debate in which principle and pragmatism variously contended.

The question of Aboriginal land rights persists in Australia. While Libby's book does not address the issue qua issue, it does help to illuminate it and reasonably informs the reader of Aboriginal circumstances in the Australian sociopolitical context. It also, of course, throws light on federalist influences, ALP politics, real or perceived public opinion movements, and the dynamics of lobbying, with special reference to business. Relationships among groups, publics, and public authorities are especially usefully treated. The application to non-Australian settings is largely inferential, but the Australian-based lessons and conclusions are transportable. The book is more suggestive than persistently overt in linking its argument to the wider literature relating to social science theory. But, as suggested, it is sufficiently clear in raising wider questions so as to be recommended as something other than a good-value, self-standing case study.

HENRY S. ALBINSKI

Pennsylvania State University
University Park

OLSON, ROBERT. *The Emergence of Kurdish Nationalism and the Sheikh Said Rebellion, 1880-1925.* Pp. xix, 229. Austin: University of Texas Press, 1989. $35.00.

The Sheikh Said rebellion of 1925 was the first large-scale Kurdish nationalist rebellion. Robert Olson's book is the first English-language work to discuss it in detail, amplifying Martin van Bruinessen's *Agha, Shaikh and State: On the Social and Political Organization of Kurdistan* (Utrecht, 1978). It is based on Olson's original research in the British Air Ministry archives, covering the period from 26 February 1926 to January 1927. The bulk of the book, therefore, is concerned with British policy toward Kurdish nationalism. However, Olson places this discussion within the overall context of Kurdish nationalism as it developed from the last quarter of the nineteenth century, and he concludes with a chapter describing the international implications of the Sheikh Said rebellion.

Among the most interesting aspects of Olson's analysis are those dealing with the continuity of Kurdish nationalist activity over the past century and, relatedly, the weaknesses within the Kurdish movement that continue to prolong the struggle. Olson carefully delineates the salient characteristics of Kurdish society in this regard: multiple dialects, urban-rural distinctions, Sunni-Shi'ite-Alevi rivalry, tribal-nontribal differences. Yet he makes perfectly clear that the exigencies of primarily British and Russian imperial politics in confrontation with post-World War I Turkish, Armenian, Arab, Greek, Soviet, and Iranian nationalism severely exacerbated inter-Kurdish rivalries. Olson also chronicles the development of international support for the idea of an independent Kurdistan, as expressed in the Treaty of Sèvres and by the League of Nations. In the process, he allows readers to judge the tragic consequences—in light of the most recent revival and frustration of Kurdish nationalism in Iraq—of imperial powers' disregard for international opinion.

The Emergence of Kurdish Nationalism offers a particularly enlightening analysis of disputes within Britain over imperial policy toward Kurdish nationalism. In a passage that could, with slight alterations, apply to the current crisis, Reader Bullard, a member of Britain's Middle East Department, criticizes in 1922 the plan to incite Kurdish nationalism as a bulwark against possible Turkish expansion: "Is it seriously proposed that we should stir up the Kurds against the Turks and then leave them to be massacred when we have secured the political advantage we desire?"

Olson's work is essential reading for scholars of the modern Middle East. It is not for beginners; the author refers to relatively obscure events such as the Franklin-Bouillon Treaty without explanation. Some scholars will find its lack of detailed analysis of the economic implications of British policy disappointing, and scholars of contemporary Islamic movements will probably take issue with Olson's scant reference to the relationship between religious and political movements in the region. Nevertheless, in light of recent events in Iraqi Kurdistan, Olson's analysis of imperial machinations acquires a chilling aura of prescience.

TAMARA SONN

St. John Fisher College
Rochester
New York

PEDLAR, NEIL. *The Imported Pioneers: Westerners Who Helped Build Modern Japan.* Pp. 228. New York: St. Martin's Press, 1990. $39.95.

Reading this book for review purposes, I was at first inclined to dismiss it as not serious scholarship, certainly lacking in appropriate documentation and containing only a cursory bibliography of what one might call oddball items on the history of modern Japan. For example, with the exception of Edwin Reischauer and Richard Storry, none of the leading post-World War II scholars of modern Japanese history is mentioned in the bibliography. One has no idea whether Pedlar has read them or not, but one suspects not.

Nonetheless, this reviewer, who immodestly admits to being one of those unmentioned leading post-World War II scholars of modern Japanese history, found himself unable to put the book down, even while feeling increasingly irritated at its poor organization, lack of documentation, inclusion of irrelevant detail, repetitions, and occasional preachiness. Why? Because on page after page, I found tidbits of information, details about individuals, situations, and relationships between foreigners in Japan and between foreigners and Japanese during the nineteenth and early twentieth centuries that I had not come across before, details that are no longer discussed in the scholarly literature on modern Japanese history.

For example, did you know that German Dr. Franz von Siebold, sneaking into Japan as a Dutchman from Batavia, brought the first smallpox vaccine to Japan, and that Britisher Sir Harry Parkes arranged a meeting in 1871 that resulted in smallpox-vaccination stations being established in Japan? I did not and was glad to find out. But, author Pedlar continues, the recent (November 1986) introduction of AIDS into Japan "has been blamed squarely on foreigners," which "xenophobic response will no doubt increase." This observation is but one example of a tendency to combine fascinating pieces of historical information with not very relevant comments on present-day Japan. Another curious juxtaposition has the book end with the U.S. occupation, while "the computer revolution" is mixed with "international marriages" in the book's introduction. One could say that Pedlar needed an editor for organizational assistance.

Let us not criticize too much, however, lest we lose sight of the fact that *The Imported Pioneers* is an immensely valuable collection of the kind of informational detail usually available only in hard-to-find primary sources, which Pedlar has assuredly scoured even though he rarely documents them. I can say this quite confidently, I believe, because on the few occasions when he does, somewhat lackadaisically, cite a source, it turns out to be correct and even precise. Thus on page 207 he quotes Clara Whitney, and sure enough *Clara's Diary: An American Girl in Japan* (edited by William M. Steele and Tamiko Ichimata [Tokyo: Kodansha, 1978], pp. 234-35) has the quote almost exactly as he puts it. He says that "1500 invitations" were sent out for the fancy-dress ball given at the Rokumeikan in November 1884. Clara actually spelled out the number "one thousand five hundred." Otherwise correct. He also shows up some phonies, such as Clive Holland, a turn-of-the-century expert on Japanese culture who probably never stepped foot in Japan (pp. 200-204).

Thus I think we may be confident that the literally hundreds of fascinating pieces of information on what foreigners contributed to "modernizing" Japan are accurately portrayed as given, even to his contention that the *jinrikisha* (man-powered vehicle) was invented, or at least reinvented, by American Jonathan Goble as suitable transport for his sickly wife,

Eliza (pp. 74-79). And far beyond rickshas were buildings, railways, newspapers, lighthouses, bridges, photography, legal system—all influenced in very specific ways by Westerners whose characters are presented in colorful detail in this book. It is well worth reading.

HILARY CONROY

University of Pennsylvania
Philadelphia

EUROPE

BEICHMAN, ARNOLD. *The Long Pretense: Soviet Treaty Diplomacy from Lenin to Gorbachev.* Pp. xiv, 303. New Brunswick, NJ: Transaction, 1991. No price.

Editor's Note: This review was written in the summer of 1991.

This is a curious book. Minor errors are very few: the order of "Socialist" and "Soviet" in official nomenclature is reversed (p. 164); the chronology of the Bolshevik Revolution and the elections to the Constituent Assembly is reversed (p. 72); Rapallo was 1922, not 1924 (p. 178); "Edward," not "Edwin," is the first name of arms specialist Luttwak (pp. 48, 232)— and that is virtually all. The book is loaded with quotations; it is difficult to remember a case where they bulk quite as large; very many of them are in the footnotes. The quotations have been assembled from fools and scoundrels, great men—who should have known better— uttering nonsense, sensible scholars, statesmen, and journalists. The division into eleven chapters seems haphazard and is neither chronological nor clearly topical; the chapter headings come from Gilbert and Sullivan, Afanasiev's Russian folktales, and an experienced journalist's flair for colorful phrase, but they do not help the reader to follow the degvelopment of the argument. The central contention of the book is that signing agreements or treaties with the USSR is unwise, as shown by seventy-odd years of Soviet diplomatic history, but much of the volume is designed to show that the Soviet domestic system has not changed and is unlikely to do so. Three appendices give a chronology of events in Afghanistan, of Soviet annexations and the like from 1919 to 1980, and a list of Soviet treaty violations.

If ever a historical treatment of a topic was called for, it is here. The nature of Soviet aims from the first and of the Soviet system under Stalin are not in dispute, even among many Soviets today. The question is, How significant are the changes in the Soviet Union since 1953 and especially since 1985? A large part of this book simply begs the question, treating the entire post-1917 period as part of the same seamless web, with some astonishing consequences. Philip Mosely's fine analysis of Anglo-American negotiations with the Soviet Union during World War II, written in 1951, is quoted as if it applies to 1991, despite Beichman's acknowledgment elsewhere that Gorbachev is, after all, not Stalin. The Berlin wall is discussed as if it still existed when the book was written.

The treatment of the Brezhnev Doctrine is especially exasperating. George Shultz is quoted as saying in 1985 that it means that "once you're in the so-called 'socialist camp,' you're not allowed to leave"—as if most of Eastern Europe had not left since then and as if in the Asian part of the "socialist camp" there had not arisen such complexities that Moscow may have better relations with Seoul than with Pyongyang. A few pages later it is suggested that the doctrine had its demise in December 1989; next, Beichman declares that the "fact is" that the Brezhnev Doctrine remains an integral part of Soviet foreign policy and "is no more amendable or revocable than the political power of the CPSU." That sounds conclusive, but there follow several more back-and-forth pages on the same point, so that the reader is finally baffled.

Beichman seems to subscribe to the view that the essence of Soviet politics and Soviet military doctrine today is "the inevitable clash—not necessarily a military clash—between the United States and the Soviet Union." This would be news to many highly placed people in both countries. No matter how Leninist President Gorbachev remains, several important changes have taken place. The Soviet economy has nearly ceased to function, and leaders acknowledge that only the West and its system offer a remedy; the republics have significantly limited the power of the central government to do anything; 60,000—by a count in 1989—voluntary groups exist outside the Communist Party and many non-Communist political parties are among them. Quite true, the KGB is still strong and the dead hand of the *apparatchiki* lies athwart the path of reform; as of July 1991 *glasnost* is an astonishing success despite recent limitations on it, and *perestroika* is largely a fiasco despite efforts to revive it. All of this requires careful calibration and cool analysis. But 1951 does not tell us what Gorbachev or Yeltsin or the USSR Supreme Soviet will do in 1991. Beichman declares—twice in three pages (pp. 257 and 259)—that "the world is leaving behind the era of Marxism-Leninism," but almost all of the book defends the thesis that "nothing fundamental has changed in the Soviet Union" and nothing can change while the USSR "bases itself on Marxism-Leninism." In fact, the world has been transformed during the last three years—this is especially true after the abortive coup of August 1991—and Beichman needs to look again at what has happened.

DONALD W. TREADGOLD

University of Washington
Seattle

KAHN, DAVID. *Seizing the Enigma: The Race to Break the German U-Boat Codes, 1939-1945*. Pp. xii, 337. Boston: Houghton Mifflin, 1991. $24.95.

David Kahn, historian extraordinaire of ciphers and codes, here gives us not only the first complete account of the role of ULTRA signals intelligence in the World War II campaign against Germany's *Unterseebooten* but also the best concise history of how Poland, France, Great Britain, and the United States broke the supposedly unbreakable ciphers created by German Enigma machines. If the reader wishes to consult one book and only one on the ULTRA secret, *Seizing the Enigma* should be it.

The word "codes" in the subtitle actually refers to the keys, the settings of the wheels or plugs of an Enigma machine, that had to be understood to permit the deciphering of German messages. It was mastering the frequently changed keys that proved the most difficult task in reading German ciphers—ciphers, that is, because they were essentially cryptograms that worked by letters rather than, as in codes, by words. The keys to the ciphers of the Kriegsmarine, the German Navy, proved particularly impervious to Allied cryptographers, and, as Kahn shows, penetrating them ultimately depended on a series of espionage ventures to capture instructions for the key settings.

Capturing the keys would have done little good, however, had it not been for the previous success of cryptanalysts in replicating German Enigma machines and their workings. The foundation was laid by Poland's Biuro Szyfrów, or Cipher Bureau, which during the 1920s and 1930s far surpassed any other country's ability to thwart German encipherment.

The Poles began reading Enigma encipherments as early as December 1932, and they continued to do so with varied success through the rest of the 1930s. This achievement is rendered all the more remarkable by the fact that, through most of this period, the French did not share with them their own success in obtaining German keys from a spy, Hans-Thilo Schmidt. Relatively full sharing of code-breaking secrets by Poland, France, and Great Britain began only at a Warsaw meeting on 24 July 1939, on the eve of war. Thereafter, the superior—because larger—resources of Great Britain combined with the fruits of the Poles' earlier breakthroughs to permit the Government Code and Cypher School at Bletchley Park, some fifty miles northwest of London, to carry Britain into the lead in seizing the Enigma.

The Germans calculated that to break the ciphers of even their early, relatively simple Chiffriermaschinen Aktien-Gesellschaft Enigmas would require computations lasting 900 million years. In theory they were correct. The breaking of the ciphers occurred not because of defects in the machines but because of human carelessness and error. Too many operatives enciphering messages, especially in the Luftwaffe and the Army, set the keys in predictable patterns. Too many messages repeated the same or similar words predictably. Too frequently the same or similar messages were entrusted to lesser codes as well as to Enigma ciphers, giving the cryptanalysts cribs in the former messages that they could use to enter the latter.

But the Kriegsmarine operatives were shrewd and careful enough not to slip up in these fashions very often. As late as 1941, Hut 8 at Bletchley Park, the Naval Section of the Government Code and Cypher School, was solving naval ciphers only irregularly and occasionally. Solutions tended to consume too much time to save ships from submarines in the Atlantic. Then, on 7 May 1941, the German weather trawler München was captured in the North Atlantic in an enterprise designed by the Operational Intelligence

Centre of the Admiralty specifically to take enemy cipher information. The seizure yielded the Wetterkurzschulüssel, or Short Weather Cipher, which, along with the fortuitous capture of U-110 off Iceland two days later, permitted Hut 8 to penetrate other Kriegsmarine ciphers with heartening regularity and often in real time, soon enough to frustrate U-boat operations. By the end of 1941, however, the Germans had again changed the keys enough that Kriegsmarine dispatches could be read only sporadically. The falling off of British countersubmarine effectiveness was so dramatic that it might well have aroused German suspicions about what had been going on since May, if the entry of the United States and the incredible carelessness of American shipping against the submarines in early 1942 had not distracted the Germans.

When the final triumphs of the Allies over Kriegsmarine ciphers at last occurred in 1943, nevertheless, "the role of the United States in breaking the naval Enigma eventually equaled Great Britain's." Just as German breaking of Allied ciphers—which Kahn also discusses—did not win the battle for the Kriegsmarine, so also the Allies had to translate deciphering victories into operational victories in order to win the war. Kahn completes his history with a judicious assessment of the contributions of all of the Allies' relevant assets, especially their air power and their eventual closing of the mid-Atlantic gap in aerial coverage.

"Exceptional" remains the operative word to describe Seizing the Enigma. Kahn's book stands out in its completeness, its judiciousness in interpretation, its accuracy, and the author's ability to make the esoteric subject of ciphers comprehensible to the layperson.

RUSSELL F. WEIGLEY

Temple University
Philadelphia
Pennsylvania

MOSKOFF, WILLIAM. *The Bread of Affliction: The Food Supply in the USSR during World War II.* Pp. xvi, 256. New York: Cambridge University Press, 1990. $49.50.

The Soviet Union during World War II was a nation of hungry people. Aside from the Party elite, everyone had less than enough to eat, many suffered from malnutrition, and several million starved. For at least the second time in a generation—the first being during the famine of 1922-23 on the Volga—cannibalism made its appearance. Of the nations allied against Nazi Germany in Europe, only Russia had to fight an all-out war against hunger at the same time that it fought a total war against the Germans.

Combining a mass of carefully assembled economic data with solid historical research, William Moskoff chronicles the sufferings of the Soviet people during World War II and explains how they survived. Integrating a thorough combing of printed and archival sources with material drawn from a series of poignant interviews with survivors, *The Bread of Affliction* is a monument to well-done research that adds a very human dimension to the impersonal statistics of suffering and death that emerge from the printed sources. Together, these tell a tragic tale, all the more so because the suffering was in part a consequence of an economic system that placed ideological truth ahead of real accomplishment.

From the beginning, the war with Nazi Germany tested the Soviet system and found it wanting. The Soviets paid a painful price for Stalin's infatuation with the bizarre theories of the quack biologist T. D. Lysenko, who believed that wheat could be made to grow in the freezing north, that sugar beets could be conditioned to flourish in the hot summers of Central Asia, and that the deadly viruses that had cut the world's output of potatoes could be overcome simply by planting new crops in the fall rather than the spring. Elevated to the status of revealed scientific truth by his admirer in the Kremlin, Lysenko's crackpot theories removed hundreds of thousands of hectares from production at the very time when every available bit of land needed to be used productively to offset the loss of 40 percent of the Soviet Union's prime agricultural lands to the Germans.

But the Lysenko fiasco was only one failure among many whose consequences condemned the Soviet people to greater suffering than other Allies had to bear. As events showed all too quickly, the Soviet system simply could not fight against the Germans and hunger at the same time, and, although Soviet planners gave highest priority to feeding the Red Army, even its best soldiers suffered hunger at the most critical moments. Soldiers defending the approaches to Moscow in November 1941 received only 200 grams of bread a day, and, although their food supplies improved after 1943, Red Army soldiers still had to forage for food in their own country until the war's end. For civilians, the situation was much more desperate, with starvation becoming a major cause of death throughout the first two years of the war.

As in their efforts to recover from the devastation of World War I and the Civil War of 1918-21, Soviet leaders turned sharply away from their system in 1941-44 so as to free private initiative to accomplish what they could not. In the end, only the peasantry, its productive forces set loose by what Moskoff describes as the Soviet government's decision to jettison ideology, "in essence turning a blind eye to 'exploitative' activities of the peasantry in the collective farm market," managed to keep the Soviet people alive. "The evidence," Moskoff tells us, "suggests a conscious policy of allowing free markets to do what the government could not do itself."

Moskoff may underemphasize the impact of U.S. Lend-Lease food shipments at the peak of the Soviet food crisis. Although the food sent by the United States during the war years came to a bit less than ten ounces per day for each soldier in the Red Army, the fact that even that small amount actually was almost half again as much as Red Army soldiers fighting in defense of Moscow received from their own quartermasters makes that figure more significant than it now seems. Such quibbling, though, is not meant to detract from Moskoff's broad and impressive accomplishment. This is the best book on the subject yet to appear in any language, and it is a delight to have it in print.

W. BRUCE LINCOLN

Northern Illinois University
De Kalb

UNITED STATES

CAPPS, WALTER H. *The New Religious Right: Piety, Patriotism, and Politics.* Pp. xii, 246. Columbia: University of South Carolina Press, 1990. $27.95. Paperbound, $12.95.

In this survey of leaders of the new religious Right and their worlds—Jerry Falwell, Francis Shaeffer, the Bob Joneses, Jim and Tammy Bakker, and Pat Robertson—Walter Capps presents some portraits and draws some conclusions relevant to the discussion of American civil religion. These portraits are based on attendance at meetings, interviews with the protagonists and their lieutenants—there are lots of direct quotations—and a reading of their literature; the portraits are evenhanded, with an effort to take the intentions and intellectual worldviews of each seriously as well as to analyze the nature of their appeal and their place in American religious and political life. The result is a balanced,

well-told account that should serve as an introduction to these figures for the general reader. But there are few surprises, apart perhaps from the inclusion of Shaeffer with the other, better-known figures. The importance of Shaeffer's thought in the evangelical and Fundamentalist worlds is brought out, with connections made between it and the political agenda of the religious Right.

It is in the opening and closing chapters that Capps develops his argument that the religious Right is, as such, more a political and nationalistic than a religious phenomenon, with its primary concern being devotion to the nation and its revitalization as a "Christian America." The movement is convinced that America has a decisive role to play in the unfolding of God's plan for the world. Capps argues that the ideas of the religious Right represent a conservative alternative to the mainstream forms of civil religion that have flourished in the United States, noting that earlier commentators such as Robert Bellah could write Fundamentalism off as marginal to American civil religion; this, he is convinced, is no longer possible.

For all its excellence as an introduction to the topic for the general reader, there are some limitations to Capps's work. The most important of these is that the religious Right is rather narrowly defined and treated in isolation from the larger history of Fundamentalism and evangelicalism in America. There is little reference to the standard literature on these subjects and little historical context. There has, after all, always been a political agenda for at least some important Fundamentalists, and much of what his subjects say about America's role and destiny under God echoes earlier themes now grown anachronistic to the wider public and thus seems to me the persistence of elements of civil religion long abroad in the culture rather than a clear-cut alternative to earlier versions of American civil religion.

DEWEY D. WALLACE, Jr.

George Washington University
Washington, D.C.

FELDMAN, EGAL. *Dual Destinies: The Jewish Encounter with Protestant America*. Pp. xi, 339. Champaign: University of Illinois Press, 1990. $34.95.

Egal Feldman has provided a detailed, comprehensive, narrative history of Protestant-Jewish relations in the United States. The scope of the volume extends from the European roots of both Protestantism and Judaism to the recent relationship between Israel and the American Christian Right. This impressive work is certain to become a standard reference in the history of American anti-Semitism.

Feldman's sensitive and nuanced analysis suggests that American Protestants have always felt a deep ambivalence about Judaism. Among more conservative, "evangelical" Protestants, Judaism has been regarded as the source of an inerrant Old Testament and as the source of Christianity itself. The state of Israel also figures prominently in the premillennialist theology that characterized many Protestant fundamentalists. The Jews' refusal to accept Christ, however, has regularly led to virulent anti-Semitism on the part of many conservative Christians. Similarly, more liberal Protestants have lacked the religious particularism necessary to sustain consistent anti-Semitic feelings but have often been repelled by what is taken to be Judaism's excessive legalism. Thus different traditions within American Protestantism have promulgated distinctive Jewish stereotypes.

Feldman's historical account suggests that Jews have suffered from negative stereotyping and prejudice from all quarters of American Protestantism. While the particular relationship between Jews and Christians varies according to circumstances, an inability to accept Judaism on its own terms is a constant characteristic of Protestantism in the United States. Along this line, Feldman's description of the "unrelenting" efforts of Christians to convert Jews is most instructive. Even among leaders or denominations relatively tolerant of Judaism, Jews are regarded as "pre-Christians" or "potential Christians" rather than as carriers of an autonomous, authentic religious tradition.

The pervasiveness of anti-Semitism in the United States suggests that the religious freedom of American Jewry cannot be attributed to any positive characteristics of Protestantism in this country. Jewish-Protestant coalitions are ultimately unreliable and unstable. Rather, the religious liberty of Jews is preserved in the United States through the diversity of American Protestantism. Protestant, anti-Jewish coalitions are difficult to form and maintain, due to the theological and stylistic diversity of Protestant churches in the United States.

The major strength of this volume is its detail and its documentation. Feldman has produced an impressive work, which is likely to guide future scholarship for some time to come. The most obvious weakness is the relatively weak analysis. Feldman does not settle on an analytical framework at the outset of his work but allows the reader to become overwhelmed in the mass of historical detail. While Feldman does draw some conclusions in a brief concluding chapter, the readability of this volume would have been enhanced if a few explicit themes had been established and if the events of particular historical periods had been organized around these themes.

Apart from this stylistic quibble, I find this volume to be a fascinating, and potentially very important, historical work.

TED G. JELEN

Illinois Benedictine College
Lisle

FOERSTEL, HERBERT N. *Surveillance in the Stacks: The FBI's Library Awareness Program*. Pp. x, 171. New York: Greenwood Press, 1991. $39.95.

The significance of this book is that it highlights the part played by libraries—and free access to them—in the maintenance of democracy, and it charts in great detail the ways in which the recent Library Awareness Program of the Federal Bureau of Investigation (FBI) undermined this function. Foerstel quotes the description by Dr. V. Gregorian, former director of the New York Public Library, of libraries as institutions to be valued because they are " 'the only unifying neutral ground for all the elements of our culture; libraries are the only tolerant institution we have in our culture.' " Foerstel argues that "tolerance is simply a commitment to personal liberty from which support for intellectual freedom flows naturally."

Foerstel poses the dilemma between, on one hand, freedom of information to all citizens and the right not to have their use of information monitored by state agencies in violation of their constitutional rights and, on the other, the national security interests of the state in regulating access to the rich technical and other information resources of the United States. Foerstel unequivocally comes down on the side of the former and dismisses the national security reasoning behind the FBI Library Awareness Program, which is viewed as the latest example of the exercise of politically unaccountable and legally questionable bureaucratic executive power in U.S. history.

The FBI Library Awareness Program involved attempts to gain access to library records in order to determine the reading habits of foreign—or even foreign-sounding—nationals and to enlist the support of library staff in monitoring the behavior of their clients. The broader context of what, at first, might appear to be laughable domestic intelligence and counterintelligence activities is the fear of the FBI and other groups that, in an age of electronic global communications systems, the Soviet Union or another potentially hostile power could take advantage of the open society that prevails in the United States in order to gather technical and scientific information to aid its economic and military efforts to compete with the United States. A central issue posed here is whether it is morally legitimate and legal for an intelligence agency to attempt to monitor and restrict the reading habits of U.S. or foreign citizens where the reading materials concerned have been given no security classification but are publicly available in libraries and their range of data bases. Here, as Foerstel suggests, the FBI has sought to develop the view that data in aggregate, gathered through data-base scanning, can be security relevant even if they are harmless when considered individually. Foerstel shows that the legal basis of this reasoning is highly questionable, however.

Much of this book recounts in detail the background of the FBI Library Awareness Program: its location in New York and its connection with related initiatives elsewhere; its public exposure and in particular the reaction of librarians to this challenge to their professional ethics. In the early chapters, the argument tends to get bogged down in a welter of rather repetitive quotations from the key individuals involved—one of whom is the author himself—so that one has to await later chapters for more sustained analysis and contextualization. Indeed, the opportunity to provide a firmer historical and institutional analysis of the FBI as a domestic intelligence agency is lost, with only brief sketches provided of this important issue.

The book regains its strength and vigor in the later chapters, where central problems concerning the law related to freedom of information, the privacy of the citizen, and the operations of the FBI are discussed ably and provocatively. Here discussion focuses on whether library records are subject to privacy rules concerning FBI and police agencies or indeed inquiries from private organizations and individuals.

As Foerstel argues with great conviction, libraries are central to the democratic process through helping to create an informed critical citizenry, free of the fear of having their legitimate reading activities illegally monitored or regulated. Insofar as national security interests provide a constraint on such activities, these interests should be subject to due legal process. Once data are in libraries, they are in the public realm and should not be subject to politically unaccountable and legally questionable activities of state agencies armed with their own definition of sensitive information. This definition as used by the FBI in relation to what Foerstel refers to as its rather paranoid intelligence activities reveals the uncertainties of this and other groups at a time when the military competition with the Soviet Union is now being eclipsed by the economic and technological competition with Japan.

CHRISTOPHER DANDEKER

King's College London
England

FRIEDENBERG, ROBERT V. *Theodore Roosevelt and the Rhetoric of Militant Decency.* Pp. xviii, 209. Westport, CT: Greenwood Press, 1990. $42.95.

CAMPBELL, KARLYN KOHRS and KATHLEEN HALL JAMIESON. *Deeds Done in Words: Presidential Rhetoric and the Genres of Governance.* Pp. ix, 275. Chicago: University of Chicago Press, 1990. $27.50.

In the middle of the Progressive Party campaign of 1912, candidate Theodore Roosevelt walked out of his Milwaukee hotel and was shot by a fanatic. The bullet smashed a rib and lodged just below the left lung. Pushing away doctors, Roosevelt rushed to the hall, boomed out to the crowd, "I have just been shot, but it takes more than that to kill a Bull Moose," then spoke for almost an hour. (John Garraty, *Theodore Roosevelt: The Strenuous Life* [New York: American Heritage, 1967], p. 123.)

Few politicians have better understood the power of rhetoric than Theodore Roosevelt, the subject of Robert V. Friedenberg's *Theodore Roosevelt and the Rhetoric of Militant Decency,* one in a series of book-length case studies of great American orators. Friedenberg, of Miami University, traces the evolution of Roosevelt's public speaking career. We see Roosevelt grow from a 24-year-old finding his public voice while serving in the New York State Legislature to one of this century's most effective speakers. A thorough review of Roosevelt's speeches—many of which are included in the second part of the book—reveals that the president was such an effective public speaker because he really believed in what he was saying. Roosevelt was, in fact, a statesman whose policy positions were a natural outgrowth of deeply held convictions about such things as the duties of citizenship, the role of government in a democratic society, and America's place in the world. Passion, however, is a necessary but not sufficient quality for effective public address. Thus Friedenberg deftly identifies many of the rhetorical strategies Roosevelt used so superbly, such as historical examples, concrete images, and powerful language.

Because Theodore Roosevelt is such a compelling subject, and the presentation is so well executed, this book is a terrific read.

The authors of *Deeds Done in Words*, Karlyn Kohrs Campbell of the University of Minnesota and Kathleen Hall Jamieson of the Annenberg School for Communication of the University of Pennsylvania, use a wider lens to analyze presidential rhetoric. They isolate and examine recurring patterns in presidential speeches. For example, they open the chapter on presidential inaugurals by arguing that presidents try to accomplish four things in their maiden speech to the nation: (1) they try to unify the audience in order to legitimate the transfer of power; (2) they remind the audience of values that they have in common; (3) they discuss the political principles that will guide the new administration; and (4) they try to demonstrate that they recognize the requirements and limitations of the office. Vivid examples culled from inaugurals illustrate different levels of rhetorical success presidents have experienced. Other chapters—which focus on State of the Union messages, war rhetoric, the rhetoric of impeachment, and the rhetoric of veto messages—are organized in a similar fashion and provide equally important insights.

Both of these books provide a useful and important framework with which to discuss and assess as well as appreciate presidential speeches. Given the power of the presidency and television's wide reach, citizens should have a better un-

derstanding of the rhetorical strategies presidents have used and still employ to win their support.

FRED SMOLLER

Chapman University
Orange
California

GORDON, LYNN D. *Gender and Higher Education in the Progressive Era*. Pp. xiii, 258. New Haven, CT: Yale University Press, 1990. $29.95.

From the 1880s until 1920, women constituted a growing minority in institutions of higher learning in the United States. In *Gender and Higher Education in the Progressive Era*, Lynn D. Gordon explores the experience of this second generation of college women. To support important conclusions linking women's college culture and the social ferment of the Progressive Era, Gordon closely examines two coeducational institutions, the University of California at Berkeley, which admitted women in 1870, and the University of Chicago, which included women from its inception in 1892, and three women's colleges: Vassar College, H. Sophie Newcombe Memorial College, and Agnes Scott Institute. The result is a good geographical mix but one that privileges the experience of students at private institutions.

Gordon uses letters from students and alumnae, faculty papers, and college newspapers and literary magazines to paint a vivid portrait of women's lives within the academy. Self-conscious about the responsibilities that educational opportunity thrust upon them, college women sought to distinguish themselves by excelling intellectually and setting high standards of campus conduct. Yet, unlike their women teachers, who were members of the pioneering generation of American college women, the second generation hoped to marry, raise children, and combine a useful life with a happy family.

At the three women's colleges, students brought arguments on woman's place into classrooms and campus social life, often confronting male adminstrators' prejudices and female professors' preconceptions. On coeducational campuses, women experienced deliberate exclusion from college traditions, extracurricular activities, and sometimes even courses themselves. There, women students mitigated the resulting emotional toll by carving out separate, woman-run and woman-centered spaces. Chicago women, with the support of strong female teachers, administrators, and local activists, created social and service organizations within the academy that produced strong female leaders. They used these organizations to influence college traditions and activities in which men participated. Berkeley women, lacking this combination of resources, failed to mobilize women's groups and remained second-class citizens on campus. Furthermore, women at Chicago and Vassar influenced the curriculum content by lobbying for and flocking to courses in social work, economics, and sanitary science.

Gordon devotes individual chapters to each institution, rather than employing a topical or chronological approach. As a consequence, her development of women students' links to Progressive Era activism is less successful than her rendering of the academic world itself. Moreover, Gordon's laudable attempt to add regional perspective by including two southern women's colleges is thwarted by her uncritical acceptance of southern conservatism. In New Orleans and Atlanta, the urban settings of Newcombe and Scott, respectively, progressive projects flourished, including suffrage associations, settlement houses, and labor initiatives led by college women. That Gordon finds little such activism among Newcombe and Scott students may be a reflection of the conservatism of these two private schools rather than the interests of southern college women at large.

Gordon's work makes an important contribution to the current debate on multiculturalism on campus. Her research suggests that accommodating special-interest groups with separate organizations can foster their identification with educational institutions and increase their influence on campus. Moreover, it reminds us that the curriculum has never been static but has reflected the needs and interests of students, as it should in a democratic society.

GLENDA ELIZABETH GILMORE

University of North Carolina
Chapel Hill

HIRSCH, ERIC L. *Urban Revolt: Ethnic Politics in the Nineteenth-Century Chicago Labor Movement.* Pp. xvii, 253. Berkeley: University of California Press, 1990. $39.95.

The creation and re-creation of an American working class is a subject that has long intrigued scholars. In part, this fascination stems from what many authorities believe are unique patterns of development in the United States. Professor Eric Hirsch's insightful study adds to this ongoing debate by exploring the dynamics underpinning the nineteenth-century mobilization of the Chicago labor movement and relating these matters to existing theories of urban social and political movements. As an ethnically diverse city experiencing the effects of massive industrialization and urbanization, Chicago offers excellent opportunities for a case-study investigation.

The main contours of Hirsch's argument can be quickly stated. He finds that the present theories of mobilization—Marxist; classical urban social movement; resource mobilization; and solidarity—cannot adequately account for the highly organized activism that took place in Chicago. By examining the adjustment patterns of Anglo-American, Irish, and German workers, he downplays the importance of class consciousness, social disorganization, and bureaucracy as critical factors in promoting revolutionary movements. Rather, he posits the central role of "ethnically based havens" in producing revolutionary ideas and tactics. Within these relatively isolated areas, a complex blend of old-world and new-world conditions shaped the ability of each cluster of workers to respond effectively to the larger forces besetting them. The social networks and cultural resources peculiar to each group were particularly important. Hence each major working-class group responded quite differently. In the end, "the use of ethnic ties, culture, and language to mobilize the revolutionary movement in Chicago proved to be a two-edged sword. It allowed the creation of a strong, highly mobilized, very militant movement, but it confined that movement to a minority of the working class."

In terms of source materials, this is a synthetic book that is based almost totally on secondary works, and all save one are in the English language. Hence Hirsch has not carried out primary research from an insider's perspective of the ethnic groups themselves. Although Chicago is unusually blessed with a body of excellent published works on ethnic life, the source foundation of the present work ensures that no original historical

material appears. Specialists in immigration and ethnicity, therefore, will find nothing new in terms of the historical narrative. Additionally, despite Hirsch's disclaimer that Chicago had such unusual traits as an urban center that it was impossible to generalize, one wonders if an attempt at larger generalization was not possible. To be sure, the book argues eloquently for the need to be attentive to the demands of historical specificity in attempting to understand movements as complex as labor mobilization among ethnically diverse workers. Yet, will it ultimately be necessary to write similar assessments of each large industrializing city in America?

These observations aside, this volume makes a decided contribution in providing a sensitive and focused discussion of the development of the labor movement in an important American urban center. Moreover, it is a skillfully written, tightly argued, and soundly organized work of scholarship. It deserves wide attention.

GEORGE E. POZZETTA

University of Florida
Gainesville

HYMAN, MICHAEL R. *The Anti-Redeemers: Hill-Country Political Dissenters in the Lower South from Redemption to Populism.* Pp. ix, 252. Baton Rouge: Louisiana State University Press, 1990. $39.95. Paperbound, $16.95.

The outlines of the political conflict that Michael R. Hyman describes in *The Anti-Redeemers* have long been familiar to students of the New South. The bitter struggles over state subsidies, taxation, and railroad regulation that divided white Southerners in the late 1870s and 1880s, pitting small farmers and producers against large planters and commercial interests, are staples of the region's political history. Hyman's book, with its close focus on the hill-country dissenters of Georgia, Alabama, and Mississippi, adds new detail to the story.

After sketching the social, economic, and political contours of his selected counties, Hyman traces the evolution of the insurgents' political ideology by examining several issues that raised the question of the proper role of the state in late nineteenth-century society. For example, proposals to build a new county courthouse or subsidize local railroad construction aroused immediate opposition among the white small producers, as did attempts to retain an appointive judiciary or establish a state agriculture department. The hill-country whites, steeped in Jacksonian rhetoric and republican values, opposed any policy that seemed to favor special interests or weaken the voice of the people. The expenditure of tax dollars for internal improvements and government programs designed to aid town dwellers, large farmers, and commercial interests was anathema to the small producers. At the heart of their ideology was the conviction that government should act in the interest of the general citizenry. That conviction also underlay their strong support for state regulation of corporations and their defense of black civil and political rights.

Hyman's admiration for the hill-country dissenters does not blind him to their weaknesses. The anti-Redeemers lost most of their battles; they were never able to present a sustained challenge to the conservative Democrats. Yet their struggle, even in defeat, helped lay the foundation for the Populist uprising of the 1890s. Hyman protests that the post-Reconstruction insurgencies were more than "merely a prelude to Populism," but his emphasis on the gradual radicalization of the small producers seems a minor revision.

Hyman's sympathetic yet balanced account of the hill-country whites who fought to keep ordinary people at the center of democratic politics is solidly grounded in the traditional sources for political history—manuscript collections, government records, newspapers—and buttressed by quantitative analyses of census figures, roll-call votes, and election returns. For all his digging, however, Michael Hyman has not really broken new ground with *The Anti-Redeemers*. At most, he has plowed some fresh furrows in an already intensely cultivated field.

CAM WALKER

College of William and Mary
Williamsburg
Virginia

JONES, NORRECE T., Jr. *Born a Child of Freedom, Yet a Slave: Mechanisms of Control and Strategies of Resistance in Antebellum South Carolina*. Pp. viii, 331. Middletown, CT: Wesleyan University Press, 1991. $24.95.

Norrece T. Jones's intention in this book is to provide a case study of the way in which South Carolinian plantation owners controlled their slaves and thereby to call into question much of our current understanding of the dynamics of plantation slavery. Jones tilts at several recent studies of slavery—Peter Kolchin's *Unfree Labor* (1987), for example—but reserves most of his sharpest criticism for Eugene D. Genovese's *Roll, Jordan, Roll* (1974), whose arguments about the paternalistic nature of slavery are, Jones implies, little more than a recycling of the planters' own beliefs. While Genovese's thesis allows him "brilliantly" to portray planter ideology and the way in which non-slaveholding whites and small slaveholders were ensnared by this worldview, it prevents him from understanding the slaves. According to Jones, there is little evidence that South Carolinian slaves internalized the paternalist ethos of their masters.

For Jones, the most appropriate metaphor for describing the slave system was not paternalism but the state of war. A small minority of white planters developed an elaborate series of repressive and brutal mechanisms that allowed them, for the most part, to keep their human property servile. Chief among these mechanisms was the threat of the sale of recalcitrant slaves out of the state. In what is clearly the best chapter in the book and, in fact, the best treatment of the subject in the literature, Jones shows how the very strength of the slaves' culture—their attachment to family, friends, the land, and the dead—made this such a potent weapon. Other chapters, which detail the way in which rewards and punishment, and religion, were used to divide and rule the slave population, support Jones's contention that the South Carolinian slaves were a constantly restive population kept in check only by a cruelly oppressive regime.

The research undertaken for this book is certainly impressive. Jones has been assiduous in mining a wide range of sources, and many who will not subscribe to his argument will nevertheless find much that is useful in this volume. The emphasis on the role of force and repression on the plantation does provide a useful corrective to some of the excesses of historians who have focused solely on slave culture; notwithstanding the vigor with which Jones puts his case, however, I at least was not fully persuaded. Jones seems somewhat blinkered in his pursuit of Genovese and at times inattentive to the nuances in his own sources that occasionally suggest ambiguity and the possibility of a less cut-and-dried interpretation. Though, in the end, the parts of this book are rather more convincing than the whole, *Born a Child of Freedom* should still be read by all those interested in the

history of the South's peculiar institution.

SHANE WHITE

University of Sydney
New South Wales
Australia

MARKS, PATRICIA. *Bicycles, Bangs, and Bloomers: The New Woman in the Popular Press*. Pp. 222. Lexington: University Press of Kentucky, 1990. $22.00.

KITCH, SALLY L. *Chaste Liberation: Celibacy and Female Cultural Status*. Pp. 225. Champaign: University of Illinois Press, 1989. $24.00.

Bicycles, Bangs, and Bloomers: The New Woman in the Popular Press by Patricia Marks and *Chaste Liberation: Celibacy and Female Cultural Status* by Sally Kitch are two fascinating studies that analyze very different topics to reach conclusions about female power and empowerment. Kitch focuses on celibate symbolic belief systems of three turn-of-the-century utopian communities—Shakers, Koreshans, and Sanctificationists—so that she can "challenge familiar constructs and suggest new visions of cultural change." Marks studies the late nineteenth-century frame of mind through the satire and caricature that appeared in the popular press of Great Britain and the United States so that she can "put the twentieth century in perspective, particularly in terms of women's expanding sphere." Yet, the emphasis in both books is the changing roles of women in the home and in the broader society and how these changes related to women's power. Kitch makes the statement that "the achievement of female power . . . is best understood in light of the taboos or barriers that have been broken." In her study, the broken taboos and barriers are sexual. Women, many of whom were married, eliminated sex from their lives and chose celibacy as the means to achieve gender equality. In the Marks book, the New Woman challenged the "old protective assumptions about . . . physical frailty and mental incapacity" when she changed her hairstyle—to short hair with bangs—and her style of dress—to bloomers—and started riding bicycles. In both books, women were rejecting male dominance by significantly changing their behavior.

Some interesting differences are found in these two studies of turn-of-the-century women. First, *Chaste Liberation* looks at the beliefs of three very nonmainstream groups while *Bicycles, Bangs, and Bloomers* uses information from the mainstream comic press, which caricatured dangerous trends in a broad spectrum of the female population. Second, one book looks at women who purposefully and voluntarily separated themselves from sex and marriage while the other identifies "redundant" women, who, because of the size of the female population, could not marry and had to support themselves outside of marriage. Third, in the Kitch study, celibacy was the key to the ideal of a cooperative, communal, unified society; in the Marks book it is education that was seen as the driving force behind the New Woman's quest for personal independence. Finally, there are differences in how changed women were perceived by those around them. The celibate Shaker, Koreshan, and Sanctificationist women were viewed positively, and it was thought that they had developed "heightened powers of spiritual perception." The behavior of the New Woman, on the other hand, was portrayed in the popular press as loose and immoral.

The similarities between the books, however, overshadow the differences. First, in both there is an emphasis on paradox. In Marks, the lives of Queen Victoria and her symbolic granddaughter, the New Woman, are similarly paradoxical. The queen's "stubbornness in dealing with affairs of state, her persistence in a mode of dress seen to be distinctly unfashionable and politically unwise . . . much of this mixture can be traced in her cultural granddaughter." The paradox for the believers in the three religious communities was that they "connected celibacy with the spiritual unity and social equality of the sexes despite the physical separation of celibate men and women."

Second, the issues discussed in both books are relevant to the world of the late twentieth century. For example, feminists of today are still dealing with the issue of gender hierarchy in both the family and the working world, the difficulties experienced by women crossing from the domestic private sphere into the public arena, and the fear and resistance of many to women's rejection of male domination in both spheres. In addition, the last chapter of *Chaste Liberation* offers a discussion of the "relevance of celibate symbolism . . . for such modern feminist issues as female reproductive freedom . . . the relationship between sex and power in today's society, and the new interest in chastity as a feminist statement." The women studied in the Kitch and Marks books threatened the traditional order of the society of their times; the same is true of women today who may not wear bloomers or practice celibacy but are economically self-sufficient and purposefully independent.

MARY ANN E. STEGER

Northern Arizona University
Flagstaff

RISHEL, JOSEPH F. *Founding Families of Pittsburgh: The Evolution of a Regional Elite, 1760-1910.* Pp. xii, 241.

Pittsburgh: University of Pittsburgh Press, 1990. $34.95.

DeVAULT, ILEEN A. *Sons and Daughters of Labor: Class and Clerical Work in Turn-of-the-Century Pittsburgh.* Pp. xii, 194. Ithaca, NY: Cornell University Press, 1990. $21.50.

Both social historians and sociologists have shared a continuing interest in the origins and nature of the American social class structure and the actual extent of status mobility within the system. Rishel's and DeVault's studies are two of the most recent efforts by social historians to improve our understanding of the nature of the American social class structure during a particularly important period in its history at the turn of the century. Each provides a longitudinal type of analysis of a different group within the Pittsburgh population's status hierarchy based on group biographies constructed from data taken from the vast array of the social historian's traditional armamentarium of data sources. Census data, in turn, are used not only to enrich the descriptions of individuals and families but to reconstruct the social and economic contexts within which their lives and work were given meaning at the turn of the century.

Founding Families of Pittsburgh, by Joseph F. Rishel, is based on an extensive longitudinal analysis of 1006 individuals traced from a sample of twenty eminent families for the period from 1760 to 1910. Every existing data source was painstakingly searched to enable Rishel to paint a detailed portrait of the lives of the early "elite" and the transformation of the relatively autonomous local social/economic structures within which the founding families lived to a national elite where professional success was measured in terms of more universalistic criteria for membership in the upper class. Rishel shows not only that eminent families composed a clearly defined coherent upper class but that they were, by and large, successful in maintaining their status over time as the local social/economic structure of the founding families was transformed to a national elite where professional success was achieved more and more through formalized instruction at preferred institutions of higher learning and where upper-class status was maintained through appropriate marriages. He attributes much of their success to the founding families' "accumulation of advantage," defined as "a combination of achievement opportunity and the psychological readiness to promote oneself to even higher levels."

A major objective of Rishel's study was to determine the degree of openness of the class system at this particular juncture in time and locale of American capitalism. Specifically, and perhaps uniquely, his tenacious pursuit of individuals through records allowed him to examine downward mobility as well as status maintenance or improvement not only for those remaining in the original study area but for those who out-migrated as well. By and large, the founding families were able to adapt their "accumulation of advantage" to the changing character of the larger society's organizational structure, achieving a remarkable stability in the percentage of successful members in each generation. While founding-family names remained prominent in the upper classes, the "accumulation of advantage" from preceding generations was not always sufficient to guarantee a secure position in the upper class. About one-fourth of the founding-family members in each generation were found to have declined in status, in spite of the fact that the old elite did not have to be displaced to make room for the new. Rapid population growth and technological change continued to produce more opportunities for upward mobility, as might be expected in a relatively open society.

Sons and Daughter of Labor, by Ileen DeVault, is also concerned with status mobility within the same population in the same era, but it focuses on the opposite end of the class structure from Rishel's elite. Specifically, it addresses the origin and growth of the white-collar class and the status ambiguities of the boundary between low-level white-collar workers and the skilled manual blue-collar worker. DeVault's work is based on a unique data set: the enrollment records of the Pittsburgh Central High School's Commercial Department from 1891 through 1903. Combining individual data gleaned from city directories, the 1900 Manuscript Census, and a Marriage License Index, DeVault created a collective biography of the students of the Commercial Department that allowed her to examine post-schooling outcomes of former students in relation to the social origins of parents or guardians.

This is worthwhile reading for those seeking a better understanding of the changing nature and degree of openness of the American class structure to mobility on the part of those with blue-collar backgrounds, but it contributes little to the resolution of the ideological debate as to whether or not the interests of the lower-level clerical white-collar workers were better served by these workers' aligning themselves with the working class, from which most of them came, or identifying themselves with the values and goals of the manager/owner class. The problem with this study, as with most studies based on secondary data sources, is that the data are seldom the most relevant for addressing the questions being posed by the investigator. In DeVault's case, many of the questions remain unanswered, but most readers will undoubtedly be more highly sensitized to the complexities of the issues and resistant to oversimplified versions of America's class structure and theories of social mobility. As noted by DeVault, the rapidly expanding clerical sector was not monolithic in growth but deeply divided by gender, worker's experience, nature of the work performed, and type of training required. At times, DeVault's explanations seem unnecessarily complex and vague. She attributes the predominance of native born of German and Irish stock among the city's clerical workers to a "convoluted interaction of employer's prejudices and desires for a malleable work force and preferences and prejudices of the women workers and their families." Consideration of a simpler immigrant-assimilation paradigm might have provided a more parsimonious explanation.

DeVault's general conclusion is that "the collar line is not so much of a social chasm as it was a social estuary, a site for the mingling of economic groups and social influences." While interesting, a "maybe" type of answer to the question as to whether or not there are real differences between blue-collar skilled manual workers and white-collar clerical workers is somewhat disappointing given the time and effort required for her research. The study is rich in descriptive detail, but the data serve more to illustrate than to test specific hypotheses. *Sons and Daughters of Labor* and *Founding Families of Pittsburgh* both have something to tell us about the American social class structure. The latter provides evidence of some downward mobility among elite families and their descendants as a demonstration of the openness of the Pittsburgh social class structure at the turn of the century. The former, in examining the emergence of the white-collar class during the same period and the feminization of the clerical and sales occupations, provides for a better understanding of the origins of current gender gaps and the bases for persisting pay inequities. It is encouraging to see social historians concerned with problems of sampling and with the statistical significance of differences between groups and to see them making greater use of population census data to fill in the details of individual cases as well as to paint the broader picture. One can only hope that social historians, like Rishel, who state that they will never undertake another study requiring such enormous expenditures of time and energy, are not really suggesting that the results were not worth the effort.

WARREN E. KALBACH

University of Toronto
Mississauga
Ontario
Canada

SCHWENINGER, LOREN. *Black Property Owners in the South, 1790-1915.* Pp. xiv, 426. Champaign: University of Illinois Press, 1990. $50.00.

DOYLE, DON H. *New Men, New Cities, New South: Atlanta, Nashville, Charleston, Mobile, 1860-1910.* Pp. xix, 361. Chapel Hill: University of North Carolina Press, 1990. $39.95. Paperbound, $12.95.

Loren Schweninger has done pioneer work in researching the struggle of black Americans to enter the mainstream of American economic life. In the past, most Reconstruction historians have concentrated on the poverty and repression of the masses of freedmen by the crop lien system and the consequent perpetual indebtedness. Schweninger does not challenge the accuracy of this well-established interpretation, but he concentrates on proving that many blacks made supreme efforts to secure their economic independence, and he shows that a considerable number succeeded.

Schweninger goes beyond the few state-specific studies of property ownership among blacks that have been made and gives us the first study of black property ownership of all the South down to 1915.

He makes a painstaking analysis of the census returns, probate records, and state and county assessment records of all Southern states as well as wills and real estate inventories.

Schweninger found the concept of private property alien to African heritage due to the emphasis on communal ownership in ancestral Africa, but black Americans soon saw land ownership as the most positive symbol of freedom. After the Civil War, blacks showed a passion for ownership of the land that they had toiled on for generations.

In the antebellum South, the greatest number of black landowners were found among the free blacks of Louisiana and South Carolina, but after the Civil War former slaves in the upper South had the largest percentage of black-owned lands. Rural blacks made small gains in the upper South, but the most dramatic change in property ownership occurred in the towns and cities of the border states.

Despite racism, lynchings, and coercive action by government and society, blacks clung to the idea that acquisition of land and property would free them from the burden of the past. "Their tragedy and the region's tragedy was that it never would," Schweninger concludes.

Don H. Doyle investigates the nature of the new order in the South after the Civil War. He finds that the business class in the New South were in the vanguard of economic and cultural change, and he concludes that the Civil War emancipated the urban South as well as the slave.

Four cities were chosen to illustrate the varying changes that occurred. Nashville and Atlanta were directed into the new order by self-made men who came from the interior of the South and exploited every avenue for progress. In contrast, Charleston and Mobile were directed by the old cotton factors and brokers who resisted change. They looked backward to the past and their cities soon became stagnant.

Doyle is at his best when discussing post-Civil War race relations in the New South. He agrees with C. Van Woodward that segregation and legalized Jim Crowism did not rise from the traditions of the plantation but were invented by the new order in the rising cities. Doyle reasons that the failure of paternalism in the developing cities of the New South was due to the fact that blacks could not always rise to the level of their talent and potential.

Charleston adhered to the patterns of the antebellum South, and strict residential segregation did not exist. Family servants enjoyed a protected status under white patronage as former slaves or as later-day servants. But, Doyle concludes, Charleston's blacks, as a group, were much worse off than Atlanta's blacks despite the fact that Atlanta's social policies were not implemented with an even-handed justice with respect to blacks.

Both books are significant additions to the study of Southern history.

VICTOR B. HOWARD

Morehead State University
Kentucky

SOCIOLOGY

BARON, LARRY and MURRAY A. STRAUS. *Four Theories of Rape in American Society: A State-Level Analysis.* Pp. xiv, 250. New Haven, CT: Yale University Press, 1989. $25.00.

In this controversial book, Baron and Straus attempt to present a structural analysis of four theories of rape: gender inequality, pornography, social disorganization, and legitimate violence. They conclude by presenting an "integrated theory," derived from the Chicago school of sociology, theoretically informed by Durkheim, and relying on social disorganization as the central explanatory variable. They present what they believe to be the evidence for these theories in close to forty tables of state-level data, all but one quantitative. There is no experiential or case material; the study is completely macrosociological. One does not hear the voices of women who have been raped or of rapists.

Baron and Straus use the Uniform Crime Reports (UCR) to measure how much rape occurs in a state, although the UCR reflects only rapes that have been reported to, and then labeled as genuine by, police. Not only are the overwhelming majority of rapes not reported, especially non-stranger rapes, but many of those that are reported to the police are not "founded" by the police or charged by the states' attorneys as sexual assault. Reported and founded rapes are disproportionately rapes by strangers. Even so, for the case to be considered a genuine rape, the police and prosecution must think that the woman would be found credible by a jury or a judge. Thus the woman must not have been known to drink, especially before the assault, must have no history of "promiscuity" or sex with the assailant, and must have no mental illness. It helps if she was physically attacked in addition to the rape and has the bruises to show it. Finally, she must be willing to be a witness for the prosecution. In the ongoing study by one of us—Bart—of acquaintance rape, only the aggravated cases met most of these criteria. Therefore, even if Baron and Straus's quantitative methods were flawless, their results would be applicable only to a small subset of actual rapes.

In fact, though, the path analysis that caps the work and purportedly demonstrates the superiority of the social disorganization theory of rape has serious flaws. It is computed from a correlation matrix of state-level indicators. Such analyses are gravely suspect, both because the number of cases is limited to 50 and because the correlations are ecological ones at best—since a state is a grouping of dissimilar communities and not a homogeneous social unit. The high degree of multicollinearity in the matrix poses further problems, as do the vague conceptual nature and debatable operationalization of most of the variables in the model. For example, "social disorganization," Baron and Straus's key variable, is assembled from measures of divorce, interstate mobility, single parenting, irreligion, and tourism. The most solidly constructed variable in the model is the variable for sex magazine circulation, whose correlation with the UCR rape rate, by state, is .64. Explaining away this correlation is an important theme of this work, which carries on a long-standing dispute between Straus and feminists on the causes of violence against women.

Baron and Straus present a path model in which social disorganization accounts for rape, sex magazine circulation, and some other things. Other strong relationships involving social disorganization—for instance, a strong association with the proportion of a state's population that is male—are labeled as exogenous correlations and not reported outside of appendix B. Baron and Straus estimate the coefficients of their path model one path at a time by ordinary least squares. Using this technique makes specification error—that is, the error of having the wrong model to start with—impossible to detect. It does not help their estimation process that they routinely reset coefficients to zero if they are not statistically significant at the .05 level, a practice that is guaranteed to eliminate real effects and bias the reported ones where, as here, the number of cases is low and multicollinearity is high.

Consequently, Baron and Straus are unsupported in their belief that they have proved their own social-disorganization-based path model better than others. But even in their own model, the effect of social disorganization on rape is mostly mediated by sex magazine circulation. Having found this unwanted effect, they claim it to be spurious, since they have "greater skepticism" that such an effect can exist than in the case of any other part of their model. This is at best a flat admission that their analysis does not test the theories it is supposed to test.

Though Baron and Straus claim to be feminists, their bias against and ignorance of feminist theory are evident. For example, in one section nonfeminist theoreticians are listed under the heading "Social Scientists, Philosophers, and Attorneys," while feminist scholars such as law professor and political theorist Catharine A. MacKinnon are listed under the contrasting heading "Feminists." Baron and Straus state that feminists say that rape is about violence, not sex; in fact, the more recent theorists such as MacKinnon and Scully say that in a society where dominance is eroticized, rape is, of course, about sex. On the basis of hearsay, Baron and Straus charge that antipornography feminists have aligned themselves with right-wing groups; in fact, conflict between the two is frequent. As a last example, Baron and Straus's categorization of pornography and gender inequality as separate causes of rape ignores the feminist analysis of pornography as a form of the subordination of women. Sexual harassment in the workplace, for example, is not only linked with pornography but often takes the form of pornography.

In positing social disorganization as the cause of rape, Baron and Straus cite the deleterious effects of the breakdown of the institutions of society, while admitting that this breakdown promotes gender equality. Thus they ignore the analysis of patriarchy that states that it is precisely social organization, not disorganization, that subordinates women and is associated with violence against women. It is the institutions of religion, the state, the economic system, and the schools that provide the support for the nuclear and extended family, in which most violence against women and children takes place. (See M. Becker, "The Politics of Women's Wrongs and the Bill of Rights: A Bicentennial Perspective," *University of Chicago Law Review*, in press.) Most child rape, for example, is done by members and friends of the family. By using the UCR as their measure of rape, Baron and Straus exclude rapes by husbands, grandfathers, uncles, brothers, priests, ministers, indeed the very upholders of those institutions of social control that in fact furnish normative support for violence.

Since all forms of violence against women are interconnected—battery, rape, incest, sexual harassment, and, in our analysis, pornography as the ideology providing the vocabulary of motives justifying the rest—all are linked to these institutions of control. Against this, Baron and Straus can argue at most that social disorganization is associated with rapes of a certain type—namely, those by strangers—occurring and/or being reported to and founded by the police.

Baron and Straus diagram a utopia in which society reorganizes around gender equality and where rape withers away like the state after the revolution. We wish!

PAULINE B. BART

University of Illinois
Chicago

PETER KIMBALL

American College of
  Healthcare Executives
Chicago
Illinois

FURSTENBERG, FRANK F., Jr. and ANDREW J. CHERLIN. *Divided Fam-* *ilies*. Pp. vi, 142. Cambridge, MA: Harvard University Press, 1991. $18.95.

One of the grand illusions of social science is that empirical data are objective and neutral and therefore can provide the grounding for rational and humane public policy. The more data we collect, it would seem, the better the policies we can recommend. One of the great self-deceptions of contemporary American society is that children are a national priority. Confusing sentiment for practice and policy, the intensity of protestations of concern about children's welfare seems inversely related to public and private actions that jeopardize their physical and psychological well-being. Perhaps nowhere is this more apparent than on that battleground we call the family. *Divided Families* represents the efforts of two highly respected sociologists to synthesize what researchers have found about the effects of divorce on children and to make recommendations regarding divorce law and public policy, recommendations intended to minimize the damaging effects of divorce on children.

Given the authors' understanding of their task, they have done a fine job—a wide range of studies from a variety of disciplines are clearly and concisely summarized and integrated in jargon-free language that is accessible even to the general reader. First, the problem of divorce is located in sociohistorical context; successive chapters focus on the process by which marriages dissolve, the disastrous economic consequences of divorce, children's troubled adjustments to divorce, and remarriage and its effects on children. One of the dilemmas of divorce is that it places parents in a position where the pursuit of their own well-being is often at odds with the needs of their children. Since Furstenberg and Cherlin's primary concern is the impact on children, they present the parents' perspective only with partial sympathy. Fathers look especially bad, providing appallingly inadequate economic support, if any, and almost as little in the way of emotional availability and relational consistency.

There is one glaring error in the discussion. Throughout the book Furstenberg and Cherlin follow the divorce history of a hypothetical couple, Helen and Herb. In describing the economic inequality of the divorce settlement they use gross income figures and fail to take into account deductions for taxes, health insurance, and retirement, thereby presenting an exaggerated picture of Herb's postdivorce affluence relative to Helen's impoverishment. The realities of divorce economics are stark enough to make the point without such distortion.

It is when Furstenberg and Cherlin turn to policy recommendations that the limits of their narrowly data-based approach are most apparent. Not one of their recommendations addresses the need to have fathers accept financial and emotional responsibilities for their children. Instead, their proposals—better economic support for the custodial family primarily through assured child support benefits and better collection of (father's) payments, which is a good recommendation, and physical custody with the primary caretaker (read "mother" even if Furstenberg and Cherlin will not say it) —are unimaginative and directed to the most narrow interpretation of children's and parents' postdivorce needs. Every feature of the current marital and familial situation in America is accepted as if it had the same inflexibility as the structure of the solar system. These recommendations, at most, can only help us manage a problem that calls out for solutions, solutions that *Divided Families* cannot even help us to imagine.

HOWARD GADLIN

University of Massachusetts
Amherst

GREEN, EILEEN, SANDRA HEBRON, and DIANA WOODWARD. *Women's Leisure, What Leisure?* Pp. xi, 189. Hampshire, England: Macmillan Education, 1990. $35.00.

PYLE, JEAN LARSON. *The State and Women in the Economy: Lessons from Sex Discrimination in the Republic of Ireland.* Pp. xiii, 202. Albany: State University of New York Press, 1990. $15.95.

One of the central lessons of feminist scholarship is that the dividing line between the workplace and the family is exceedingly porous. Policies and strategies aimed at changes in one arena may lead to unexpected results in the other if attention is not paid to the complex ways in which women's work and home lives intersect.

In her important study of economic policy in the Republic of Ireland, Jean Pyle examines one such unexpected finding: between 1961 and 1981, the share of Irish women who participated in the labor force remained virtually unchanged and women's share of the labor force rose only slightly, in sharp contrast to changes in the rest of Western Europe and in other countries pursuing similar export-led development.

Pyle rejects a number of alternative explanations for this stagnation, including changes in relative wages—neoclassical economic theory predicts that women's share of employment will fall if women's wages rise relative to men's— and distributional shifts—women's share of employment will fall if employment in female-dominated industries shrinks relative to male-dominated industries. Instead, she argues convincingly for a feminist approach, using "a theory of gender inequality which incorporates the role of the state and assesses the impact of a broad range of state policies (employment policies along with reproductive rights and family policies)."

During the period in question, a number of policies favored men's employment, including a marriage bar for service industries until 1973, restrictions on night work and heavy lifting through much of the period, limited access to contraceptives, and laws against divorce and abortion. Pyle argues that these policies kept women out of specific jobs and, by keeping fertility rates high, in the home. In addition, the agency responsible for attracting multinational industry to Ireland explicitly favored industries that would employ men, putting forward men's employment as a criterion for the award of financial incentives. In a creative blending of public choice theory, Marxist theory of the state, and feminist theories of the patriarchal state, Pyle argues that these policies were maintained because state personnel faced contradictory ways of furthering their own tenure in office: through successful economic development and by supporting the traditional, male-dominant family.

The contemporary importance of these findings cannot be exaggerated, as export-led development continues to dominate development thinking. Careful coordination of work and family policies and consideration of the conflicting agendas of policymakers are needed if women are to benefit from economic development. This book should prove useful to scholars of economic development, the role of the state, and public policy affecting women. Technical material such as regression analysis is confined to appendices, so the book is accessible to nonspecialists.

In *Women's Leisure, What Leisure?* Eileen Green, Sandra Hebron, and Diana Woodward draw on a range of British theoretical and empirical work to study a realm of women's experiences about which relatively little is currently known. The first two chapters are devoted to a reconceptualization of leisure that rejects the dichotomy between work and leisure and sees them as "a complex set of experiences involving degrees of freedom and constraint." This is especially important since the home, the site of much of women's leisure, is also simultaneously the site of most demands on their time from partners and children. In contrast, much of men's leisure takes place in public arenas such as pubs and sport stadiums.

Working within a socialist feminist theoretical framework, Green, Hebron, and Woodward argue that historically constituted structures and processes within patriarchal capitalism have served powerfully to constrain women's leisure. The authors devote attention to the effects of women's low pay, the sexual division of labor in the family and the workplace, and mechanisms of social control such as violence against women, which confines women to the home, regulates their access to public spaces, and delimits their opportunities to enjoy leisure.

Later chapters draw on a variety of sources to explore the social history of women's leisure and contemporary gender differences in leisure. Much of the information is drawn from a 1984 survey of adult Sheffield women, and they quote extensively from these interviews to support a number of conclusions: women enjoy less leisure time and spend most of it in the home, expenditures for women's leisure have low priority in household budgets, and conventional definitions of acceptable womanly pursuits constrain the range of activities from which women can choose. In keeping with their argument that social class, age, ethnicity, labor force, and marital status all work to differentiate the content, the meaning, and the amount of leisure enjoyed by women, special attention is devoted to Afro-Caribbean, Asian, and elderly women.

The book concludes with a brief discussion of ways in which public policies might expand women's access to leisure. In common with Pyle, the authors of *Women's Leisure, What Leisure?* point out the need for policies that address the broad range of women's experiences and the complex ways in which women's workplace and family lives condition one another.

TERESA L. ARNOTT

Bucknell University
Lewisburg
Pennsylvania

HELWEG, ARTHUR and USHA HELWEG. *An Immigrant Success Story: East Indians in America*. Pp. xvi, 297. Philadelphia: University of Pennsylvania Press, 1990. $29.95.

This is a timely volume in light of a growing realization that the so-called new immigration, set into motion by the Immigration Act of 1965, is an ongoing phenomenon. East Indian communities —usually referred to in official documents since the census of 1980 as Asian Indians—are therefore in need of documentation as they come to represent an extraordinary new dimension in U.S. immigration history. An elite population in terms of professional qualifications and income, their story differs greatly from that of earlier waves of immigrants. As exhibited by each additional census since 1970, the East Indian population has grown at a rate that defines it as one of the fastest-growing U.S. minorities. A population that numbered under 35,000 in the census of 1970 has exceeded 800,000 in the census of 1990.

Helweg and Helweg have produced a well-documented volume that will be of interest to specialist and lay person alike since its statistical and sociological data are matched by an easily readable and often personalized style of writing. Many of the interviews, quoted at great length, project a human dimension with which any reader can readily identify.

A particularly valuable feature of the volume is the comprehensive nature of its bibliography, which includes significant materials relating to the East Indian diaspora. Anyone wishing to undertake a study of the origins and historical development of the East Indian communities in the United States would do well to consult this bibliography. One sees the volume, due to the quality of the study as well as its bibliography, as the basic source book on the East Indian experience.

Although one cannot fault the Helwegs for their emphasis on the experiences of the dominant Indian immigrant communities—almost 90 percent of all immigrants are Gujarati or Punjabi and Hindu, Sikh or Jain—a bit more attention to nondominant communities could have added an additional dimension to the study. The complete absence of any reference to Christian or Muslim communities is a notable omission. Mar Thoma Christians who have generated an entirely new ecclesiastical structure for North America, Kerala Roman Catholics who have evolved parishes parallel to existing American parishes in major cities, and Indian Muslims who have played a dynamic role in Pan-Islamic organizations may represent some interesting and different nuances in the East Indian immigrant story.

All in all, *An Immigrant Success Story* represents a major contribution to the literature of the East Indian immigrant experience.

ROBERT YOUNG

University of Pennsylvania
Philadelphia

ISAAC, RAEL JEAN and VIRGINIA C. ARMAT. *Madness in the Streets: How Psychiatry and the Law Abandoned the Mentally Ill.* Pp. ix, 436. New York: Free Press, 1990. $24.95.

At first glance, this volume appears to be a carefully documented study of the political and cultural forces that collectively led to deinstitutionalization—the wholesale release of those mental patients previously housed in long-term institutions. The authors, a sociologist and a journalist, posit a domino theory to explain how deinstitutionalization happened: the first domino fell during the 1960s, when a group of "anti-psychiatrists" led by Thomas Szasz destroyed the existing system of care by closing all the state mental hospitals in the "delusion" that the mentally ill could be better cared for in more normal settings; and the next domino fell during the 1970s, when the "mental health bar" rewrote all relevant laws to prevent any return to involuntary care. Betrayed and abandoned by mental health and legal professionals alike, the families of the mentally ill were left to pick up the pieces, with all the burdens of their relatives' care but with none of the resources that Rael Jean Isaac and Virginia C. Armat consider essential: psychosurgery; electroconvulsive therapy, also known as shock treatment; forced medication; and involuntary hospitalization on demand.

Closer examination, however, reveals Isaac and Armat's heavy dependence on secondary sources, chiefly from disciplines whose interest in mental illness is tangential—the sociology of deviance, for example, is overrepresented, just as clinical material is underutilized—and their pattern of citing only those experts with whom they agree, omitting all mention, except by the occasional snide dig, of opposing views and contradictory evidence. The chapter on electroconvulsive therapy, for instance, presents only one side of a long-standing, complicated debate about a treatment whose effects are poorly understood even by its partisans,

but whose efficacy Isaac and Armat promote without reservation. The authors rely most heavily on interviews, many of them extremely emotional, which they present, largely unexamined, as truth. In the most curious of these, a parade of well-known psychiatrists is permitted to pass off or recant decades of their own work that tends to support the ideas behind deinstitutionalization, with no questions asked.

In the end, *Madness in the Streets* provides no insight into the profound political, social, and economic changes in the way our culture has chosen to deal with the mentally ill over the past several decades, because its real purpose is partisan and confessional, not scholarly. By focusing exclusively and melodramatically on the sufferings of families and the intellectual crises of theoreticians, and by avoiding any suggestion that mental illness might also be a serious problem for the mentally ill, Isaac and Armat arrive at a simple solution that is both emotionally gratifying and politically expedient: turn back the clock and reopen the old custodial institutions where crazies are out of sight and out of mind. If the authors had done any real research into their topic, they would understand at once why this is unlikely ever to happen: long-term custodial care of the mentally ill simply costs too much.

ANN BRADEN JOHNSON
Rikers Island Health Services
Montefiore Medical Center
New York City

LINDHOLM, CHARLES. *Charisma.* Pp. vii, 238. Cambridge, MA: Basil Blackwell, 1990. No price.

This book tries to give an understanding of the relationship between leaders and followers in charismatic movements, primarily in the West. It begins with an elaborate and very helpful discussion of sociological and psychological theories of the passions involved in these movements. Charles Lindholm does not get stuck in the quagmire of what "charisma" means in Weber's work and in that of his followers. In an interesting way, he deals with Hume and Nietzsche and argues that Nietzsche's charismatic leader with his "will to command" is not only an answer to a prevailing utilitarian worldview but is also, as such, intimately related to it.

The more general argument is that there is a tension in modern society "between development of autonomous personal identity and an opposing tendency for self-loss in states of merger." This argument relates Freud's view of the dialectics of attachment and separation involved in love for the leader to a sociological understanding of modern society. What I find missing in this theoretical overview is a discussion of Foucault's theories of desire and modernity. The theoretical part is followed by case studies that deal with the charisma of Adolf Hitler, Charles Manson, and Jim Jones. Although Lindholm calls them ethnographic, they are really not much more than rather sketchy illustrations of his general argument. Moreover, since they are overstudied already, they do not offer the reader much new information. Another difficulty with them is that Lindholm's decision to limit himself to these Western examples—only briefly compared with Bushmen shamanism—seems to imply that modernity is restricted to the West. It would have been very illuminating to include Gandhi in a discussion of charisma and modernity. With these reservations, however, I see this as a useful introduction to the subject for undergraduate and junior graduate teaching in the social sciences and religious studies.

PETER VAN DER VEER

University of Pennsylvania
Philadelphia

ROTHMAN, DAVID J. *Strangers at the Bedside: A History of How Law and Bioethics Transformed Medical Decision Making*. Pp. xi, 303. New York: Basic Books, 1991. $24.95.

David Rothman offers a well-written, lucid—yet surprisingly superficial—account of a significant development: the sharp reduction in medical authority over the last 25 years. Rothman identifies a number of factors contributing to the decline of public confidence in physicians: the 1966 Beecher exposé of dubious research ethics on the part of some medical investigators; the increasing separation of doctors and hospitals from patients and the community exacerbated by the growth of specialization; the technological advances that raised a host of ethical questions ranging from access, as in the case of organ transplants, to the right to die, typified by the Quinlan and Cruzan cases.

Rothman gives less weight than is deserved to developments outside of medicine that had a profound effect: the growth in the 1960s of a challenge to all institutional authority coupled with an ideology of rights that eventually embraced so-called patients' rights as well.

Strong on identifying the factors that led to the challenges to physicians' preeminence in medical decision making, Rothman scarcely attempts to answer the question he raises at the outset: "Was the cure worse than the disease? Did bringing new rules to medicine prove more mischievous than helpful?"

Part of the problem is that Rothman takes at face value much that requires exploration. He assumes that patients have been "victors," achieving greater autonomy through the right to "informed consent" to medical treatment. He does not even refer to the many studies that show patients—even those with average or above average intellectual capacity—have significant difficulties comprehending, not to say evaluating, the information they are now given. Rothman does not explore the extent to which informed consent has come to mean signing informed consent forms, hardly the same thing.

Amazingly, Rothman never discusses psychiatry, the specialty suffering the greatest erosion of medical authority with the most problematic results. Perhaps Rothman avoided psychiatry precisely because he would have been forced to confront uncomfortable issues that he glides over. If informed consent is, as Rothman feels, an obvious ethical requisite in research, how are new psychiatric drugs to be tested on severely psychotic patients whose capacity to give informed consent is by definition in question? As one physician has noted caustically, perhaps the classical medical credo "First of all, do no harm" is to be superseded with a new research dictum, "First of all, do nothing."

In psychiatry, the impact of the right to informed consent has been less to empower patients than to transfer decision making from physicians to lawyers and judges. In many states, patients who refuse treatment—as studies have shown, often on delusional grounds or because they do not realize they are ill—must be brought to court; judges decide whether they shall be treated. In one of the groundbreaking cases, *Rennie* v. *Klein*, a federal judge micromanaged the patient's care to the extent of ruling at different times which antipsychotic medications the patient's psychiatrists should prescribe.

In psychiatry it is impossible to miss that "power to the patient" has been a smoke screen behind which lawyers have maneuvered themselves into dominance over medical practitioners. To a much larger extent than Rothman seems willing to recognize, in other branches of medicine as well this slogan has disguised the transfer of power from one

professional elite to another less qualified to make the relevant decisions.

RAEL JEAN ISAAC

Irvington
New York

ECONOMICS

FINE, LISA M. *The Souls of the Skyscraper: Female Clerical Workers in Chicago, 1870-1930*. Pp. xx, 249. Philadelphia: Temple University Press, 1990. $43.95.

Secretary, bookkeeper, clerk: today we think of these as women's jobs, but it was not always so. Only 120 years ago virtually all U.S. workers in these jobs were men. The office was a male domain, complete with spittoons. The notion of a female secretary was as odd and disconcerting to nineteenth-century Americans as that of a male secretary is now. For a long time, this dramatic change in the sex type of the large occupational category of clerical work did not receive scholarly attention. Traditionally, the interest of labor historians was drawn to workers who were blue-collar, organized, and male. In the last 15 years, however, with the growing interest in women's history, a substantial literature on clerical workers has developed. With *The Souls of the Skyscraper*, Lisa Fine contributes to this literature a carefully researched and richly textured study of clerical workers in Chicago.

Fine takes the title of her book from a poem by Carl Sandburg entitled "Skyscraper," in which he writes that the laughter and sorrows of office girls become part of the soul of the tall building. This literary beginning helps set the tone of the book, which fits more within the realm of cultural than social scientific history. This is no criticism. Fine is well versed in the work of others who have described and tried to explain the feminization of clerical work. She knows what other historians, including those of a more obvious social scientific bent, have offered, and she reviews these contributions carefully and fairly. She does not so much reject social scientific explanations as she adds to them a thick description of the culture in which women clerical workers emerged and took over the office.

This is not to say that she neglects quantitative analysis. Data from the census, the Bureau of Labor Statistics, and the National Industrial Conference Board are all there, clearly displayed and discussed. Additionally, she has exploited a plethora of other data sources: city directories; corporate records; newspaper want ads; information from schools, public and private, that offered training for office jobs; and records of social and charitable organizations such as the Young Women's Christian Association (YWCA), Hull House, and the Eleanor Association, which offered housing and support to many clerical workers.

The sheer quantity of scholarly digging that went into pulling together so much disparate information is impressive. But if Fine had stopped there, this would have been only an ordinary good book. What makes the book extraordinary is the sensitive analysis of the cultural milieu in which women's role in the workplace changed so dramatically. The story takes us from the early days, in which the first brave, pioneering women in the office were "conquering" clerical workers, through the 1920s, by which time women office workers were "conventionalized." Fine uses many elements of popular culture—magazine stories, novels, cinema, advertisements, even postcards—to show us the ways in which women clerical workers were portrayed as they moved from conqueror to convention. Importantly, the voices of the

women workers themselves are heard as well; they are not silent objects in this history. By using their own writings and actions, Fine finds ways of showing us how these women saw themselves.

The Souls of the Skyscraper is an excellent addition to the literature of U.S. social and cultural history. Anyone interested in the changing role of women in the work force will profit by reading this painstakingly researched and well-written book.

ELYCE J. ROTELLA

Indiana University
Bloomington

RICCUCCI, NORMA M. *Women, Minorities and Unions in the Public Sector*. Pp. 189. Westport, CT: Greenwood Press, 1990. No price.

Norma Riccucci has written a painstaking, meticulous, but still inconclusive study of the record of public sector unions in championing the rights of women and minority workers. She begins with doubts about the popular assumption that public sector unions are invariably—or even frequently—progressive on issues concerning affirmative action and equal employment opportunity. Indeed, the evidence she musters shows that her doubts are well grounded. The union record is spotty at best in championing the rights of previously excluded workers. Inconsistencies appear between industrial and craft unions, between union federations and their locals, between greater receptivity to women in some settings and to minorities in others.

To arrive at her conclusions Riccucci surveys the role of public sector unions in a variety of contexts: as participants in joint labor-management committees, as spokespersons for comparable-worth wage policies, as litigants on behalf of workers' rights. In fact, Riccucci's data are drawn almost entirely from appellate court cases involving public sector unions and affirmative action issues. Using appellate court opinions, briefs, and exhibits, Riccucci is able to enumerate some of the structural constraints and uncertainties that shape union behavior: for example, the changing demographics of the labor force, legal obligations to fairly represent all union members and yet to defend existing seniority systems, and ferocious resistance to women by craft unions.

This book represents a useful compilation of information. Its value would have been enhanced, however, by a discussion of the relationship between these data and the larger world of work. We already know that few workplace grievances eventuate in legal complaints, that many complaints are settled before trial, and that only a tiny minority of trial results are challenged at the appellate level.

Some of Riccucci's interpretations also seem problematic. For example, on page 76 she argues that craft unions have been particularly effective in resisting affirmative action because access to their ranks is gained through apprenticeship programs and these, in turn, recruit only from the family or neighborhood networks of already established members. Yet two pages later, on pages 78-79, Riccucci's own data show that craft unions have been relatively more open to minority men than to white women. Are we, then, to conclude that the informal social networks of white male craft workers have expanded to include black men but not the white women in their own homes and neighborhoods? Some discussion of this apparent contradiction would have been in order.

Riccucci's volume, the twenty-eighth in Greenwood Press's series Contributions in Labor Studies, is a helpful compendium, reviewing the role of public sector unions in pressing for affirmative action at the appellate level. It demonstrates that the legal environment within which unions act is inconsistent and that union behavior itself is varied. Therefore, the aspirations of women and minority workers are played out in a field of value conflict and structural uncertainty—with commensurately uneven results. It remains for others to formulate viable strategies at the work-site level for advancing minority interests in this unpromising terrain.

EVE SPANGLER

Boston College
Chestnut Hill
Massachusetts

SHERRADEN, MICHAEL. *Assets and the Poor: A New American Welfare Policy*. Pp. xviii, 324. Armonk, NY: M. E. Sharpe, 1991. $34.95.

The basic argument of this book is that welfare policies for the poor are consumption oriented and, as a result, do not encourage the accumulation of assets. In contrast, welfare policies for the nonpoor tend to come through tax expenditures that facilitate the acquisition of wealth, such as pensions and home equity, while perpetuating the illusion that these benefits are wholly earned by their recipients. For example, federal tax expenditures allowing the nonpoor to exclude or defer taxation on contributions to retirement accounts and to deduct interest on home mortgages almost equals the total direct expenditures on welfare to the poor. As a consequence of this dual welfare system—tax expenditures for the nonpoor and stigmatizing direct welfare expenditures for the poor—the poor are not able to experience the refracted benefits of asset accumulation, which, according to Sherraden would include (1) improved household stability by virtue of the cushion that assets provide for income shocks and crises; (2) the increased concern about the future that can emerge when assets are acquired and their use anticipated; (3) the development of other assets, such as educational credentials and real estate, that becomes possible with even modest wealth holdings; (4) the increased focus and specialization of activities that are possible with the options that asset accumulation allows; (5) the enhanced personal efficacy and sense of personal control that come from possessing assets and using them to achieve goals; (6) increased social influence stemming from social networks that become viable with assets to facilitate communication and negotiation in diverse social spheres; (7) the increased political participation that comes with a financial stake in the society; and (8) the increased welfare of offspring that emerges when assets are accumulated and used to establish long-range goals for children.

The current welfare system encourages just the opposite of these eight outcomes, and, in so doing, it keeps the poor not only financially impoverished but unable to mobilize other resources that they could employ to get out of poverty. What Sherraden proposes is that welfare for the poor should provide the same capacity for asset accumulation that tax expenditures now offer to the nonpoor. For as long as welfare provides only bare subsistence income—both cash and in-kind—that must be consumed, it prevents asset accumulation and encourages short-term thinking, behavior, and consumption. But if savings can be encouraged and subsidized by government, the accumulation of assets will make for higher levels of consumption in the long run, while fostering the eight benefits of asset accumulation previously listed. What is needed, therefore, is an asset-based welfare policy.

At the household level, such a policy would—rather than punish individuals, as current policy dictates—allow them to accumulate assets. It would also promote family stability and enable family members to think about their future and to set goals for their lives. At the more macro, national level, asset-based policies would reduce poverty permanently, develop a more economically sophisticated and astute citizenry, improve the savings rate of Americans, and help the United States be more competitive in the world economy.

The principles guiding this asset-based policy should complement—not completely replace—current income-based policies of the welfare system. But unlike the current income-based welfare system, an asset-based system should be universally available to all citizens, provide greater incentives to the poor and nonpoor alike to save, avoid defining people as on or off welfare, encourage gradual wealth accumulation, provide diverse investment options, promote economic information and training, and foster personal development. To realize these principles, Sherraden proposes the creation of a system of individual development accounts (IDAs), which would be similar to individual retirement accounts (IRAs) and which, like IRAs, would be available to everyone. Such accounts would be structured into employment settings, schools, and community organizations, thereby encouraging every citizen of any age to contribute to the accumulation of assets for their own development. There would be various types of IDAs—for example, ones designed to meet future needs for education, housing, self-improvement, and retirement. To pay for these subsidized IDAs, Sherraden proposes tapping into the current system of tax expenditures for the nonpoor.

Sherraden makes a strong case, backed up with relevant data, which should appeal to both conservatives and liberals alike. He may be somewhat optimistic about the psychological and behavioral benefits to those who accumulate assets, but such a program could hardly make the situation of the poor any worse. Moreover, Sherraden may be underestimating the fiscal costs of his proposal, and he is certainly underestimating the political costs of trying to eliminate current tax expenditures for the nonpoor. Finally, it is hard to imagine that the political climate exists for serious consideration of new domestic initiatives. Yet, Sherraden's proposal is imaginative, and hence it deserves to be kept alive in the debate over welfare policies. For at some time, perhaps in the near future, there may come a new effort to do something about the poor. The ideas in this book offer some stimulating proposals for this future effort, and, for this reason, it marks an important contribution to the literature on inequality, poverty, and welfare policy.

JONATHAN H. TURNER

University of California
Riverside

STEIN, ROBERT M. *Urban Alternatives: Public and Private Markets in the Provision of Local Services*. Pp. xv, 250. Pittsburgh, PA: University of Pittsburgh Press, 1990. $39.95.

City governments continue to face paradoxical demands for traditional service levels and low taxes. Affluent urban actors are mobile within the limits of the metropolitan arena, well informed, and highly sensitive to differences in local tax rates as well as the kind and quality of services locally provided. It follows that the respective tax burdens of voters living within the various municipalities of a metropolitan region had better appear equitable, or else. Acknowledging that there is no single policy measure adequate to the task of resolving the paradox, Stein examines the limited policy option of diversifying the modes of public service provision through municipal service contracting.

This comparative analysis of various means of providing local services is well crafted and is worth reading, carefully, by policymakers and academic urbanologists alike. Stein provides a crisp and critical summary of recent conceptual developments that reflect pressures on local administrations to emphasize infrastructural—such as transportation—over redistributive—such as housing or health—services. His review also explores the convergence tendency of municipal tax burdens within metropolitan regions, and the trend toward minimal service provision among more recently incorporated cities.

A large, national survey of municipal revenues and expenditures provides the empirical basis for the evaluation of existing assumptions about the forces that drive local policy. The survey includes localities under 25,000 in population, providing an important advantage over earlier studies. In his analysis Stein presents a measured explanation of important differences that make the dilemmas of service provision more difficult in some cities than in others. For example, the fixed municipal boundaries between city core and suburban periphery in older metropolitan areas coincides more clearly with social-class divisions and deepens the conflict over taxpayer service preferences.

The study reflects the fact that choices involved in service contracting, and their consequences, are complex, not simply a matter of the privatization of former government functions. Administrative decision makers will be interested in the detailed analysis of the varying impacts that different service-contract choices have on jobs, wages, and service costs. On a service-by-service basis, local governments must weigh the relative advantages of partial versus complete contracting. In addition to the option of contracting with private, for-profit firms, localities also have the option of using nonprofit private firms, or purchasing services from other levels of government—which turns out to be a popular and effective contract choice for many types of services. Stein shows that the rationale for adopting the contract option is often not purely economic. For example, many smaller municipalities elect to contract because some services simply cannot otherwise be justified by the small numbers of individuals who will make use of them. Stein also argues that any savings that result from contracting for services will not be translated into reduced taxes but will be absorbed at the bureau level.

Despite the focus on local service-delivery strategies, Stein does not lose sight of the broader context of policy considerations in which his work must be placed. He warns that local service-contracting strategies are in no way equal to the enormous task of service provision that localities face today and will face in a future of shrinking federal supports. As the responsibilities of cities continue to expand, and as the federal government attempts to curb spending, it would be "naive and irresponsible to suggest that the fiscal plight of America's cities can be remedied by the diversification of municipal service arrangements."

Although Stein does place the limited goals of the book in a broader context, I am left with three concerns, the first two of which are addressed in some measure by the author. The narrowest of these is that Stein was unable to test for differences in the quality of services produced under the various modes of contract. Second, one worries whether the details of the comparative analysis of delivery modes will obscure the warning that contracting for services is a limited and inadequate response to the future service needs of local populations. Finally, there is the conceptual tradition within which Stein operates and to which he addresses his findings. The assumptions contained in this literature are clearly equilibrial, finding expression in the concern for retaining affluent and "productive" elements of the population. This has the unfortunate effect of making the problem the needs of the poor for redistributive services.

Local administrators and policymakers with constant or shrinking resources may find in this volume a practical guide for optimizing the service product they can present to voters. Social scientists, who may be expected to assume a broader view, whether they are political economists or advocates of human agency, should find insight into the structures that constrain imagination and choice at the local level.

WILLIAM G. FLANAGAN

Coe College
Cedar Rapids
Iowa

OTHER BOOKS

ABADINSKY, HOWARD. *Law and Justice: An Introduction to the American Legal System*. 2d ed. Pp. xii, 403. Chicago: Nelson-Hall, 1990. Paperbound, $21.95.

ALLWORTH, EDWARD A. *The Modern Uzbeks: From the Fourteenth Century to the Present, a Cultural History*. Pp. xiv, 410. Stanford, CA: Hoover Institution Press, 1990. Paperbound, $24.95.

ANTOLIK, MICHAEL. *ASEAN and the Diplomacy of Accommodation*. Pp. xiii, 208. Armonk, NY: M. E. Sharpe, 1990. $39.95.

ARONSON, GEOFFREY. *Israel, Palestinians and the Intifada: Creating Facts on the West Bank*. Pp. xxiii, 376. New York: Kegan Paul International, 1990. $29.95.

BANERJEE, TRIDIB and MICHAEL SOUTHWORTH, eds. *City Sense and City Design: Writings and Projects of Kevin Lynch*. Pp. 853. Cambridge: MIT Press, 1990. $50.00.

BARTHOLOMEW, PAUL C. and JOSEPH F. MENEZ. *Summaries of Leading Cases on the Constitution*. 13th ed. Pp. xix, 538. Savage, MD: Rowman & Littlefield, 1990. Paperbound, $19.95.

BARTLEY, NUMAN V. *The Creation of Modern Georgia*. 2d ed. Pp. x, 279. Athens: University of Georgia Press, 1990. $27.50. Paperbound, $12.95.

BEAN, FRANK D., BARRY EDMONSTON, and JEFFREY S. PASSEL, eds. *Undocumented Migration to the United States: IRCA and the Experience of the 1980s*. Pp. 292. Lanham, MD: Urban Institute Press, 1990. $38.75. Paperbound, $21.75.

BERRY, NICHOLAS O. *Foreign Policy and the Press: An Analysis of the New York Times' Coverage of U.S. Foreign Policy*. Pp. 184. Westport, CT: Greenwood Press, 1990. $39.95.

BIANCHI, ROBERT. *Unruly Corporatism: Associational Life in Twentieth-Century Egypt*. Pp. ix, 268. New York: Oxford University Press, 1989. $34.95.

BOHM, ROBERT M., ed. *The Death Penalty in America: Current Research*. Pp. xii, 148. Cincinnati, OH: Anderson, 1991. Paperbound, no price.

BRILMAYER, LEA. *Justifying International Acts*. Pp. x, 164. Ithaca, NY: Cornell University Press, 1989. $19.95.

CALLAGHAN, JOHN. *Socialism in Britain since 1884*. Pp. viii, 279. Cambridge, MA: Basil Blackwell, 1990. $37.95.

CARMINES, EDWARD G. and JAMES A. STIMSON. *Issue Evolution: Race and the Transformation of American Politics*. Pp. xvii, 217. Princeton, NJ: Princeton University Press, 1990. Paperbound, $14.95.

CARTER, APRIL. *Success and Failure in Arms Control Negotiations*. Pp. xi, 308. New York: Oxford University Press, 1989. $55.00.

CHANG, PARRIS H. *Power and Policy in China*. 3d ed. Pp. xv, 352. Dubuque, IA: Kendall/Hunt, 1990. Paperbound, $29.95.

CLARKSON, C.M.V. and H. M. KEATING. *Criminal Law: Text and Materials*. 2d ed. Pp. xlvii, 822. London: Sweet & Maxwell, 1990. Paperbound, no price.

COHEN, RAYMOND. *Culture and Conflict in Egyptian-Israeli Relations: A Dialogue of the Deaf*. Pp. 208. Bloomington: Indiana University Press, 1990. $27.50.

COOK, KAREN SCHWEERS and MARGARET LEVI, eds. *The Limits of Rationality*. Pp. ix, 426. Chicago: University of Chicago Press, 1991. $49.95. Paperbound, $19.95.

COOK, TIMOTHY E. *Making Laws and Making News: Media Strategies in the U.S. House of Representatives*. Pp. x, 210. Washington, DC: Brookings Institution, 1989. $26.95.

CUMBLER, JOHN T. *A Social History of Economic Decline: Business, Politics* and Work in Trenton. Pp. xii, 302. New Brunswick, NJ: Rutgers University Press, 1989. $42.00. Paperbound, $15.00.

DAHL, ROBERT A. After the Revolution? Authority in a Good Society. Rev. ed. Pp. vii, 145. New Haven, CT: Yale University Press, 1990. $25.00. Paperbound, $9.95.

DARLING, ARTHUR B. The Central Intelligence Agency: An Instrument of Government, to 1950. Pp. xxiv, 509. University Park: Pennsylvania State Press, 1990. $60.00. Paperbound, $17.50.

DE GRAMONT, SANCHE. The Strong Brown God: The Story of the Niger River. Pp. 350. Boston, MA: Houghton Mifflin, 1991. Paperbound, $10.95.

DEERE, CARMEN DIANA et al. In the Shadows of the Sun: Caribbean Development Alternatives and U.S. Policy. Pp. xvii, 246. Boulder, CO: Westview Press, 1990. $38.50. Paperbound, $12.85.

DESAI, PADMA. Perestroika in Perspective: The Design and Dilemmas of Soviet Reform. Pp. x, 221. Princeton, NJ: Princeton University Press, 1990. Paperbound, $12.95.

ESTERLINE, JOHN H. and MAE H. ESTERLINE. "How the Dominoes Fell": Southeast Asia in Perspective. 2d ed. Pp. 440. Lanham, MD: University Press of America, 1990. $73.00. Paperbound, $41.25.

EVERS, WILLIAMSON M., ed. National Service: Pro & Con. Pp. 270. Stanford, CA: Hoover Institution Press, 1990. $21.95. Paperbound, $14.95.

EWING, K. D. and C. A. GEARTY. Freedom under Thatcher: Civil Liberties in Modern Britain. Pp. vi, 305. New York: Oxford University Press, 1990. No price.

FELDMAN, S. SHIRLEY and GLEN R. ELLIOTT, eds. At the Threshold: The Developing Adolescent. Pp. x, 642. Cambridge, MA: Harvard University Press, 1990. $39.95.

FEREJOHN, JOHN A. and JAMES H. KIKLINSKI, eds. Information and Democratic Processes. Pp. 421. Champaign: University of Illinois Press, 1990. $44.95. Paperbound, $16.95.

FESLER, JAMES W. and DONALD F. KETTL. The Politics of the Administrative Process. Pp. 480. Chatham, NJ: Chatham House, 1990. Paperbound, $24.95.

FINGER, SEYMOUR MAXWELL and ARNOLD A. SALTZMAN. Bending with the Winds: Kurt Waldheim and the United Nations. Pp. 144. New York: Praeger, 1990. $37.95.

FORBATH, PETER. The River Congo: The Discovery, Exploration, and Exploitation of the World's Most Dramatic River. Pp. xii, 404. Boston, MA: Houghton Mifflin, 1991. Paperbound, $10.95.

FREDERIKSE, JULIE. The Unbreakable Thread: Non-Racialism in South Africa. Pp. 304. Bloomington: Indiana University Press, 1990. $37.50. Paperbound, $15.95.

FRIEDMAN, WILLIAM J. About Time: Inventing the Fourth Dimension. Pp. x, 147. Cambridge: MIT Press, 1990. $19.95.

GALATY, JOHN G. and DOUGLAS L. JOHNSON, eds. The World of Pastoralism: Herding Systems in Comparative Perspective. Pp. x, 436. New York: Guilford Press, 1990. No price.

GENICOT, LEOPOLD. Rural Communities in the Medieval West. Pp. x, 185. Baltimore, MD: Johns Hopkins University Press, 1990. $30.00.

GEREFFI, GARY and DONALD L. WYMAN, eds. Manufacturing Miracles: Paths of Industrialization in Latin America and East Asia. Pp. xv, 416. Princeton, NJ: Princeton University Press, 1990. $49.50. Paperbound, $16.95.

GLAD, BETTY, ed. Psychological Dimensions of War. Pp. 384. Newbury Park, CA: Sage, 1990. $39.95. Paperbound, $19.95.

GORDON, DAVID. *Resurrecting Marx: The Analytical Marxists on Freedom, Exploitation, and Justice.* Pp. ix, 155. New Brunswick, NJ: Transaction, 1990. Paperbound, no price.

GOULD, PETER. *Fire in the Rain: The Democratic Consequences of Chernobyl.* Pp. xi, 163. Baltimore, MD: Johns Hopkins University Press, 1990. $19.95.

GREEN, ROY E., ed. *Enterprise Zones.* Pp. 270. Newbury Park, CA: Sage, 1990. $36.00. Paperbound, $17.95.

GREENBERG, EDWARD S. and THOMAS F. MAYER, eds. *Changes in the State: Causes and Consequences.* Pp. 260. Newbury Park, CA: Sage, 1990. $36.00. Paperbound, $17.95.

HAGAN, KENNETH J. *This People's Navy: The Making of American Sea Power.* Pp. xiii, 434. New York: Free Press, 1990. $27.95.

HARRINGTON, MICHAEL. *Socialism: Past and Future.* Pp. xv, 320. New York: Plume, 1990. Paperbound, $9.95.

HESS, BETH B. and ELIZABETH W. MARKSON, eds. *Growing Old in America.* 4th ed. Pp. 618. New Brunswick, NJ: Transaction, 1990. Paperbound, $22.95.

HUDELSON, RICHARD. *Marxism and Philosophy in the Twentieth Century: A Defense of Vulgar Marxism.* Pp. 272. Westport, CT: Praeger, 1990. $45.00.

INCIARDI, JAMES A., ed. *The Drug Legalization Debate.* Pp. 230. Newbury Park, CA: Sage, 1990. $29.95. Paperbound, $14.95.

JESSOP, BOB. *State Theory: Putting Capitalist States in Their Place.* Pp. xii, 413. University Park: Pennsylvania State Press, 1991. $45.00. Paperbound, $14.95.

JOHNSON, NEVIL. *The Limits of Political Science.* Pp. vi, 142. New York: Oxford University Press, 1989. $35.00.

JUDD, DENNIS and MICHAEL PARKINSON, eds. *Leadership and Urban Regeneration: Cities in North America and Europe.* Pp. 311. Newbury Park,

CA: Sage, 1990. $38.00. Paperbound, $17.95.

KAKAR, SUDHIR. *Intimate Relations: Exploring Indian Sexuality.* Pp. 161. Chicago: University of Chicago Press, 1989. No price.

KHAYUM, MOHAMMED F. *Macroeconomic Modeling and Policy Analysis for Less Developed Countries.* Pp. xi, 203. Boulder, CO: Westview Press, 1990. Paperbound, $26.95.

KIRK, JOHN M. *Between God and the Party: Religion and Politics in Revolutionary Cuba.* Pp. xxi, 231. Tampa: University of South Florida Press, 1988. $22.00. Paperbound, $15.00.

KIRKPATRICK, JEANE J. *The Withering Away of the Totalitarian State . . . and Other Surprises.* Pp. 300. Lanham, MD: AEI Press, 1990. $21.95.

KRIEGER, MARTIN H. *Marginalism and Discontinuity: Tools for the Crafts of Knowledge and Decision.* Pp. 206. New York: Russell Sage Foundation, 1989. $25.00.

LAPIDUS, GAIL W. and ALEXANDER DALLIN, eds. *The Soviet System in Crisis: A Reader of Soviet and Western Views.* Pp. xv, 711. Boulder, CO: Westview Press, 1991. $59.95. Paperbound, $21.95.

LAVRAKAS, PAUL J. and JACK K. HOLLEY, eds. *Polling and Presidential Election Coverage.* Pp. 244. Newbury Park, CA: Sage, 1990. $36.00. Paperbound, $17.95.

LEE, CHIN-CHUAN, ed. *Voices of China: The Interplay of Politics and Journalism.* Pp. 353. New York: Guilford Press, 1990. $40.00. Paperbound, $19.95.

LEMERT, CHARLES C., ed. *Intellectuals and Politics: Social Theory in a Changing World.* Pp. 188. Newbury Park, CA: Sage, 1990. $35.00. Paperbound, $16.95.

LUKE, TIMOTHY W. *Screens of Power: Ideology, Domination, and Resistance in Informational Society.* Pp. x, 264. Champaign: University of Illinois Press, 1990. $34.95. Paperbound, $14.95.

MAXWELL, NAN. *Income Equality in the United States, 1947-1985.* Pp. 227. Westport, CT: Greenwood Press, 1989. $42.95.

MEDINA, VICENTE. *Social Contract Theories: Political Obligation or Anarchy?* Pp. 188. Savage, MD: Rowman & Littlefield, 1990. $39.95.

MICHELMANN, HANS J., JACK C. STABLER, and GARY G. STOREY, eds. *The Political Economy of Agricultural Trade and Policy: Toward a New Order for Europe and North America.* Pp. xix, 242. Boulder, CO: Westview Press, 1990. Paperbound, $28.50.

MOHL, RAYMOND A., ed. *Searching for the Sunbelt: Historical Perspectives on a Region.* Pp. xi, 249. Knoxville: University of Tennessee Press, 1990. No price.

NEWBOULD, IAN. *Whiggery and Reform, 1830-41: The Politics of Government.* Pp. x, 401. Stanford, CA: Stanford University Press, 1991. $45.00.

NEWSOM, DAVID D., ed. *The Diplomatic Record, 1989-1990.* Pp. xii, 250. Boulder, CO: Westview Press, 1990. $50.00.

NOVAK, MICHAEL. *This Hemisphere of Liberty: A Philosophy of the Americas.* Pp. 168. Lanham, MD: AEI Press, 1990. $18.95.

OBEYESEKERE, GANANATH. *The Work of Culture.* Pp. xxv, 354. Chicago: University of Chicago Press, 1991. $49.95. Paperbound, $17.95.

OOMMEN, T. K. *Protest and Change: Studies in Social Movements.* Pp. 309. Newbury Park, CA: Sage, 1990. $32.50.

OOMMEN, T. K. *State and Society in India: Studies in Nation-Building.* Pp. 225. Newbury Park, CA: Sage, 1990. $26.00.

OWEISS, IBRAHIM M., ed. *The Political Economy of Contemporary Egypt.* Pp. xiii, 334. Washington, DC: Center for Contemporary Arab Studies, 1990. $34.95. Paperbound, $16.95.

PIORE, EMANUEL. *Science and Academic Life in Transition.* Edited by Eli Ginzberg. Pp. 93. New Brunswick, NJ: Transaction, 1990. $24.95.

PROCTER, DAVID E. *Enacting Political Culture: Rhetorical Transformations of Liberty Weekend 1986.* Pp. 144. New York: Praeger, 1990. $37.95.

RABOW, GERALD. *Peace through Agreement: Replacing War with Non-Violent Dispute-Resolution Methods.* Pp. xi, 189. New York: Praeger, 1990. No price.

RADU, MICHAEL. *The New Insurgencies: Anticommunist Guerillas in the Third World.* Pp. 300. New Brunswick, NJ: Transaction, 1990. $32.95.

RAKOVE, JACK N., ed. *Interpreting the Constitution: The Debate over Original Intent.* Pp. x, 357. Boston, MA: Northeastern University Press, 1990. $45.00. Paperbound, $16.95.

REAGAN, RONALD. *An American Life: The Autobiography.* Pp. 748. New York: Simon & Schuster, 1990. $24.95.

RIPLEY, RANDALL B. and GRACE A. FRANK. *Congress, the Bureaucracy, and Public Policy.* 5th ed. Pp. xiii, 223. Pacific Grove, CA: Brooks/Cole, 1991. Paperbound, $21.75.

SIMONTON, DEAN KEITH. *Psychology, Science, and History: An Introduction to Historiometry.* Pp. xi, 291. New Haven, CT: Yale University Press, 1991. $30.00.

SISMONDI, J.-C.-L. SIMONDE DE. *New Principles of Political Economy: Of Wealth and Its Relation to Population.* Translated by Richard Hyse. Pp. xlix, 658. New Brunswick, NJ: Transaction, 1990. No price.

SISSON, RICHARD and RAMASHRAY ROY, eds. *Diversity and Dominance in Indian Politics.* Vol. 1, *Changing Bases of Congress Support.* Pp. 312. Newbury Park, CA: Sage, 1990. $35.00.

SMOKE, RICHARD and ANDREI KORTUNOV, eds. *Mutual Security: A New Approach to Soviet-American Relations.* Pp. 430. New York: St. Martin's Press, 1991. $49.95. Paperbound, $19.95.

SOBELL, VLAD. *The CMEA in Crisis: Toward a New European Order?* Pp. 120. New York: Praeger, 1990. $34.95. Paperbound, $11.95.

SOLOMON, ROBERT C. and MARK C. MURPHY, eds. *What Is Justice?* Pp. xi, 359. New York: Oxford University Press, 1990. $38.00. Paperbound, $14.95.

STARR, CHESTER G. *The Birth of Athenian Democracy: The Assembly in the Fifth Century B.C.* Pp. 86. New York: Oxford University Press, 1990. $16.95.

STICKER, MARTIN. *The Genesis of the State.* Pp. 176. New York: Praeger, 1990. $39.95.

STOCKHOLM INTERNATIONAL PEACE RESEARCH INSTITUTE. *SIPRI Yearbook 1990: World Armaments and Disarmament.* Pp. xxxi, 714. New York: Oxford University Press, 1990. No price.

SULEIMAN, EZRA N. and JOHN WATERBURY, eds. *The Political Economy of Public Sector Reform and Privatization.* Pp. ix, 388. Boulder, CO: Westview Press, 1990. $47.50.

TEMIN, PETER. *Lessons from the Great Depression.* Pp. xv, 193. Cambridge: MIT Press, 1989. $16.95.

THOMPSON, JOEL A. and G. LARRY MAYS, eds. *American Jails: Public Policy Issues.* Pp. xv, 288. Chicago: Nelson-Hall, 1990. $28.95. Paperbound, $15.95.

TORRES-RIVAS, EDELBERTO. *Repression and Resistance: The Struggle for Democracy in Central America.* Pp. vii, 165. Boulder, CO: Westview Press, 1989. $28.95.

VALELLY, RICHARD M. *Radicalism in the States: The Minnesota Farmer-Labor Party and the American Political Economy.* Pp. xviii, 258. Chicago: University of Chicago Press, 1989. $29.95.

WALKER, CHARLS E., MARK A. BLOOMFIELD, and MARGO THORNING, eds. *The U.S. Savings Challenge: Policy Options for Productivity and Growth.* Pp. xxi, 408. Boulder, CO: Westview Press, 1990. $38.50.

WELLINGTON, HARRY H. *Interpreting the Constitution: The Supreme Court and the Process of Adjudication.* Pp. xii, 196. New Haven, CT: Yale University Press, 1991. $22.50.

WILMSEN, EDWIN N. *Land Filled with Flies: A Political Economy of the Kalahari.* Pp. xviii, 402. Chicago: University of Chicago Press, 1989. $60.00. Paperbound, $17.95.

WOLIN, RICHARD. *The Politics of Being: The Political Thought of Martin Heidegger.* Pp. xvii, 221. New York: Columbia University Press, 1990. $29.50.

WOODWARD, GARY C. *Persuasive Encounters: Case Studies in Constructive Confrontation.* Pp. 216. New York: Praeger, 1990. $45.00. Paperbound, $14.95.

YALKOWSKY, STANLEY. *The Murder of the Rosenbergs.* Pp. ix, 462. New York: Stanley Yalkowsky, 1990. Paperbound, no price.

INDEX

New from Sage!

How Many Candles Were On Your Cake The Last Time You Thought About Buying Insurance?

Face it—it's been a long time. Styles have changed. So has your family, maybe even your job. And most likely, the insurance you bought then isn't enough to cover your family today. That's why you need coverage that you can easily update as your life changes—AAPSS Group Insurance Program.

We Understand You.

Finding an insurance program that's right for you isn't easy. But as a member of AAPSS, you don't have to go through the difficult task of looking for the right plans— we've done that work for you. What's more, the program is constantly being evaluated to better meet the needs of our members.

We're Flexible.

Updating your insurance doesn't have to be a hassle. With our plans, as your needs change, so can your coverage. Insurance through your association is designed to grow with you—it even moves with you when you change jobs.

We're Affordable.

We offer members the additional benefit of reasonable rates, negotiated using our group purchasing power. Call 1 800 424-9883 (in Washington, DC, (202) 457-6820) between 8:30 a.m. and 5:30 p.m. Eastern Time for more information about these insurance plans offered through AAPSS:

Term Life • Excess Major Medical • In-Hospital • High-Limit Accident • Medicare Supplement

AAPSS Insurance
Designed for the way you live today. And tomorrow.

Explore the ethical

traditions affecting

global change in

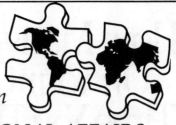

ETHICS & INTERNATIONAL AFFAIRS

Published annually by the Carnegie Council on Ethics and International
Affairs, ETHICS & INTERNATIONAL AFFAIRS shows concrete
applications of ethics to current issues in international affairs.

Volume 6: Democracy and the New World Order

[ ] Please send me_____ copies of the 1992 edition of ETHICS & INTERNATIONAL AFFAIRS,
Volume 6 for $10 per copy. ($12 outside U.S. and Canada).

Enclosed is $_____. Make checks payable to Carnegie Council. Payment must accompany
order.

Name _____

Address _____

City, State, Zip _____

Telephone _____

Mail to: Publications Fulfillment Department
Carnegie Council on Ethics and International Affairs
170 East 64th Street, New York, NY 10021-7478